HEALTH STUDIES

Also by Jennie Naidoo and Jane Wills

Health Promotion: Foundations for Practice 2nd edition
Practising Health Promotion: Dilemmas and Challenges

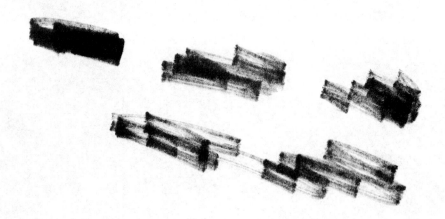

Health Studies

An Introduction

EDITED BY

Jennie Naidoo

AND

Jane Wills

First published 2001 by
PALGRAVE
Houndmills, Basingstoke, Hampshire RG21 6XS and
175 Fifth Avenue, New York, N.Y. 10010
Companies and representatives throughout the world

PALGRAVE is the new global academic imprint of
St. Martin's Press LLC Scholarly and Reference Division and
Palgrave Publishers Ltd (formerly Macmillan Press Ltd).

ISBN 0–333–76008–5 paperback

This book is printed on paper suitable for recycling and
made from fully managed and sustained forest sources.

Editing and origination by
Aardvark Editorial, Mendham, Suffolk

11 10   9   8   7   6
10 09 08 07 06 05

Printed in Great Britain by
Ashford Colour Press Ltd, Gosport, Hants

Contents

CHAPTER 3   **HEALTH PSYCHOLOGY**   **69**
                        Jane Ogden

CHAPTER 4   **SOCIOLOGY**   **101**
                        Norma Daykin

CHAPTER 5   **CULTURAL STUDIES**   **133**
                        Sarah Burch

List of Figures

List of Tables

Notes on Contributors

Sarah Burch is Senior Lecturer in Social Policy at Anglia Polytechnic University and an associate lecturer in the same subject with The Open University. Prior to this, she was a researcher with the NHS. Her main teaching interests include work centred on older people, childhood, social care, comparative health studies and gender. Her current research centres on the evaluation of rehabilitative services for older people. Sarah is also currently completing a PhD, which is a methodological study evaluating the health of older people.

S.H. Cedar is Senior Lecturer in Biological Sciences in the Faculty of Health at South Bank University. After completing a PhD in cell biology, investigating human leukaemic cells in vitro, post-doctoral research included work in developmental biochemistry and gene cloning. Her current research projects are in bioethics, particularly genethics and the public understanding of science.

David Cohen is Professor of Health Economics and Head of the Health Economics Research Unit, which has an ongoing portfolio of research covering a wide area of health service areas. The Unit is part of the Medical Research Council's Health Services Research Collaboration and the Capricorn network of primary care research. David has published widely on a variety of issues in health economics and has also acted as an adviser to the World Health Organization and to the House of Commons Select Committee on Welsh Affairs.

Norma Daykin is Head of the School of Health Sciences, University of the West of England, Bristol. Her research interests include health promotion, gender and workplace health issues. She is co-editor, with Lesley Doyal, of *Health and Work: Critical Perspectives*. She is currently working on a collaborative multidisciplinary project evaluating the impact of user involvement in the development of cancer services.

Peter Duncan is Senior Lecturer in Health Education in the School of Education at Kings College, London. He has a background in health promotion in both the voluntary and the public sector. His current research interests are: health care ethics (especially the ethics of preventive activities); health promotion theory and practice; the history of health promotion; and the relationship between politics and health care (particularly health promotion).

Judy Hubbard has recently retired after a long teaching career at the University of Central England in Birmingham. She taught physiology on a range of courses for students preparing for or already working in the health care professions, these courses including medical laboratory sciences, speech therapy, nursing, midwifery, combined health studies and orthoptics. She has extensive experience in course development as well as in course-directing and tutoring. Prior to joining the University, Judy worked for the Medical Research Council.

Liz Lloyd is Lecturer in the School for Policy Studies at the University of Bristol. She has experience of teaching and research in health policy and community care, with a particular focus on the roles of family carers. Her primary academic interest lies in gerontology, and she has written and researched on the provision of health and community care for older people at the end of life. Liz worked in the voluntary sector prior to her career in education, and she has maintained an active involvement in community-based organisations.

Anne Mulhall is an independent Research Consultant. Her previous posts include Senior Scientific Officer at Queen Charlotte's Hospital, London, and Deputy Director of the Nursing Practice Research Unit, University of Surrey. Her particular interests are evidence-based practice, the dissemination and implementation of research, ethnography, epidemiology and infection control. She has written three books on nursing research.

Jennie Naidoo is Principal Lecturer in Health Promotion and Public Health at the University of the West of England. She has a background in sociology, health promotion and education. Jennie worked in health promotion and research for several years prior to taking up her post at UWE. Her research interests include gender and health, and health promotion in primary care settings. She has written extensively on health promotion practice and theory, including co-authoring, with Jane Wills, two books on health promotion.

Jane Ogden is Reader in Health Psychology at the Department of General Practice at Guys, Kings and St Thomas' School of Medicine, London University. She is involved in teaching health psychology to medical and psychology students at both undergraduate and postgraduate levels. Her current research relates to eating behaviour and obesity, sexual behaviour and reproductive issues, and doctor–patient communication. She is the author of over 50 research papers on aspects of health psychology, and of three books.

Martin Walter is Senior Lecturer in Health Service Management at South Bank University. Previously, he worked in the NHS for 33 years, where he became interested in the application of computers to solve laboratory data-processing problems. Martin worked on four short-term consultancies during 1995 and 1996 in Pakistan to solve management problems in the Metropolitan Corporation of Lahore's health department. He is currently researching the possibilities of online course delivery with a view to providing this service for his Master's students.

Jane Wills is Senior Lecturer in Health Promotion and Public Health at South Bank University. Her career started in education, initially as a school teacher and later as local education authority adviser. Her first degree was in history so she is familiar with crossing disciplinary boundaries. Jane has been involved with health promotion practice for many years and has published many education and training resources and several textbooks, including the popular text *Health Promotion: Foundations for Practice*, which she co-authored with Jennie Naidoo.

Acknowledgements

The editors would like to thank Helen Lewis for her information about South Africa, Chrissie Littler for her invaluable administrative support and Aardvark Editorial for their diligence. We are especially grateful to the contributing authors for the enthusiasm with which they approached the hard task we set and for their patience as the book developed, and once again we thank our long-suffering families who have been so understanding and supportive.

We are also grateful to the following for their kind permission to use the undermentioned copyright material:

Blackwell Publishers for Table 6.2, Comparative welfare regimes from *The Three Worlds of Welfare Capitalism* by Esping-Anderson.

The Guilford Press for Figure 3.5, The protection motivation theory, from Cognitive and physiological processes in fear appeal and attitude change: a revised theory of protection motivation edited by Cacioppo and Petty in *Social Psychology: A Source Book*, 1983.

Harcourt Health Sciences/Baillière Tindall for Table 10.1, Lalonde's health field from *Promoting Health: A Practical Guide*, 4th edn, Ewles and Simnett, 1999.

Routledge for Figure 10.2, Beattie's model of health promotion from *The Sociology of the Health Service* edited by Beattie, Gabe, Calnan and Bury, 1991.

The World Health Organization for Table 4.1, Causes of death from the *World Health Report*, 1998.

Every effort has been made to trace all the copyright holders but if any have been inadvertently overlooked the publishers will be pleased to make the necessary arrangements at the first opportunity.

List of Abbreviations

AIDS	acquired immune deficiency syndrome
ATP	adenosine triphosphate
CT	computed tomography
DNA	deoxyribonucleic acid
DoH	Department of Health
EU	European Union
FSH	follicle stimulating hormone
GDP	gross domestic product
GMC	General Medical Council
HIV	human immunodeficiency virus
ICD	International Classification of Diseases
IMF	International Monetary Fund
LH	luteinising hormone
MHC	major histocompatibility complex
MRI	magnetic resonance imaging
NHS	National Health Service
NICE	National Institute for Clinical Excellence
ONS	Office of National Statistics
PCG	Primary Care Group
PEST	political, economic, sociological and technological
PET	positron emission tomography
QALY	quality adjusted life years
RCT	randomised controlled trial
UKCC	United Kingdom Central Council for Nursing, Midwifery and Health Visiting
WHO	World Health Organization

Introducing Health Studies

JENNIE NAIDOO AND JANE WILLS

Health Studies is a relatively new field of enquiry that draws on theoretical perspectives from a wide range of fields. This book sets out to explore the diversity of those perspectives, illustrating the many ways in which health may be studied and how ideas from different disciplines contribute to our understanding of 'health'. It shows how there are different epistemologies or theories of knowledge for studying and trying to understand health. In academic language, interdisciplinary means the coming together and contribution of different academic disciplines. Strictly speaking, 'inter' means 'between', 'multi' means 'many' and 'trans' means 'across'. We shall use the term 'interdisciplinary' here to describe the way in which theory and knowledge from cognate and applied disciplines can be brought together.

By studying health in an interdisciplinary way, through Health Studies, students who wish to embark on a related career will find themselves better equipped to work with other professionals, patients, managers and the general public. Acknowledging and understanding the diversity of perspectives that people bring to the concept of health is the first step in successful partnership working.

This introductory book will help the reader to:

- become familiar with a variety of perspectives on health issues
- explore different constructions of health and its management for individuals and populations
- relate these perspectives to the ways in which health and welfare services should be organised
- understand the different ways in which health may be studied
- identify some of the core health issues and challenges that face contemporary society
- identify areas that might merit further study.

There is no agreed view on what constitutes Health Studies. For some, it should be approached as a human and social subject with an emphasis on the whole person in his or her environment. Predominant in Western societies, however, is a biomedical perspective that focuses on the processes influencing health and illness. Those who study health may also be interested in its practical

1

application in the care of the ill and the organisation of health services. This book is inevitably, in the absence of a commonly accepted syllabus, a partial selection of the fields making up Health Studies, the rationale for inclusion of particular disciplines being to demonstrate its breadth.

There is no general paradigm for understanding health within which theories and models can be fitted. Each discipline has its own perspective, concepts and methodologies that it uses to answer questions. What we have are numerous models and explanations that highlight biological, social and psychological processes, and you will be introduced to these in the relevant chapters. The degree of connection between the different elements has only recently begun to be explored. Stansfeld (1999), for example, asks whether a lack of social support (a psychologically perceived and socially produced process) can influence bodily physiology and contribute to cardiovascular disease. The evidence from epidemiological studies might suggest there is a relationship between the two variables, but the causal mechanism is not known. The value of Health Studies is that, by drawing on many disciplines, it can provide a fuller account of health and begin to challenge existing boundaries of knowledge that lead to partial understandings of health.

This book is about the study of health. Most students probably have a clear idea of what they will be studying when they look at health. Yet as individuals, groups and societies, our understanding of health differs. Our view of health is also likely to change as we get older. Most children see health as 'eating the right things' and 'being fit'. For older people, health is likely to be much more about their ability to cope and do the things that they are used to doing. The importance of physical fitness in people's conceptualisation of health is demonstrated by some research conducted with Californian women (Crawford, 1984). This study showed how women in particular conceptualise health as the control of their physical bodies, which is achieved through dieting and exercise.

A holistic view of health was encapsulated in the World Health Organization (WHO) definition of 'health is a state of complete physical, mental and social well-being, not merely the absence of disease or infirmity' (WHO, 1946). Health may, in this definition, seem idealistic and unattainable, but the frequent quotation of this statement reflects its symbolic significance in highlighting the importance of a multidimensional view. More recent pronouncements from the WHO emphasise the dynamic nature of health and its many social and environmental correlates:

> [Health is the extent to which an individual or group is able] to realise aspirations, to satisfy needs, and to change or cope with the environment. Health is, therefore, seen as a resource for everyday life, not the objective of living. Health is a positive concept emphasising social and personal resources, as well as physical capacities. (WHO, 1986)

More recent definitions of health therefore conceptualise it not as a state, but as a process towards the achievement of each person's potential (Seedhouse, 1986). This is often part of people's own definitions of health and illness too. In studies of lay perceptions of health, health is seen positively. People often talk of being fulfilled or whole. Blaxter (1990), in a comprehensive study of health and lifestyles, noted how 'positive health' was associated with the ability to cope with stressful situations and having a strong support system. People related their health to their relationships, their socio-economic status and their mood.

Health has many different meanings that are linked to the social and cultural context of its use. In Western societies, health tends to be associated with the presence or absence of disease or illness. This derives from the dominance of medicine, which offers a framework of scientific knowledge and understanding of the body. Disease is an objective state that is capable of being scientifically proven. It is manifested via signs and symptoms in various parts of the body, indicating a pathological abnormality. Someone has a disease if tests can verify the presence of a disease process such as a compromised immune system.

Illness is distinct from disease. Illness refers to the individual experience of ill health and feelings of discomfort, pain or unease. People may feel ill but have no diagnosed disease. The illness may not be sited in the physical body but have a social or psychological dimension. This view of health is almost a return to the early Greek school of thought that *hygeia* (health) and *euexia* (soundness) occur when there is a balance between the bodily 'humours' of blood, phlegm, yellow bile and black bile. The theory was that these four fluids normally remained in balance, but if the equilibrium was upset, illness ensued. Galen (AD 130–199) believed that the body's constitution could be put out of balance by too much wetness, dryness, heat or cold.

In the 16th and 17th centuries, these ideas were challenged, and scientists began increasingly to view the body as a machine that could be reduced to its component parts. This paradigm shift was underwritten by Descartes' famous treatise proposing that body and soul are separate. Cartesian dualism, as this is called, allowed the study of these two realms as quite distinctive entities. A person's spiritual being, emotions and feelings remained with the soul, but the corporeal body was freed up for exploration through the methods of science. Nature was considered to be orderly and predictable, its explanations lying in logic rather than spiritual meaning. This legitimised the exploration of the human body through dissection, something that had already been described by Vesalius in 1543.

There then followed a general trend towards empiricism (the idea that knowledge derives from observation or experiments rather than from theory). This in turn led to an era of laboratory medicine that focused not on patients as whole beings but on their organs, tissues or even cells. Such studies required an even greater input from natural scientists. The Flexner Report (1910) stated that medicine should be underpinned by a thorough training in biology and laboratory science.

In recent years, the biomedical perspective has been challenged. Medicine is not as effective as is often claimed. The steady reduction in mortality and increased longevity in the Western world in the 20th century that was attributed to medical advances has now been attributed to improved sanitation and nutrition and general improvements in living conditions (McKeown, 1976). Social factors such as income, housing and employment have been shown to have a greater impact on health status than health care. In addition, it has been claimed that medicine contributes to a loss of individual autonomy. Medical decisions and techniques have encroached into ordinary stages of the life cycle such as birth and death. Illich (1975) argues that health is a personal task and a fundamental human right that should be pursued by everyone as they wish. The rise in the number of self-help groups indicates a general belief that people believe that they know what is best for them and that other people in similar circumstances may be helpful and supportive. The growing number of people using complementary therapies reflects a dissatisfaction with conventional medicine and health care. Complementary therapies adopt a more holistic approach, challenge the dualism of medicine and actively engage the person who is seeking to recover or maintain their health.

When students begin to study health, the frequent assumption is that they will be looking at the human body and its functions – perhaps the nature of human tissue and how particular foods can encourage regeneration, or how muscles react to stress. The human body is a stable structure that is fundamentally similar in all members of the species. Biological explanations for the way in which the body works are important because they do not vary and are least influenced by the external environment. S.H. Cedar, with Judy Hubbard, explores some of the major concerns of physiology in Chapter 1, showing how individuals are biological entities determined by their anatomy and the chemical reactions inside their cells. Physiology employs rigorous scientific methods to investigate physiological mechanisms and processes such as the reaction to stress or pain.

Epidemiology, the study of the patterns of disease within populations, is particularly linked to public health. Identifying patterns of disease and then causal agents, associated factors or triggers for disease provides statistical data upon which efforts to improve the health of populations can be based. Epidemiology has traditionally relied on the techniques of scientific enquiry, the study designs it uses being outlined in Chapter 2. Anne Mulhall also argues for a broader view of epidemiology that looks at the interrelationship between individuals and their environment in the causation of disease.

There is thus no simple, linear model of health, but illness can be caused by a combination of biological (for example a virus), psychological (for example behaviours and beliefs) and social (for example employment) factors. Psychological explanations for health acknowledge that mental functioning affects behaviour, and both may be influenced by wider social factors. Health psychology aims to understand and explain the role of psychological factors in the cause, progression and consequence of health and illness. In Chapter 3, Jane Ogden explores what contributes to people's behaviour and how the views of patients may differ from those of health professionals.

Health and ill health are strongly patterned by social factors. People do not have an equal chance of enjoying health or living to a ripe old age. There is now a mass of evidence showing that deprived groups in the population experience poorer health and a higher level of mortality. Most of the discussion in the UK focuses on health differences in different social classes, but we are beginning to recognise that other structural factors such as gender, sexuality and ethnicity produce health differences. Norma Daykin, in Chapter 4, reviews the evidence on health inequalities and examines the different explanations for why these inequalities persist in a modern democracy with an established national health service. Using the example of work, she shows how sociology as a discipline explores below the surface of the taken-for-granted naturalness of social life and questions our assumptions and long-held beliefs about how society functions.

Medical knowledge sees health and illness as objective states that can be discovered and measured, yet this is at odds with the public perception, which is to think of health and ill health as an individual experience – as personal and unique. Our perception and understanding of the experience is shaped by the shared meanings that we possess in our culture. A disease such as cancer, for example, is often seen as an uncontrolled invasion (Sontag, 1989), and wellness is expressed through independence and control. The growing interest in the body reflects our emphasis on the individual, and it is through our bodies that we express and shape our identity. In Chapter 5, Sarah Burch examines the language and visual signs with which we describe health. She shows how there has been a shift in the knowledge and ideas about the body so that our ways of knowing are no longer bounded by a single agreed discipline (science) but are varied and contested (cultural).

The need to rationalise the rising cost of health care has been a major feature of most health policy throughout the developed world. The difference in national systems of health care reflects different political and ideological decisions. In Chapter 6, Liz Lloyd discusses different views on service provision and the emergence of a welfare state in the UK. She offers a historical perspective, showing how the idea of health as a right emerged in the post-war period, and how this led to the state managing the health service and funding it through taxation and National Insurance. The welfare state has been challenged, and there has been a recent 'retreat from welfare'. Health care is increasingly being provided by a plurality of sources, including public and private medicine, informal caring and voluntary sector provision. There has been an ideological shift towards liberal, anti-collectivist views that stress individual responsibility as well as the need for people to insure themselves against risks and not become dependent on the state.

Health policy is a complex process involving different groups. Students of Health Studies will be curious about why some issues, but not others, make it onto the policy agenda and how ideas about service delivery are shaped. Since 1997, health policy in the UK has undergone a radical change, with a commitment to public involvement in decision-making, the development of local Health Improvement Programmes, a commitment to tackle waiting times and hospital waiting lists, and quality standards. Members of the public are no longer merely patients with something wrong with them that requires treatment but consumers with an expectation of a quality service and a right to a say in that service. Chapter 6 examines the policy-making process from initiation and development, through implementation to evaluation and monitoring.

Chapter 7, by Martin Walter, illustrates how and why health services change. He looks at the organisation of health care and at why national systems may differ in their degree of centralisation or local autonomy. In the 1980s, the British government tried to increase the capacity of the NHS by introducing an 'internal market' for health services. It was thought that if service providers such as hospitals and clinics had to compete, they would be more efficient and responsive to local needs. The NHS thus became less a provider of health services and more a regulator or contractor with a growing role in assessing quality and clinical governance. Chapter 7 therefore looks at the practice of management in a large and complex organisation such as the NHS.

In the past two decades, economists have been active in deciding priorities in resource allocation. While cost reduction is a major incentive, efficiency is a broader criterion within which resources are used to maximise specific outcomes. The health economics discourse of cost utility, cost benefit and quality adjusted life years suggests an objective, rational approach and one in which the objectives are agreed. David Cohen argues in Chapter 8 that health economics is the only ethical approach to resource allocation and 'hard decisions'. Complex decisions can, he argues, be reduced to simple and quantifiable comparisons of cost and benefit, but there are continuing controversies over how health services can be made available to the population. Should health services be made available in proportion to need or in proportion to the ability or willingness to pay? This chapter on health economics discusses whether a free market can ensure that there is equal access for those who need health care.

Rationing dilemmas are just one example of the kind of ethical and legal problem faced by health professionals. Increasingly, health workers and services are being held responsible for the services they provide, which means that they can be held to be negligent if, for example, they do not provide an appropriate quality or level of care. The advances in technological medicine mean that health care workers are faced with decisions about the nature and value of life and in what circumstances it is ethical to end or sustain life. Peter Duncan explains in Chapter 9 why it is important for anyone studying health to explore the nature of values and to have a framework for exploring their own actions. This chapter on ethics and law explores how far people are allowed the freedom to choose how to live their lives and discusses the role of the state in protecting people's health.

Chapter 10 explores the ways in which health promotion brings together the strands of controlling disease, a concern with the individual and a recognition of the social determinants of health. Health promotion, through screening, immunisation and health education, tries to control human bodies. At the same time, health promotion also tries to take account of people's lives and facilitate decision-making and choice. The empowerment, of both individuals and groups, is said by some to be the central task of health promotion and the key to health improvement. Others see a greater role for government in regulating the social, economic and environmental factors linked to ill health. Health promotion combines these different perspectives, recognising the importance of individual perceptions of health and the ways in which systemic and macro structures pattern disease and health care systems.

Questions such as what are the most effective means of getting people to stop smoking or what is the best way of spending X amount of money to reduce coronary heart disease inform the methodological base of health promotion. The search for a strong evidence base upon which to plan health promotion interventions is complicated by the fact that many health promotion outcomes are qualitative in nature. Increasing self-esteem or social capital, for example, are legitimate health promotion goals, but they are not amenable to controlled investigation in a scientific manner.

Each of the disciplines presented in this book is located within different paradigms or ways of seeing the world. Each therefore poses different sorts of question and requires different methods for answering them. It is usual to find that a health issue is investigated and discussed in terms of one explanation – for example the psychological. This book shows that other explanations exist and that 'health' is far too complex to be interpreted in a single embracing explanation. The second part of each chapter discusses theoretical and methodological perspectives: there are extended discussions of different methodologies ranging from scientific methods (Chapter 1) and epidemiological designs (Chapter 2) to social constructionism (Chapter 4).

Traditionally, a scientific approach tries to identify the cause of ill health and aims to produce predictive models that can say that, in certain circumstances, x will happen. It does this through the observation and measurement of variables, ideally in the context of a controlled investigation. Social and natural sciences have a common logical framework that tries to understand the relationship or association between different variables. The assumption is that there is a single objective reality that can be discovered through this approach. Epidemiology, physiology, economics and psychology all use this kind of approach and employ scientific methodologies. This approach is associated with the philosophy of positivism. The quest to understand *why* something happens varies according to different disciplinary values. A physiologist, for example, may be interested in the physical reactions that take place under stress, an epidemiologist might be interested in the extent to which stress is associated with certain diseases, whereas a psychologist might be interested in why certain situations are stressful.

At the opposite end of the spectrum lies the social constructionist epistemology or theory of knowledge. According to this perspective, there is no single, fixed reality or truth about health, people instead having a variety of different descriptions and accounts of health. We all try to interpret our experiences and all learn to understand 'what health is' (for us). We can thus begin to understand health as a social product, influenced and formed by class, gender, family life and so on. People's 'worlds of meaning' are also shaped by and reflected in all the customs and practices of the culture in which they live. We can begin to understand this by looking at accounts of health and illness in discourse, narratives and media representations. The chapters on sociology and cultural studies explore this different approach to understanding health.

In between the two extremes lies a range of epistemologies and methodologies that subscribe to elements of both science and social constructionism. Sociology, social policy and health promotion use a scientific approach and quantitative data while simultaneously advocating a critical stance towards such data. The mortality rates of different social classes, for example, tell us important things about health and employment status but obscure the impact of other factors, such as gender or ethnicity, that may be equally important. Why are the data on social class more widely available than the data on gender or ethnicity? How do data sets construct social class? Is it primarily an economic or social concept?

While a scientific approach is appropriate for some questions, others demand a different approach. Exploring people's core values, ideals and principles calls for qualitative methodologies investigating the meanings that people construct and maintain. An in-depth investigation of a small number of people or key events is more rewarding if this kind of information is sought, although it cannot be claimed that such information is generalisable to whole populations. In their different ways, management, ethics and law, sociology, social policy and health promotion all use these types of methodology.

This book presents each discipline separately, showing what it can contribute to the understanding of 'health'. The chapters all follow a similar layout, connections or links being made to other chapters relating to concepts or methodologies that are common. Complex health issues such as stress or pain are discussed throughout the book, suggesting that one level of explanation or single field of knowledge is inadequate and encouraging the reader towards a more holistic interpretation. The book is clearly signposted and structured for ease of reading and study. Each chapter starts with an overview of its contents and ends with a bullet point summary of the main points. Key terms are high-lighted in the text and explained in the margins. An extended case study applies the concepts and frameworks discussed in the chapter to a contemporary health issue. Interspersed in the text are interactive features:

- **questions** for discussion, reading and exploration
- **thinking about** to enable readers to use their experience to understand and apply concepts
- **examples** to illustrate concepts or methodologies or explore contemporary issues.

We hope this book will introduce readers to a variety of different disciplines, clarify how they contribute to our understanding of health issues, and inspire readers to pursue their studies into the meanings, measurement, management and promotion of health.

REFERENCES

Blaxter, M. (1990) *Health and Lifestyles*. London: Routledge.

Crawford, R. (1984) 'A cultural account of health: control, release and the social body', in McKinlay, J. (ed.) *Issues in the Political Economy of Health Care*. London: Tavistock, pp. 60–103.

Illich, I. (1975) *Medical Nemesis*. London: Calder & Boyers.

McKeown, T. (1976) *The Role of Medicine: Dream, Mirage or Nemesis*. Oxford: Nuffield Provincial Hospitals Trust.

Seedhouse, D. (1986) *Health: The Foundations for Achievement*. Chichester: John Wiley & Sons.

Sontag, S. (1989) *AIDS and its Metaphors*. London: Penguin.

Stansfeld, S. (1999) 'Social support and social cohesion', in Marmot, M. and Wilkinson, R.G. (eds) *Social Determinants of Health*. Oxford: Oxford University Press, pp. 155–78.

WHO (World Health Organization) (1946) *Preamble of the Constitution of the World Health Organization*. Geneva: WHO.

WHO (World Health Organization) (1986) *Ottawa Charter for Health Promotion*. Geneva: WHO.

Physiology

S.H. CEDAR WITH JUDY HUBBARD

Learning outcomes •••••••••••••••••••••••••••

This chapter will enable readers to:

● Gain an appreciation of the scope of human physiology, the framework of homeostasis and the principles of control by nervous and hormonal systems
● Be aware of the variety of scientific methods used by physiologists
● Understand how physiology can contribute to the analysis of physical aspects of human health.

OVERVIEW

The aim of this chapter is to explore the ways in which physiology can be used to analyse physical aspects of states of health. Physiology contributes to Health Studies by providing a knowledge of the body's functions and how these are interlinked. These issues are illustrated using a physiological analysis of hypoxia (oxygen defi-ciency). Human physiology concerns how the body functions in terms of its cells, tissues and body systems. Each body system contributes to the maintenance of a constant internal environment (homeostasis) for its cells. The two principal systems for regulating activity are the nervous and endocrine (hormonal) systems. The essen-tial mechanisms used by these systems are explained in the first part of this chapter. Physiology uses scientific methods variously described as induction, deduction, falsi-fication and hypothetico-deduction. The second part discusses experimental research methods and includes a personal account of using such research. An extended case study of the physiology of pain concludes the chapter.

INTRODUCTION

Science seeks to explain the natural world. Biology deals with the living world, physiology being a subdivision of biology that studies the mechanisms of life. Human physiology aims to unravel how the body functions. What are the mechanisms by which a person sees, feels pain, pumps blood round the body, breathes in and out, and absorbs food, for example?

Science in general seeks answers for 'how' things happen rather than 'why' they happen. In relation to physiology, this difference is crucial. If, for example, the question 'why do people sweat when they get hot?' is asked, the answer might be 'in order to lose heat'. Inferences might be drawn, such as the need to replenish lost fluids in hot countries or when exercising vigorously. For a physi-ologist, however, the key question concerns not why people sweat but how people sweat and what are the physical consequences of sweating?

physiological pathway – this connects a sequence of events starting with a challenge to homeostasis (for example a fall in body temperature) and ending with mechanisms tending to restore the status quo (in this case, raising the body temperature again)

A physiological analysis of 'how does sweating occur and what does it do?' includes the response of sensory receptors to a rise in body temperature, the action of a control centre that receives neural input from the receptors and increases activity in the neural pathway to the sweat glands, how the sweat glands produce sweat and how the subsequent evaporation of fluid from the skin takes heat from the body. This sequence of events constitutes a **physio-logical pathway** that regulates the body, in this case maintaining a relatively constant temperature.

The analysis of such processes involves the study of mechanisms occurring inside cells, how cells communicate with each other and how the composition (and temperature) of the fluid within and surrounding the cells is maintained at a relatively constant level. This involves studying these processes at a micro level in controlled laboratory settings. The application of scientific methods of investigation means that the findings are generalisable, that is, they apply to all human beings.

THE CONTRIBUTION OF PHYSIOLOGY TO HEALTH STUDIES

 What examples are there of physiological knowledge contributing to human health?

Physiology is a scientific discipline that contributes to our understanding of the bodily processes and functions that keep us alive in various states of health. The example of hypoxia (see below) illustrates how a physiological framework can identify the cause of a health problem and contribute to its management or cure. Similarly, a knowledge of the composition of fluids enables effective rehydration in drought situations. However, as a discipline, physiology is removed from any practical activities designed to promote or protect health.

Central concepts in physiology are homeostasis (maintaining a stable internal environment) and nervous and hormonal control mechanisms. The body's building blocks – blood and other body fluids, cells, tissues and organs – are all involved in complex ways in these processes.

There are many areas of Health Studies to which physiology does not contribute; for example, whether or not an individual is declared to be healthy or unhealthy, normal or abnormal, is not part of the subject's remit. The distinction between physiology and medicine is therefore an important one. Physiology studies body functions; it is not of itself clinical. Physiology informs medicine but has a separate identity. This chapter demonstrates the use of a physiological framework in the analysis of physical aspects of health.

FRAMEWORK AND LEVELS OF ORGANISATION IN PHYSIOLOGY

To study how living organisms survive and flourish, biology divides itself into separate levels of explanation based on size. We can start from the lowest level and work up to the whole organism:

- atoms and molecules
- organelles
- cells
- tissues
- organs.

proteins – macromolecules composed of amino acids. Various proteins exist depending on the order or assembly of their amino acids. The chemical make-up of proteins is mainly carbon, hydrogen, oxygen and nitrogen

fats – macromolecules composed of long chains of fatty acids. Used to store energy, provide insulation and protect the organs, fats can be converted into energy. Fats are mainly composed of carbon and hydrogen

carbohydrates – macromolecules composed of sugars such as glucose and fructose. Carbohydrates are used by the mitochondria in the cells in conjunction with oxygen to make energy in the chemical form of ATP, which stores energy for the cells. Carbohydrates are mainly composed of carbon, hydrogen and oxygen

organelle – a structure within a cell carrying out specific functions

cells – the smallest self-contained living units in the body. Some, like those in the blood, are separate; others are connected to each other to form tissues

tissues are composed of cells and are subdivided into four primary groups: muscle, nervous, epithelial (which lines structures) and connective (which supports structures)

organs are composed of tissues that form a structure such as the heart, stomach, liver or skin

At the lowest level are atoms, of which all matter is composed and which can combine to make molecules and macromolecules. In biological systems, living organisms, only a few types of atom are found in large quantities, for example carbon, hydrogen and oxygen. Molecules are combinations of atoms: one oxygen atom and two hydrogen atoms, for example, combine to make one molecule of water. Some molecules are very big, for example **proteins**, **fats** and **carbohydrates**, but if broken down into their constituent atoms, they are also mainly composed of carbon, hydrogen and oxygen. Molecules and macromolecules are studied by biochemists.

The macromolecules combine to make small structures called **organelles**, 'little organs', which are found in cells. These organelles are studied by cell biologists. Each has its specialised function so that the process of, for example, converting food into energy is carried out by an organelle called a mitochondrion.

Cells are the smallest functioning unit within which life can be carried out; they are like little chemical factories. Some organisms are composed of just one microscopic cell and are said to be unicellular. Humans are composed of billions of microscopic cells and are thus multicellular. Figure 1.1 shows a typical animal cell.

Tissues are groups of structurally and functionally similar cells. Tissues can be solid such as skin, or liquid such as blood.

Organs are specialised structures composed of tissues that carry out certain functions. The heart, for example, is an organ that pumps blood, whereas the stomach is an organ that breaks down (digests) food. Organs can work together in systems to carry out particular functions involved in sustaining the life of the

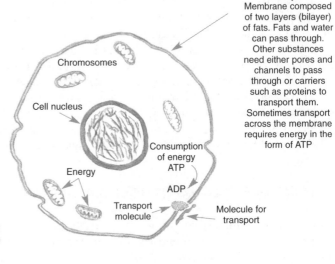

Genetics
The nucleus of the cell contains genetic information. This information, in the form of genes on long DNA strands called chromosomes, instructs the cell on how to make proteins

Energy
Mitochondria are organelles (little organs) found in cells. Their role is to convert glucose and oxygen into energy in the form of ATP (adenosine triphosphate). When energy is needed, ATP is converted into ADP (adenosine diphosphate) and releases energy during this reaction

Transport
Membrane composed of two layers (bilayer) of fats. Fats and water can pass through. Other substances need either pores and channels to pass through or carriers such as proteins to transport them. Sometimes transport across the membrane requires energy in the form of ATP

Chromosomes

Cell nucleus

Consumption of energy ATP

Energy

ADP

Transport molecule

Molecule for transport

Figure 1.1   Typical animal cell

organism by maintaining optimal conditions for the cells, of which the organism and its organs and tissues are composed.

Physiology studies systems, organs and tissues. Each specialist area, however, needs to be aware of other levels of explanation so that when we are discussing, for example, an organ, we must be aware that it is composed of millions of cells and that each cell behaves in a certain way as a result of the chemicals from which it is made.

A multicellular organism, such as a human, carries out the functions necessary to keep itself alive; the link between large structures such as organs and small, microscopic structures such as the cell, or subcellular organelles such as the mitochondria, will become clear.

The types of function that must be carried out by a multicellular organism such as a human and the organs that carry out these functions are illustrated in Figure 1.2 and explained below.

Digestion

Single-celled organisms only need to get food molecules such as proteins and fats into their one cell. All cells are surrounded by a bilayer of fats called a **membrane**, which encloses the cell, keeping the contents, the organelles and molecules, inside and excluding other molecules (see Figure 1.1 of a typical animal cell). Only certain substances are soluble in this fatty membrane; that is, it only allows certain substances to enter the cell. The cell must transport food molecules across the cell membrane to provide energy to keep the cell alive, and remove waste products, which, if they remained in the cell, would be toxic. Transporting molecules such as water and fats is easy across the cell membrane as these are soluble in the membrane. Proteins and carbohydrates do not cross easily and must be carried through the membrane, which sometimes takes energy.

> **membrane** – fatty bilayer surrounding a cell and presenting a semi-permeable barrier

Energy (calories) comes from food such as carbohydrates and fats, which can be converted by the cell into a chemical called adenosine triphosphate, (ATP). One of the main purposes of feeding is to extract energy from foods, the other being to extract from food materials such as proteins that can be recycled into new proteins to enable the cells to carry out their various functions. Most of the chemical reactions carried out in the cell and the organelles of the cell are performed by proteins.

Multicellular organisms such as humans cannot take food into each cell quite so readily. We find our food as much larger compounds, sometimes as large as the parts of animals or plants, rather than of the molecular size needed to enter a cell. Diminishing the size of these large food particles to small molecules such as proteins, fats and carbohydrates requires digestion. The digestive system is composed of various organs all with the aim of reducing the size of the food initially taken in to molecules that can enter microscopic cells. Every cell needs food to provide energy to sustain itself.

The digestive system begins with the mouth and teeth, which start to grind the food mechanically to smaller pieces (see Figure 1.2). There are also chemicals released in saliva that begin to break down food. Once the food has been chewed and swallowed, it enters the stomach, a stretchable organ that churns it up mechanically into smaller particles. The stomach also releases a strong acid that helps to kill the bacteria entering with the food.

> *Thinking about...*
>
> What do you think might be the advantages and disadvantages of the size of the food that humans eat, for example a baked potato or a steak?

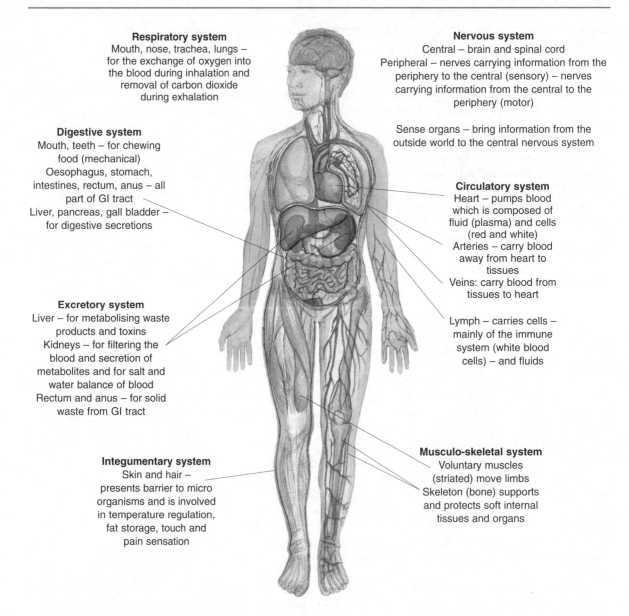

Respiratory system
Mouth, nose, trachea, lungs –
for the exchange of oxygen into
the blood during inhalation and
removal of carbon dioxide
during exhalation

Nervous system
Central – brain and spinal cord
Peripheral – nerves carrying information from the
periphery to the central (sensory) – nerves
carrying information from the central to the
periphery (motor)

Sense organs – bring information from the
outside world to the central nervous system

Digestive system
Mouth, teeth – for chewing
food (mechanical)
Oesophagus, stomach,
intestines, rectum, anus – all
part of GI tract
Liver, pancreas, gall bladder –
for digestive secretions

Circulatory system
Heart – pumps blood
which is composed of
fluid (plasma) and cells
(red and white)
Arteries – carry blood
away from heart to
tissues
Veins: carry blood from
tissues to heart

Lymph – carries cells –
mainly of the immune
system (white blood
cells) – and fluids

Excretory system
Liver – for metabolising waste
products and toxins
Kidneys – for filtering the
blood and secretion of
metabolites and for salt and
water balance of blood
Rectum and anus – for solid
waste from GI tract

Musculo-skeletal system
Voluntary muscles
(striated) move limbs
Skeleton (bone) supports
and protects soft internal
tissues and organs

Integumentary system
Skin and hair –
presents barrier to micro
organisms and is involved
in temperature regulation,
fat storage, touch and
pain sensation

Figure 1.2   Organs and body systems

The semi-digested food then enters a long tube-like structure called the intestine. Here, chemical secretions from other organs, such as bile from the liver, help to digest the food into macromolecules. All food that is not broken down is eliminated at the end of the intestine via the rectum and anus. The entire length from the stomach to the rectum is part of the gastrointestinal tract, or alimentary canal. In fact, food passing through this tract is not really considered to be part of the body. Only once it is small enough to be absorbed, that is, to cross from the tract into the body, is it ready for use by all the cells of the body.

Why do we need to eat bulky fibre to keep us healthy?

Fibre is composed of a type of carbohydrate that is not digestible by humans. Even once it has been chewed and mechanically sheared into smaller pieces, it cannot be chemically broken down in the gastrointestinal tract to macromolecular size for absorption. It remains too large to cross into the body and therefore remains in the tract. Fibre, however, helps to push other food through the gastrointestinal tract and therefore aids digestion and elimination.

Digestion, then, is the process of taking large food particles and breaking them down mechanically and chemically into smaller macromolecules and molecules for absorption into the body so that all the cells can use them for energy or as building blocks to replace worn out parts of cells. Once the food particles are small enough, they can be absorbed into the rest of the body. This requires that they cross the membranes of the cells lining the gastrointestinal tract. After this has been done, the digested food particles or macromolecules must be available to every cell in the body rather than just those in the vicinity of the gastrointestinal tract. To be available, these macromolecules must therefore be transported to all parts of the body.

Transport

Macromolecules and molecules from food digestion are transported around the body to reach the cells. Transport is carried out by the circulatory system, which is composed of a series of tubes and a transport medium. The tubes or vessels are akin to roads, with large motorways and small branch roads going to local areas. In the circulatory system, the large tubes are the arteries and veins, and the small tubes the capillaries (see Figure 1.2 above). The transport medium carrying the food molecules around is the blood, which comprises a watery fluid, plasma, as well as cells and molecules. Some food molecules cannot float freely in the blood and must be carried by other molecules – transport proteins, such as albumin. Blood can squeeze into the small spaces of the capillaries to transport food molecules to every part of the body. To aid transport, there is a pumping device pushing the blood and its contents around the blood vessels. The pump is the heart, a large, muscular organ (see Figure 1.2 above).

Food molecules such as carbohydrates are thus available for all the cells of the body. Cells take in the carbohydrates across their membrane and transport them to the mitochondria (see Figure 1.1 above), where they are converted into energy. To convert a carbohydrate into energy, the carbohydrate must undergo a chemical reaction similar to that of converting petrol into energy to propel a car. Carbohydrates are the cells' main fuel and must be 'burnt' to release their energy. This burning takes place by a reaction called oxidation, in which oxygen is added. The main difference between our reactions and that of a car is that we carry out the oxidation at 37°C whereas cars oxidise petrol at a very high temperature. We can operate at this lower temperature because we have proteins called enzymes in our mitochondria that can perform this reaction at this temperature.

> *Thinking about...*
>
> Think about some everyday things that move. What types of energy are used to make them move?

Respiration

The air around us is composed of various molecules, including oxygen. We thus need to extract the oxygen from this mixture to combine it with the carbohydrates to release energy. In order to do this, we have a respiratory system composed of two lungs (see Figure 1.2 above), bag-like organs that expand each time we breathe in. During inspiration, air enters the lungs. The oxygen must be collected from this and transported to all the cells in the body. Around each lung are millions of capillaries, oxygen passing or diffusing from the lungs into the blood in these for transport to the cells. The blood contains a transport protein, haemoglobin, which specialises in transporting oxygen. Haemoglobin does not float freely in the blood but is contained in specialised cells called red blood cells whose sole purpose is to transport oxygen to the cells.

The transport system thus carries food from the digestive system and oxygen from the respiratory system. It links these systems together, each system being redundant without the other.

 Why is heart failure so dangerous?

If the heart stops pumping blood around the circulatory system, fuel and oxygen do not reach the cells so these cannot make the energy they need to carry out all their living processes. Within a very short time, the mitochondria run out of fuel and energy. The cells cannot maintain themselves, and molecules start to enter and leave them as the control that the membrane usually exerts disappears. The cells thus become poisoned and die. This may be local and reversible if the heart starts beating again; too many cells may, however, die, causing death of the whole organism.

EXAMPLE 1.1

Hypoxia

In hypoxia, the body's cells become deficient in their oxygen supply, the oxidation to provide energy being impaired and ATP production being reduced. If someone shows signs of hypoxia, such as mental fatigue, drowsiness or general weakness, how can physiology assist our understanding of what is happening and help us to address the problem?

A logical way of analysing the possible causes of hypoxia is to draw up a list of the mechanisms whereby oxygen is transferred from the outside air to the cells in the tissues. Any impairment of function involving any of these processes is a potential cause of hypoxia.

● *Nerves and respiratory muscles*

Nerves control the movement of muscles, including those involved in respiration – respiratory muscles – which cause inhalation and exhalation to occur. If these nerves are damaged by, for example, head injury or too much morphine, they stop innervating the muscles, and the muscles will not be able to contract adequately and ventilate the lungs.

Anything that interrupts the conduction of impulses from the brain to the respiratory muscles will cause hypoxia. A cervical transection of the spinal cord (a broken neck), for example, or motor neurone disease, which affects the nerve cells (neurones), will impair ventilation. In addition, the respiratory muscles themselves may present a problem if their function is altered in some way by one of the many diseases affecting muscles, collectively known as myopathies.

- *Conducting airways*

The process by which the lungs are ventilated requires not only the actions of the respiratory muscles, but also an airway through which the air can move. The airways consist of the nasal cavity, the pharynx, the larynx, the trachea, the bronchi and those bronchioles without alveoli (see below). A variety of changes can increase airway resistance by narrowing the tubing, as is seen with the muscular spasm of asthma or the excess mucus of bronchitis.

- *Pleurae*

The pleurae are double membranes that attach the lungs to the chest wall and the diaphragm so that when the thorax expands, the lungs move with its walls. If the adhesion between the lung and the chest wall is broken, for example by a pneumothorax (air from a ruptured lung entering between the membranes), the lung collapses and ventilation cannot occur.

- *Lungs*

The inhaled air must also be able to diffuse across from the lungs into the blood. It does this in regions of the lung called alveoli, which are sacs composed of very thin tissue to facilitate diffusion. Alveolar tissue is normally light and distends easily as the thorax expands. However, if the nature of the tissue changes, for example by thickening, the ability of the lungs to take up oxygen is reduced, and ventilation is compromised. Such thickening can be due to the accumulation of fluid, for example in pneumonia, or the formation of scar tissue after an infection. Any condition in which lung tissue is destroyed, such as emphysema, reduces its surface area and compromises ventilation.

- *Circulation of oxygen from the lungs to the tissues*

After entering the blood, the oxygen is transported mainly attached to haemoglobin in the red cells. It follows therefore that anaemia, in which the number of red blood cells falls, is a cause of hypoxia. The effective transport of oxygen also requires the heart to be an adequate pump, so a fall in cardiac output, for example in heart failure, is also a cause of this condition. In some congenital heart defects, venous blood (containing less oxygen) is mixed with arterial (oxygen-rich) blood so that the blood pumped to the tissues has less oxygen in it than unadulterated arterial blood. Narrowing of the arteries, as in atherosclerosis, can reduce the blood flow and lead to hypoxia.

A physiological framework can therefore be used to understand the causes of the symptoms of hypoxia (lethargy) as well as assisting the identification of which particular mechanism or function is impaired and causing the hypoxia. Once the causal mechanisms are understood and identified, attempts may be made to manage, control or remove the symptoms of hypoxia.

Excretion

metabolism – the chemical
processes occuring within
the cells. The breakdown of
large molecules into smaller
ones is known as
catabolism, whereas the
synthesis of larger molecules
from smaller ones is known
as anabolism

As well as food being digested for energy production, in combination with oxygen, particles such as proteins are taken in and broken down to their constituent parts, amino acids, to be reformed into new proteins. All of these processes are part of a series of reactions, called **metabolism**, aimed at keeping the cells alive. From all these processes, waste products such as carbon dioxide, protein fragments and cell debris are formed. These must be removed as their build-up is toxic to the cells. The circulatory system, which has access to all the cells, transports the waste away. Carbon dioxide is excreted from the lungs each time we exhale. Food and cell debris is generally metabolised into less harmful chemicals in the liver and excreted via the rectum (in the faeces) or the kidneys and urethra (in the urine).

The kidneys (see Figure 1.2 above) act as filters for the blood. Blood is pumped through them at high pressure, solid particles – solutes – are extracted from the blood solvent carrying them. Some water from the blood also passes into the kidney tubules and, together with the solutes, forms urine, which is stored in the bladder until excretion via the urethra. The kidneys are not only filters, but are also involved in water and salt balance in the body, reabsorbing water in times of dehydration so that the urine becomes more concentrated.

Movement

The bodies of most animals are capable of moving. Movement is necessary to reach food and avoid being some other animal's food. Although each cell is in fact capable of movement, sheets of specialised cells form muscle tissue. The muscles are capable of contraction, electrical messages from the nervous system innervating muscles causing them to contract. There are various types of muscle:

● muscle that forms the heart (cardiac muscle) which contracts throughout life
● muscles that squeeze food around and through the stomach and intestines (smooth or involuntary muscle)
● muscle that moves the limbs around (striated or voluntary muscle).

Voluntary muscle is attached to the skeleton via tendons. The skeleton is composed of a hard substance, bone, which protects the internal organs and gives support to the body. Voluntary muscle is so called because we control its movement by sending it electrical messages from our brain.

Muscle contraction requires energy, which is why muscles have a very good blood supply. When we cause our muscles to contract faster, more blood is required to deliver the fuel and oxygen needed for conversion by the mito-chondria in the muscle cells into energy.

All the systems described above must therefore work together to maintain the integrity of the body and its constituent cells. When more oxygen is needed, for example when the body is using up more energy during exercise, the heart must pump blood to the lungs and around the body more quickly. All these systems can be speeded up, or slowed down as appropriate, by two other systems of the body:

- the **endocrine system** – involving chemical signals called hormones
- the **nervous system** – sending messages via electrical signals called action potentials.

These two systems act to integrate, co-ordinate and communicate information arising both within the body and from the world in which the body finds itself, thus maintaining the body under the optimal conditions for cell chemistry. Maintaining such conditions requires homeostatic mechanisms.

Homeostasis

All cells, whether from plants, bacteria, frogs or humans, have some common properties and need to carry out certain functions to maintain themselves – to keep themselves alive. To be able to carry out these activities, cells must maintain themselves within very strict and quite narrow ranges. Humans have cells that function only within a temperature range around 37°C and strict oxygen/carbon dioxide limits. Other cells, such as those of aquatic organisms or plants, have different ranges, but they still need to be kept within their optimal limits for the cell to survive and flourish. When the conditions veer outside these limits, life is threatened, and the cell, or the whole organism if it is composed of billions of cells, may die. Knowing what these limits are is part of the subject of physiology.

The mechanisms enabling a cell to stay within its optimal range are part of a system called **homeostasis**. Claude Bernard, in 1857, first observed that 'it is the constancy of the internal environment which is the condition of free and independent life. All vital mechanisms, however varied they may be, have only one object, that of preserving constant the conditions of life in the internal environment.'

Bernard's concept remains the framework within which physiology operates. Cells are bathed by interstitial fluid, which is their internal environment. This fluid provides nutrients and oxygen to sustain the life of each cell. Waste products from the cell's metabolism are added to the internal environment before being removed to the blood and then disposed of in various ways. If the nutrient and oxygen supply were compromised and the waste products accumulated, the cells would clearly die.

Walter Cannon, in 1929, coined the term 'homeostasis' to denote the constant and optimal internal environment. The paradigm of physiology is essentially simple: if something happens to change the internal environment, physiological pathways are in place to reduce the extent of the change and return to the status quo.

CONTROL MECHANISMS IN PHYSIOLOGY

The two body systems that control all others are:

- the nervous system, composed of cells called neurones that generate nerve impulses and synthesise chemical neurotransmitters
- the endocrine system, which uses hormones circulating in the blood.

---

endocrine system – endocrine glands produce hormones that are secreted into the blood and thereby circulate to other organs, where they control activity

nervous system – the central nervous system comprises the brain and spinal cord, which is connected to the tissues by nerves. The nervous system co-ordinates sensory and motor processes as well as enabling thoughts and feelings to occur

homeostasis – the constant and optimal internal environment. Cells are bathed in interstitial fluid, which is maintained at a constant temperature and chemical composition by the physiological systems of the body

A particular cell may be controlled by the neural or the hormonal system, or the two together. Both systems exert some degree of control over their effectors, systems such as muscles or glands that bring about a response. Apart from the different mechanisms that the two systems use to effect control, their timing is different. Neural control can be extremely rapid – some impulses being transmitted along neurones at over 100 metres per second – causing a fast response, for example pulling the arm away from a source of pain before the brain has actually sensed it. The effects are also short lived. Hormonal control, on the other hand, relies on the blood for transport and then elicits chemical changes in the cells, which can take some time to become apparent. Thyroxine, the main hormone produced by the thyroid gland, takes 2–3 days from its release from the gland until its actions (raising the metabolic rate) appear, and its effects can last for as long as 60 days.

Neural control mechanisms

The nervous system gathers information from the outside world, so that we can react to our environment, and from the inside world, so that we are kept in homeostasis and motivated to drink, urinate, feed, breathe and maintain our internal temperature. It links signals, or stimuli, to responses or effectors (Figure 1.3).

To gather information from the outside world, we have a number of sense organs, composed of receptors each tuned to a different energy form, each being capable of receiving a particular type of signal. Our eyes are tuned to electromagnetic light, our ears to oscillating air, our noses to chemical emissions and our skin to mechanical pressure (via touch receptors) and temperature (temperature receptors). All our sense organs or receptors translate the signal that they receive into an electrical impulse that is carried along the sensory nerves from the periphery of our bodies to our brain. The electrical impulses, called action potentials, move along a part of a nerve cell called an axon, which is an elongated stretch of the nerve cell's membrane.

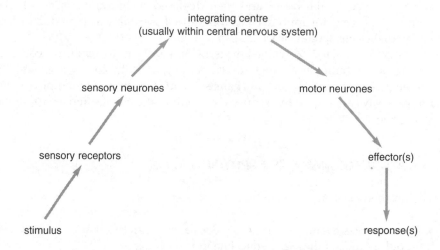

Figure 1.3   Stimulus–response

Information is assimilated in the central part of our nervous system, the spine and brain, and acted upon. Information in the form of electrical impulses can be taken to the muscles along motor axons and cause the muscles to contract (Figure 1.3). Information can be relayed to internal organs such as glands, leading to the release of hormones. Information taken to internal organs can also cause the contraction of the smooth muscles, for example those around the gastrointestinal tract which push food along. This occurs without our conscious control. This internal effect is instigated by a part of the nervous system called the autonomic nervous system, to distinguish it from the sensory and motor pathways that innervate voluntary, skeletal muscles.

A study of the mechanism of the nerve impulse, the release of neurotransmitters and nerve actions in the tissues demonstrates how physiology operates at the cellular level and gives rise to manifestations that can present as physical signs and symptoms.

The *nerve impulse* (action potential)

Nerve cells, like any other cells, have a lipid membrane, one part of this being elongated in neurones to form an axon. Fats can cross the membrane of the axon, but charged atoms – ions – cannot. Nerve transmission relies on this fact. The differing concentration of ions on either side of the axonal membrane causes a voltage difference. If tiny pores are opened in the axon, ions will move to reduce this difference. When they move, a current is formed that is exactly like the current flowing through electrical wiring. The nervous system thus runs on an electric current. Each time an electrical impulse (action potential) is sent along an axon, a piece of information is relayed in the form of a current. All our thoughts, feelings, sensations and movements are thus electrical messages.

Giving electrical stimulation to the heart is akin to jump-starting a car. Electrical impulses innervate muscle, including cardiac muscle. If your heart stops, an electrical impulse can be given to stimulate your heart muscle. Running on electricity is also the reason why we can be electrocuted.

> **nerve impulse** – an electrical impulse, also known as an action potential, that travels along the axon of a nerve cell, or neurone. The impulse carries information in the form of electrical current brought about by voltage changes

 Why does the brain consume so much oxygen and glucose that, without oxygen, we are brain-dead after 4 minutes?

> *Thinking about...*
>
> Popular hospital dramas show doctors applying electrical stimulation to people whose hearts have stopped. Why do you think this is?

Oxygen and glucose combine to release energy, this energy being used by, among other organs, the brain to set up the concentration difference of ions on either side of the axon membrane. This is called the resting potential, which is a misnomer as it takes a lot of energy to establish the different concentrations of ions on either side of the impermeable nerve axon membrane. There are billions of nerve cells in the brain, each needing energy to establish and maintain this resting potential. Energy is needed not for sending an action potential along an axon but for opening the little channels in the axon that allow the ions to flow. Once this has happened, the axon must re-establish the resting potential for future use.

A single action potential does not actually travel along a whole neurone; instead a succession of individual action potentials are generated along the axon which thereby 'conducts' impulses. The rate of movement along the axon of many neurones is about 100 metres per second. Electrical nerve conduction, the action potential, is thus very fast.

Neurotransmission

neurones – the nervous system is composed of millions of nerve cells called neurones. These have an elongated section of membrane called an axon along which electrical impulses can travel. At the end of each axon is a gap between it and the next cell in the pathway, this gap being called a synapse

The junction between **neurones** in a nerve pathway always includes a gap, this being called a synapse. A chemical called a **neurotransmitter** is released from the axon terminal and diffuses across the gap, becoming attached to receptors on the post-synaptic or effector cell membrane. This can cause an action potential to be generated in the next axon, thus taking electrical messages from the sense organs to the brain, around the brain and from the brain to the muscles.

 If the action potential is so fast (100 metres per second), why is the fastest running speed of athletes only 10 metres per second (that is, 100 metres in 10 seconds)?

neurotransmitters – chemicals released by the presynaptic neurone in response to an action potential. These chemicals are released into the synaptic gap and bind to receptors on the post-synaptic neurone, affecting the ability of the latter to conduct an electrical impulse in a nervous pathway

Electrical impulses travel around our bodies at about 100 metres per second, innervating the muscles and causing them to contract. The faster the muscle contracts, the faster we can move the limb. There is, however, an optimal rate of contraction of muscle, which is much less than the contraction of a nervous impulse. We can seldom run at the fastest muscle contraction rate as this requires all our muscle tissue to contract at a high rate synchronously, which could cause great pain and tissue damage.

Autonomic nervous system

Motor neurones, which innervate smooth muscle, cardiac muscle and some glands, constitute the autonomic nervous system, which is in turn subdivided into:

● The sympathetic nervous system
● The parasympathetic nervous system.

The sympathetic division is stimulated when an increase in, for example, metabolic rate is required; the parasympathetic system is innervated when a decrease is required. The parasympathetic division generally counterbalances the sympathetic division in 'rest and refuelling', dominating during sleep and digestion. Both branches are therefore involved in homeostasis.

Many changes brought about in the body are thus carried out automatically, without our conscious decision, by the autonomic nervous system. Much of what we consider to be motivation is part of homeostasis – the motivation to drink, sleep, urinate or eat is brought about by homeostatic mechanisms within the autonomic nervous system to aid our survival. In stressful conditions, for example being anxious or frightened, or engaging in some kind of physical activity, the sympathetic branch of the autonomic nervous system is brought into play. This is associated with 'fight or flight' response.

Sympathetic nervous system and stress

Sympathetic actions associated with fear or anxiety also produce familiar physical signs:

- dilated pupils
- a dry mouth, making it difficult to speak and swallow
- a strong, rapid heart rate, which can be described as palpitations
- pale, cold skin
- difficulty in passing faeces or urine
- a cold sweat.

A person thus affected can be described as being stressed, and the changes incurred are not promoting homeostasis but disturbing it. Digestion is inhibited, blood pressure rises, and many organs receive less blood flow and therefore operate less efficiently. Furthermore, the additional actions of circulating epinephrine (adrenaline) result in a rise in blood glucose and fatty acid level and an increased tendency for blood clots to form. This is why chronic stress, which may be associated with social factors, is deemed a health risk factor.

> **CONNECTIONS**
>
> Chapter 3 (Health Psychology) looks at the psychological processes leading to stress

The sympathetic nervous system is recruited in relation to the 'fight or flight' response. The heart beats faster and more strongly, and the arterioles constrict, both actions raising the arterial blood pressure. This propels the blood around the active body more quickly, thereby delivering nutrients and removing waste at an increased rate. Blood is diverted from the skin and gastrointestinal tract to the heart and skeletal muscles. The airways dilate, facilitating breathing. The sweat glands increase their output of sweat, which will tend to cool the body. Circulating hormones from the endocrine system reinforce and prolong the actions of direct sympathetic stimulation.

The mechanisms by which the sympathetic and parasympathetic nervous systems bring about opposing actions are based on the nature of the neurotransmitters involved. Sympathetic neurones release norepinephrine (noradrenaline) in the tissues, whereas the parasympathetic neurones, some of which innervate the same tissues, release a different neurotransmitter, acetylcholine. The changes brought about by the nervous system are thus mediated by chemicals that combine with receptors on the effector cell membranes.

EXAMPLE 1.2

Neural mechanisms and drugs

A knowledge of the processes by which impulses are generated, conducted and transmitted across synapses is clearly important for understanding how drugs work at a cellular level and their effects on people. A few examples are given here:

- *Local anaesthetics* act by preventing channels in the axon opening, thus stopping electrical impulses travelling along the axon. If the anaesthetic is applied to sensory neurones, action potentials will not be generated, and sensation will be lost. Anal-gesics, used for example by dentists, work in this way.

● *Laevodopa* (L-dopa) is taken up by neurones and converted into dopamine. This drug is used to treat Parkinson's disease, in which there is a deficiency of dopamine in the brain.

● *Amphetamine* stimulates the release of the neurotransmitter norepinephrine (nora-drenaline) from the sympathetic nerve endings in the tissues. The resultant 'high' can be attributed to the effects of excess norepinephrine in the system.

● *Salbutamol* is used in the treatment of asthma, in which there is a constriction of the airways. Salbutamol stimulates the cell membrane receptors to which epinephrine (adrenaline) and norepinephrine (noradrenaline) bind, thereby causing dilatation of the airways.

● *1-Propranolol* is called a beta-blocker because it physically combines with a type of receptor (beta-receptor) found in various sites including the heart. It thereby prevents epinephrine (adrenaline) and norepinephrine (noradrenaline) binding to the receptors, thus slowing the heart rate and reducing its force of contraction.

● *Atropine* blocks the effects of acetylcholine in the tissues by combining with the acetylcholine receptors. The action of atropine on the heart therefore reduces the action of the parasympathetic nervous system and increases the heart rate.

Hormonal control mechanisms

hormones – chemicals released by a gland. These chemicals are transported in the bloodstream. The hormone must bind to its appropriate receptor, which may be at some distance from the site of release. The binding affects the cell if the cell has a receptor for the hormone

Hormones are chemical messengers, most of which are secreted directly into the blood by endocrine glands. Hormones regulate many of the biochemical reactions taking place within the cells and consequently exert an influence upon a range of cellular processes, including metabolic rate, growth and the uptake, synthesis and secretion of materials. They do not initiate new reactions but modify the rates of those already taking place.

Some hormones, for example thyroxine and growth hormone, affect all, or most, tissues in the body, whereas others have a more limited action. Adrenocorticotrophic hormone, for example, acts only on specific cells in the adrenal cortex.

Negative feedback

negative feedback – a control mechanism such that when a value strays out of its set range, mechanisms are invoked to return it; an example is the action a thermostat has on a central heating system

Most hormone release is regulated via a *negative feedback* mechanism (Figure 1.4). A stimulus promotes the release of the hormone by an endocrine gland. The hormone then brings about a physiological response, which tends to reverse the stimulus, leading to a reduction in hormone output. That is, the response has a negative feedback effect on the rate of secretion of the hormone. In this way, the hormone level in the blood remains relatively low.

After a meal, for example, the blood glucose level tends to rise as the digested food enters the bloodstream. The increased glucose concentration stimulates the cells in the pancreas that produce the hormone insulin, so that the level of insulin in the blood rises in turn. Insulin stimulates the uptake of glucose by a variety of tissues as well as inhibiting the liver from releasing it; thus its actions lower the blood glucose level again. The negative feedback mechanism exerts a

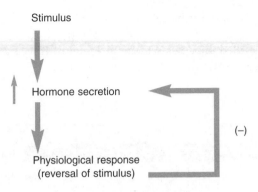

Stimulus

Hormone secretion

(–)

Physiological response
(reversal of stimulus)

Figure 1.4   Negative feedback

brake on the degree to which the blood glucose level drops and represents the essence of maintaining homeostasis.

Diabetes mellitus is a relatively common condition in which either there is a deficiency of insulin production in the pancreas or the insulin that is produced has a reduced action in the tissues. The primary effect of insulin deficiency is a rise of blood glucose concentration which is why people with diabetes mellitus regularly check their blood glucose level.

 How does negative feedback influence the hormones involved in reproduction?

The hormones follicle stimulating hormone (FSH) and luteinising hormone (LH) regulate the female sex hormones (oestrogen and progestogen). FSH and LH also stimulate the growth of follicles containing eggs in the ovaries. In the menstrual cycle, a surge in the release of LH from the anterior pituitary into the blood triggers the release of a mature egg from the ovary. Contraceptive pills containing oestrogens and progestogens suppress the concentrations of FSH and LH in the blood by negative feedback, the result being that the follicles do not grow and ovulation does not occur, thereby preventing conception.

Genes and genetics

All human cells, apart from mature red blood cells, have a nucleus. The rest of the cell within the cell membrane is known as the cytoplasm. The nucleus contains the genetic material deoxyribonucleic acid (DNA), which codes for the synthesis of proteins.

Proteins are macromolecules that are essential nutrients in our diet. They are composed of amino acids. Organisms require about 20 amino acids to synthesise all the proteins they need. Humans can synthesise some amino acids, but must obtain eight from their diet.

Proteins carry out most of the functions of the body. Many neurotransmitters and hormones, for example, are proteins. Muscles are composed mainly of two types of proteins: actin and myosin. Oxygen is transported around the body by binding to the protein haemoglobin. There are also other transport proteins such

gene – a section of genetic material (DNA) that codes for a protein, that is, instructs the cell how to assemble amino acids into proteins. As there are thought to be about 100,000 proteins in humans, there are about 100,000 genes

as albumin. The ability of the cells to convert fuel such as glucose and oxygen to energy at 37°C rather than the high temperature a car needs is due to chemical converters called enzymes which are proteins. It is essential therefore that every cell can synthesise proteins when required and that the cell knows how to synthesise these.

EXAMPLE 1.3

Human Genome Project

The ongoing Human Genome Project aims to plot the precise sequence of genetic codes in human cells. It is hoped that this will allow the development of new knowledge on the causes and mechanisms of disease, particularly those such as hypertension or mental illness which have a complex origin. These illnesses have already been the subject of much genetic investigation, building on the partial knowledge of the human genome already available. It is now clear that whereas many such conditions have an inherited component, this is more in the nature of increased risk than a direct cause.

The ability to carry out routine genetic screening has wider implications that could affect the lives of apparently healthy people. The presence of specific genes may result in individuals having difficulty getting life insurance, for example, and some employers (particularly in the USA) are requiring potential employees to undergo genetic screening for particular diseases. There are moves to regulate the use of this scientific information by the insurance industry and for changes to employment and anti-discrimination law.

The Human Genome Project will be completed by 2003. The challenge for molecular biologists following the sequencing of the genome will be to find out what kinds of protein are encoded in the DNA and, more importantly, what they do in living cells. This represents a much greater task than the genome project itself. A new name, proteomics, has been coined to cover this field of study, which, it is anticipated, will be technically much more challenging than the sequencing of the genetic codes in the DNA.

Sources: the website of the Wellcome Foundation contains details of the Human Genome Project, see www.wellcome.ac.uk; Cedar and Terry (2000)

Our genetic material contains information on how to synthesise all the proteins that humans need, each gene containing the instructions for how to make a particular protein. We are composed of about 100,000 proteins, so there are about 100,000 genes with instructions for how to synthesise these. Each species, humans being one among many, has its own set of genes that define that species and code for the proteins needed to keep that species alive. Our set of genes, the human genome, is what is currently being analysed. Our set of genes is about 98 per cent the same as our nearest cousins, the apes.

Apart from each cell being able to synthesise proteins because it has the instruction manual of genetic material telling it how to do so, organisms are also able to pass on this information from generation to generation via reproduction.

Disease

The systems discussed above are all involved in maintaining the life of the organism. If they do not operate correctly, the internal environment will not be kept under the optimal condition for the cell and its chemicals to survive.

Diseases are brought about in various ways, the causes of which are the subject of many scientific and medical disciplines. Many theories abound as to the causes of disease. Coronary heart disease, for example, is said to be linked to family history and specific risk factors such as the blood lipid level. The study of physiology and the physiological pathways whereby life is maintained by homeostatic mechanisms helps to explain the normal workings of the body and what goes wrong in disease. It therefore has a major impact on health and medicine.

There is, however, also an area of study that has not been mentioned but has a great impact on health. Diseases can be caused by micro-organisms such as bacteria, parasites, fungi, protozoa and viruses. Humans tend to think that they are at the top of the food chain by virtue of farming and using other organisms such as wheat, barley, cows and sheep for human consumption. However, we are merely *in* the food chain, eating organisms and trying to avoid being eaten ourselves. It is not only large animals that threaten us: by far the most dangerous are micro-organisms, which look on us as their lunch and use us as a source of nutrients. As humans are made up of proteins, fats and carbohydrates, we provide a very convenient source of nutrition for micro-organisms.

Most micro-organisms are harmless, which is just as well as there are millions of them in the environment. Some are beneficial and help us digest our food, living in our gastrointestinal tract. Some protect us by merely living on us: our skin is covered with harmless micro-organisms that stop harmful ones from gaining a foothold by competing for space. Some micro-organisms are, however, harmful, causing disease in their hosts, such as us humans. These micro-organisms are pathogens. Luckily for us, we have a system that has evolved to protect us from pathogenic diseases – our immune system.

Immune system

The immune system is composed mainly of cells – white blood cells – that patrol through our blood and around our tissues to monitor any invasion by pathogens. All the cells of our bodies have a marker which distinguishes the cell as belonging to one individual rather than another. The molecule is called the MHC (major histocompatibility complex). Each one of us has an MHC molecule on every one of our cells, which is different from the MHC of any other individual. It is our individual signature. Our immune system recognises this molecule as self. All other cells from other individuals or other organisms have different marker molecules on their cell surface. Our immune system sees them as non-self and attacks and kills them.

Apart from the ability to differentiate self from non-self, the immune system also has a memory to avoid suffering the same disease twice. We get the initial disease while the immune system learns to recognise the new invader. If the invader multiplies more quickly than our system can kill it, the invader wins and we die. Mortality is a part of life, a characteristic of living organisms.

Thinking about...
Think about a disease you have encountered. What do you think caused it?

CONNECTIONS
Chapter 10 (Health Promotion) discusses interventions to reduce and prevent coronary heart disease

Thinking about...
Why do you think that the use of anti-bacterial soaps might be harmful?

When can the immune system present problems to the individual?

1. The immune system sometimes goes wrong, recognising the individual as non-self and attacking its own cells or parts of cells. This is called an auto-immune disease; examples are rheumatoid arthritis and systemic lupus erythematosus.

2. In transplant surgery, the immune system of the host, the person about to receive the donor organ, must be suppressed as the donor's MHC will be different from the host's MHC. The immune system of the host will start to attack the donated tissue if it is not suppressed.

3. We can have an immune reaction to harmless particles such as pollen.

Clean water, the removal and separation of waste and sewerage from water supplies, washing the hands before preparing and eating food, and the sterile, aseptic techniques of the operating theatre during surgery have all helped to reduce the chance of death from micro-organisms. Antibiotics, which can kill bacteria, have also been very useful, but the bacteria can evolve by mutation faster than we can, and can thus become resistant to antibiotics. An overuse of antibiotics removes the harmless bacteria and allows the pathogens to take a grip. The misuse of antibiotics in, for example, viral infections, viruses not being susceptible to antibiotics, has further eroded their effectiveness.

In hospital, many people succumb to infection that they did not have on admission. In the USA, the Centre for Disease Control and Prevention has claimed that there was a 36 per cent rise in the number of hospital-acquired infections between 1975 and 1995. It estimates that 2 million patients develop an infection in hospital each year, 90,000 of these dying as a result. Most of this is caused by poor hygiene, the lack of cleaning of lavatories, beds, sinks, tables and equipment, and cross-contamination between patients by staff who have not washed their hands or changed their gloves when moving from one patient to another.

The immune system is excellent at maintaining our bodies free of pathogens. Meanwhile, the pathogens are evolving in their search for new hosts. There is a constant balancing act between pathogens and our immune system. It is claimed that more people have died from diseases caused by micro-organisms than in all the world's wars.

Physiology and health

All the findings described above seek to make a direct link between cause and effect rather than an indirect link or a correlation. Consider, for example, the link between scurvy (a disease suffered particularly by sailors in the 17th and 18th centuries when they were at sea for a long period of time) and a lack of vitamin C. Americans may still describe British people as 'Limeys', a reference to the sailors who carried fresh fruit, particularly lemons and limes, on voyages, this fruit containing vitamin C. The link to scurvy is a direct scientific finding, which also presents a direct solution.

Indirect explanations for the high incidence of scurvy in sailors might be socio-economic and refer to men from poor backgrounds being forced (by press gangs) into being sailors in 18th century Britain to develop British trade routes

CONNECTIONS

Chapter 2 (Epidemiology) examines how cause and association are identified in the study of disease and colonisation. Many illnesses in the past were blamed on the patient because of religion, superstition or prejudice. Contemporary explanations for scurvy might look to a lack of access to fresh fruit, to a lack of education on nutrition, to the relatively high cost of fresh fruit or possibly to cultural reasons for not eating fresh fruit. All of these indirect reasons do not deny that the cause is lack of vitamin C, a scientific finding. The cure is known only because of scientific investigations into normal physiology and biochemistry. Therefore physiology, albeit not a medical science, still has a direct impact on our health.

THEORETICAL AND METHODOLOGICAL APPROACHES

Physiology is a scientific discipline, science often being typified as a rational means of acquiring knowledge through the observation of physical phenomena. Its methods are rigorous and systematic. Scientific truths are popularly believed to be objective, that is, independent of any particular researcher's beliefs or views (Chalmers, 1983). Science includes the different approaches of induction, deduction and hypothesis testing.

> **CONNECTIONS**
>
> Chapter 2 (Epidemiology) considers the nature of the scientific method in relation to the study of patterns of disease in populations

INDUCTION

Induction is the process of recording a large number of observations over a wide range of conditions until a universal statement or law can be induced that applies to all the individual observations.

The example of the endocrine glands illustrates the inductive approach. Observations by many scientists showed that the underfunctioning of an endocrine gland caused a deficiency syndrome. Such observations were made on people with diseases such as diabetes mellitus, which results from a deficiency of the hormone insulin, produced by the pancreas. Symptoms such as loss of weight, hunger, thirst and the production of a large amount of sweet urine were observed. The experimental removal of the pancreas from animals also resulted in the deficiency state.

Induction therefore identified the universal law that the underfunctioning of an endocrine gland causes a deficiency syndrome. This description of science could really only apply to its origins, when virtually nothing was already known and extensive recordings of aspects of the natural world preceded the generation of laws or theories.

> **induction** in science is the process of reaching a generalisation or law from many individual specific observations

DEDUCTION

The description of science as entirely inductive misses out the mental processes of theorising. Science often progresses via suggesting an explanation or scientific theory, an 'informed guess' on how something might work, which lends itself to testing. *Deduction* is essentially logical reasoning. Deduction in science allows predictions to be made from its laws and theories as a way of testing them.

> **deduction** is the converse of induction, whereby a specific inference or prediction is made from a generalisation

Back to the endocrine glands. The universal statement is so far rather vague – an underfunctioning gland causes disruption in the body. This could apply to any gland or indeed organ. A criterion for endocrine glands, however, is that they secrete hormones into the blood, the hormones acting on tissues distant from the gland itself. Logically then, if the gland is an endocrine gland, injecting extracts of the gland into the blood will reverse the deficiency syndrome.

PROOF AND FALSIFICATION

How do we know when a law or theory is true or proven? Induction and deduction have their place, but can it ever be said that enough observations have been made to prove a law, or that enough predictions based on that law have been tested? Scientists are not naive observers – they make sense of observations through pre-existing theory, building on previous scientific information. Indeed, they have to obtain funding for their research and need to produce 'findings' to stay in work. The notion of value-free, objective investigation thus does not stand up to scrutiny.

Falsificationism, as propounded by Karl Popper in the 1950s, acknowledged that scientists do have some preconceptions about the work they are doing, some kind of **hypothesis** on how the thing works and also that it is not absolutely possible to prove that something is true. Popper (1959) suggested that good science starts with a hypothetical explanation that is falsifiable. Logically, deductions can be made from the hypothesis, and these can be tested. If the hypothesis does not stand up to testing, it is rejected; if it does, the hypothesis is not rejected, instead being subjected to even more rigorous testing. This description of science, the hypothetico-deductive method, is still reasonably well accepted today. It can, however, be argued that this does not really describe the reality of scientific endeavour. Scientists may be reluctant to discard their beliefs, either modifying their hypothesis or finding some alternative explanation, such as faulty or misused equipment, for contrary findings instead of rejecting long-held beliefs.

Kuhn (1962) suggested that science progresses by a series of revolutions. A number of contrary findings may be accommodated until an alternative paradigm or framework is proposed that explains existing incompatible findings. A 'paradigm shift' then occurs, whereby scientists adopt a new explanatory system. Einstein's law of relativity is an example of a paradigm shift from Newtonian physics.

EXPERIMENTATION

Science is a systematic discipline involving the painstaking recording of observations made under carefully controlled conditions. The aim of scientific research is that the same piece of work could be repeated by another person and identical results obtained. The equipment used must be accurate and must reliably measure whatever data are being recorded.

The unravelling of a biological pathway usually requires some intervention or interference whereby the changes can be noted and inferences drawn, for example if it is suspected that a gland in one part of the body controls another

falsification – Karl Popper suggested that it was more realistic to falsify a scientific hypothesis than to prove it to be true

hypothesis – a proposed explanation for a phenomenon

experimentation – experiments are characteristic of science as a way of testing a hypothesis. The aim is to reduce the number of factors that may affect the results so that the procedures are reproduceable

by hormones, the removal of that gland will result in physiological changes in the effector. If the hypothesis is that one part of the body controls another by nerves, cutting or inactivating the nerves will prevent the control system working and there will be clear differences between the observations recorded in the control (uncut) group and in the experimental (cut) group.

CONNECTIONS

Chapter 2 (Epidemiology) discusses the nature and process of 'social' experiments (randomised controlled trials)

Techniques

In vitro (literally 'in glass') studies are those undertaken outside the body. It is possible to keep organs alive outside the body by providing them with fluid that mimics interstitial fluid, the internal environment. It is clearly easier both to manipulate the organ concerned and to observe and measure its responses when it is separated from the rest of the body. In vitro techniques have the potential to affect health. Techniques developed in studying cells have, for example, resulted in the possibility of in vitro fertilisation (IVF) and the subsequent birth of babies to couples who are unable to conceive and bear children naturally.

Measurements on living human beings

Techniques can be subdivided into invasive and non-invasive, in other words, in terms of whether or not they involve introducing substances into the body. Arterial blood pressure can be measured invasively by inserting a cannula into an artery and connecting it up to a pressure-measuring machine. Alternatively, the sphygmomanometer measures blood pressure non-invasively.

Clinical observations of patients with congenital deficits or hyperfunction, particularly in the field of endocrinology, have led to information on the actions of hormones. An overactive gland exaggerates the normal effects of the hormone(s) secreted. For example, patients with an overactive thyroid gland show symptoms of a raised metabolic rate, including weight loss, feeling hot and an increased pulse rate. The actions of the thyroid hormones are revealed. Conversely, an underactive thyroid results in symptoms of a reduced metabolic rate, such as mental and physical lethargy, and a tendency to put on weight, feel cold and have a slow pulse. Such non-invasive observations preceded the experimental manipulations of endocrine glands, followed by isolating and purifying the hormones from the gland, identifying the hormone structure and in some cases synthesising it.

New imaging techniques introduced in the 1970s have enabled studies of internal organs be undertaken for both research and clinical investigation. The techniques or 'scans' include computed tomography (CT), magnetic resonance imaging (MRI) and positron emission tomography (PET). CT scans use rotating X-rays projected through the body to produce a series of images that are combined by computer to produce a 'slice' through the body. MRI uses magnetic fields and radio waves to energise hydrogen atoms in the body. Three-dimensional colour images are produced of tissues (soft and hard), comparative metabolic activity and blood flow. PET scans are taken following the injection of a radioactive molecule such as glucose into the bloodstream. The more active a tissue is, the more glucose it takes up, the fate of the radioactivity being analysed by the computer, which produces a colour map reflecting different levels of metabolic activity. By such means, particular areas of the brain can be 'seen' to be associated with specific functions: the occipital lobes

EXAMPLE 1.4

Scientific research

The following summary of a piece of work carried out for the Medical Research Council provides an example of the reality of the scientific process.

Background:

At the time of this research apprenticeship (the early 1970s), it was known that, at the beginning of a period of physical exercise, muscle cells increased their oxygen consumption, producing extra ATP, which was used in the contraction process. The prevailing view at that time was that the oxygen supply to the exercising muscle initially lagged behind its utilisation, the manifestation of this being the production of lactic acid (which dissociates into lactate and hydrogen ions). Once the exercise was underway, the cardiovascular and respiratory systems delivered oxygen to the cells at the required rate and lactic acid production ceased, although the lactate level remained high. In summary, then, the prevailing view was that lactic acid production was an initial event in exercise.

The hypothesis:

This project aimed to test the hypothesis that lactate production is an initial event in exercise. The research design needed to attempt to falsify, or disprove, this hypothesis.

Testing the hypothesis:

The experimental design was to use four human volunteers, all men (to exclude any sex difference), each acting as his own control. If the subjects exercised sufficiently hard to produce a constant, raised level of lactate in their blood, the lactate would, if the hypothesis were confirmed, be produced at the beginning of the exercise and then be 'trapped' in the circulation until the exercise ceased. If, however, the hypothesis was falsified, lactate would be being produced and removed all the way through the exercise at an equal rate.

The experimental techniques consisted of injecting each subject with a small intravenous dose of lactate in which the normal carbon atoms were replaced with radioactive carbon-14. Each subject walked on a treadmill sufficiently hard to produce a raised, constant concentration of lactate in the blood. A sample of blood was taken every few minutes during the exercise and recovery periods. The radioactive carbon was used to trace the fate of the lactate in the blood as well as in the carbon dioxide expired. Each subject acted as his own 'control' by being given the radioactive tracer and then resting rather than exercising. Blood and expired gas samples were taken in an identical pattern, these being analysed in each exercise and resting experiment.

The findings:

The results revealed that the radioactivity disappeared from the blood and appeared in carbon dioxide much more quickly during exercise than at rest. These findings were interpreted as being caused by the metabolism of lactate during exercise. If the concentration of lactate was steady, it followed that the production of lactate must have equalled the rate of its removal, as evidenced by the conversion of radioactive lactate into carbon dioxide in exhaled air. The initial event hypothesis was therefore falsified.

Some philosophers of science might argue that this should have had a revolutionary impact on this area of physiology. The change in view on lactate was, however, assimilated into the established 'information' by simply stating that lactate is not produced only at the beginning of exercise because the delivery of oxygen lags behind its usage. Instead, exercising muscle cells do not have the capacity to use the oxygen at a sufficient rate to avoid lactate production, so lactate production is ongoing.

are, for example, more active when the eyes are open, whereas the hippo-campus is active in memory tasks.

Scientific research thus involves much repetition and rigorous attention to detail, including considering cleanliness of equipment, timing and recording. Scientific information cannot be proved to be true, so the challenge is to fit new information into the field, cite other work that supports the findings and criticise work that does not. The interpretation of the data is the part involving human ideas and debate. Scientists may support a particular view but this is not entirely related to scientific rigour, reason and logic, being influenced by:

- aesthetics (it appeals to you)
- politics (your funding body expects a certain outcome)
- morals (for example you do not wish to support a view that one race has a higher IQ than another)
- conformity (how revolutionary you are prepared to be).

CASE STUDY – PAIN

Most of us have been ill at some time and visited the doctor or a hospital. One of the main ways in which we know we are ill is that we have a pain. But what is pain, and how do we know that we have it?

There are receptors over the surface of our body that respond to touch and to warm and cool stimuli. These convert the stimuli into electrical impulses or action potentials that travel along the axon of the neurone, carrying information about the stimulus to the brain. Each receptor has its particular sensitivity, so that touch receptors respond only to touch, and warm receptors respond only to warmth. Pain can be an extreme mechanical stimulus or a temperature stimulus, and there appear to be particular receptors that respond to these intense stimuli. These receptors, called nociceptors, are said to have a higher threshold than touch or normal temperature receptors, meaning that they respond only to more intense stimuli. They are not called pain receptors as the stimulus is not itself pain; instead, it is our perception of the stimulus that is interpreted as pain.

Nociceptors stimulate electrical impulses in their associated nerves, which take information to the brain. This we perceive as pain. These intense stimuli relate to their own receptors and nerves, and can therefore be thought of as a sense, just like any other sense. However, while, physiologically speaking, it can be seen that nociceptors are the same for everyone, our responses to this stimulation differ. Individuals are said to have different thresholds of pain tolerance, meaning that their response to an identical stimulation of the nociceptors may vary.

If we arrive at the doctors or hospital with a pain, there are particular conventions for the investigation.

1. Where is the pain?
The nervous system is able to detect the location of pain. Receptors on the surface of the body respond to mechanical pressure or temperature changes by trans-

mitting electrical signals along the neurone associated with the particular receptor that is being stimulated. The electrical stimulus travels along this neurone and enters the spinal cord. The electrical information from the original receptor is carried up the spinal cord along other neurones to the brain, forming a pathway of neurones and synapses. The electrical information from a particular receptor travels along its own unique pathway, this information being kept separate from electrical information from other receptors. The information goes to a particular region of the brain, which is in turn stimulated. Thus, a pinprick on the right fourth finger will stimulate local receptors to emit electrical activity along their associated neurones, which will send impulses to a particular area in the brain, different from the area corresponding to stimulation of the fourth finger of the left hand or the fourth toe of the right foot. The brain can therefore locate exactly where in the body the stimulus is coming from.

Where we feel the pain tells the doctor about possible problems. If we have a pain in our leg after having fallen, there is the possibility of a broken bone. If we have a pain in the region of our intestine, other possibilities arise. This may seem obvious, but it is necessary to consider it. Sometimes people have a pain in their left armpit, but there is no damage to the tissue or limbs in the area. This may be indicative of heart problems and is an example of 'referred pain'. A pain in the left armpit is associated with the heart because the heart originates in the same area during embryological development, gradually moving towards the centre of the chest as the embryo develops, but taking its own nerve supply with it. The nervous system is sometimes fooled by this. Knowing about referred pain requires a knowledge of embryology and neuroanatomy.

2. How long has the pain been going on?

Acute pain has a sudden onset and tends to be sharp. Chronic pain, pain that has been with us for more than 6 months, is usually duller but can have acute episodes. Acute pain that has no obvious cause, such as a broken bone, tends to make us anxious with regard to its cause. Chronic pain tends to make us depressed as it interferes with our day-to-day activities.

The receptors that are stimulated to cause electrical impulses along their associated neurones have a threshold below which they do not set up an electrical impulse or action potential in their neurone. The stimulus for a particular receptor must therefore be sufficient for the brain to receive an action potential from that particular area of the body. After the brain has been told of this once, there may not be any great benefit in continually telling it about a stimulus. Thus receptors are able to adapt, and some can stop sending messages after a while. Different receptors have a different length of time over which they adapt: some do this quickly, some more slowly. Once you have your clothes on, you do not need to be continually told that they are on your body. As your clothes continue to touch your body, your touch receptors should be stimulated, but they adapt. Only if your clothes are suddenly yanked across your body do you become aware of them, because new receptors are then being stimulated. The pain receptors (nociceptors) can also adapt. Although it is not known how this might happen, it is possible with chronic pain that the receptors that are stimulated are very slow or unable to adapt.

Acute pain is usually treated differently from chronic pain. There is often a direct cause such as appendicitis, which indicates the course of action. Chronic pain, such as back pain or the pain associated with terminal cancer, does not have an easily removed cause. In the case of appendicitis, surgery rather than painkillers is required, but there is a strong case for painkillers for backache or cancer.

Painkillers, or analgesics, operate at various levels of the pain stimulus–response. If tissue damage has been caused in, for example, a finger, by cutting, substances called prostaglandins are released to recruit the immune system. They also, however, cause swelling and inflammation, which can cause pain by stimulating local receptors. Analgesics such as aspirin prevent the release of prostaglandins and therefore reduce pain. The aspirin may be swallowed and travel through the digestive system and transport system before reaching the affected area, but it affects only the area where prostaglandins are being released so its effect is local and highly successful.

Local anaesthetics such as lignocaine act by blocking the movement of ions across the membrane of the neurone so that an action potential cannot travel. They are used in dentistry to numb the area. It is not yet possible to inject just the axon carrying the electrical impulse from the receptor that has been stimulated, for example by high mechanical pressure. Other axons are also influenced by the injection, and the action potentials cannot travel in them either. Thus pain, touch and motor information are affected.

A person with terminal cancer might be prescribed a strong analgesic, such as morphine. Central analgesics like morphine act in the spinal cord or brain at the synapses. They prevent neurotransmitters binding and therefore stop the continual transmission of an impulse from the first neurone in a sequence to the next neurone carrying the information up the spinal cord to the neurone receiving the information in the brain. Morphine was until recently not prescribed in the treatment of cancer as it was believed to be addictive and that patients gradually gained tolerance to the drug. Both of these claims have little physiological evidence.

Tolerance has many connotations. In terms of pain physiology, either one is becoming tolerant to the pain or one is becoming tolerant to the pain-relieving drugs and they are not having the effect that they should, one thus sensing the pain. Tolerance to pain can be caused by receptor adaptation or by the blocking of electrical signal transmission either in the neurone or at the synapse. At the synapse, the interruption of transmission could be due to endogenous analgesics being released. These are produced by the brain, and we presumably have some conscious control over them. Touch pathways can also block the transmission of nociceptive information (see gate control theory of pain below).

There may also be psychological reasons for tolerance to pain. If we are occupied with other things, we can forget our pain. For example, soldiers who have been wounded on the battlefield do not always feel the pain until they are back in a safe place. Our brains can focus on only a certain amount of information at a time, and we filter information continually. If you are in a crowded room, you do not hear all the conversations going on even though your ears are functioning. This is peripheral filtering. If somebody mentions your name, you will often hear it; it is relevant to you. This is central filtering. One can imagine the same with pain. If you make pain the centre of your existence, you will probably find that you are suffering from a low level of chronic pain all the time. Luckily, most of us are busy concentrating on other things. It is only when pain is perceived to be at a dangerous level that we need to take notice.

The second tolerance is to painkillers. Drugs fit into and bind to a specific receptor. Because of its chemical composition, each drug has a particular shape, so binding is specific to its receptor, as with a key fitting into a lock. There are a limited number of receptors. If there are not enough to prevent the transmission of action potentials from nociceptive neurones, pain will be felt. If the drugs are broken down (metabolised) faster than they can bind, pain will also be felt. The number of receptors can increase, but there is probably a maximum level. The dosage of drugs must also be kept within certain limits because of side-effects and toxicity. All chemicals, even ones we think of as good, such as vitamins, can be toxic in large quantities.

3. What type of pain is it?

The type of pain – stabbing, burning, itching and so on – helps us to assess the severity of the pain. Pain is, however, a particularly difficult problem. Most of us know what pain is, but pain has an individual quality. We cannot see or measure objectively other people's pain. With other stimuli such as light or sound, we have objective ways of measuring them. However, whereas there is a neurological link between a painful stimulus at a receptor and the receptor sending an electrical impulse along a sensory axon to the central nervous system, the effect it has on each individual varies.

4. What is the purpose of pain?

Pain has a function: to warn us of damage and to encourage us to rest and recuperate. Sometimes, however, it is dangerous to rest, for example on a battlefield, so we can shut down the sensation of pain. If we put our hand on something hot, sensory receptors in our skin send electrical impulses to our central nervous system to cause us to remove our hand before burning occurs. The cells of our skin can survive a range of temperature in various regions of the world but are happiest at around 20°C. At extreme temperatures, damage is done and cells die. If, however, we are able to shut down our perception of pain, perhaps pain is not merely a physiological pathway.

5. How does the perception of pain vary?

CONNECTIONS

Chapter 3 (Health Psychology) explains the gate control theory and the role of psychology in pain perception

One explanation of the variation in people's perception of pain can be found in the gate control theory of pain. This says that when nociceptors are stimulated to cause an electrical impulse in neurones, mechanisms can interrupt the synaptic transmission of this impulse along a chain of neurones. These mechanisms can be caused by the body releasing its own endogenous analgesics such as enkephalins and endorphins, substances that bind to the post-synaptic receptors and block the binding of neurotransmitters released by the presynaptic neurone carrying the action potential from the nociceptive receptor. Thus, the transmission is interrupted. There are various ways of causing the release of endogenous analgesics. One way seems to be rubbing the affected area, thus releasing normal touch responses and neurotransmitters, which bind to and block the post-synaptic receptors in the nociceptive pathways. It also appears to be possible for our brain to release these endogenous analgesics. Athletes can go through the pain barrier. Perhaps they are increasing the release of endogenous analgesics or learning to ignore the warning signs of tissue damage.

Personality also plays a part in a person's perception of pain: our tolerance to pain seems to differ according to our personality. If the same stimulus is applied to various people, the threshold for initiating an electrical stimulus in the nociceptive pathway seems to be similar, but how painful we say we find the pain differs from person to person. This tolerance may be learnt in childhood. Those of us who have been picked up and cuddled each time we cry may have a perception and manipulation of our perception of pain different from those who have experienced a more stoic childhood. Pain, therefore, does not have only a sensory cause, a stimulus: there is also a perception of or emotive relationship to pain. This can be seen clearly with the placebo effect.

All drugs coming onto the market must be tested in a double blind trial in which neither the administrator nor the receiver of the drug knows whether they are using the test drug, a drug already known to alleviate the symptoms, or a placebo, an innocuous substance consisting mainly of sugar and made to resemble the test drug. It is known that for most drugs, including painkillers, there is a large placebo effect whereby 30 per cent of people feel better having been given only the placebo. All drugs released onto the market must be more effective than the placebo. Does this mean that many illnesses or pains are psychosomatic and merely imagined, or does this indicate the healing power of positive reinforcement and belief? Is there a personality type that is more susceptible to suggestion than others?

Pain is clearly explicable in a physiological manner: there is a stimulus, and there are receptors that respond to that stimulus by causing action potentials to travel along nerves to the brain. Physiological mechanisms are gradually emerging to explain why different people are tolerant to a different level of pain. Physiological mechanisms are also being identified that explain why when there is an appropriate stimulus pain is not felt, and why when there is no stimulus pain is felt.

Pain is a continuing area of research. Currently, not all the answers are known, and in our search for answers we may make new discoveries that upset current thinking. It is this characteristic open mind that is the hallmark of science.

SUMMARY

- For most people, health is associated first and foremost with a physical state of being. Having a knowledge of physiological frameworks, pathways and mechanisms contributes to our understanding of this physical state of being

- The scientific discipline of physiology helps us to uncover universal mechanisms that regulate the body (homeostasis). The interlinking nature of different body pathways and systems is also investigated in physiology

- People's interpretation of bodily symptoms and states is highly varied and is related to many other non-physical factors, such as social factors and cultural beliefs. Physiology provides a means of arriving at a common baseline understanding of what is occurring inside the human body by means of rigorous scientific methods

● Physiology contributes in many ways to human health. Once processes have been understood, effective interventions may be proposed and refined. Physiology is, however, distinct from medicine, its investigations and research being neither limited nor dictated by medicine

● Understanding physiological concepts, frameworks and research methods enables us to discover the complexity and self-regulating nature of the human body. This in turn assists us in understanding what is happening in altered states of health, whether caused by assaults from the external world (for example infection or an extremely hostile environment) or internal errors in regulation (for example genetic conditions such as haemophilia). Understanding physical states of being is a crucial aspect of the wider task of understanding human health.

QUESTIONS FOR FURTHER DISCUSSION

1. Select two physical symptoms displayed by someone with diabetes mellitus. Write an essay plan/strategy for analysing the physiology causing these symptoms.

2. During exercise, blood supply and oxygen supply to exercising muscles increases. What physiological mechanisms are involved?

3. Smoking tobacco is a major risk to health affecting heart rate, blood composition, cell activity and lung capacity. What physiological mechanisms are involved? Does a physiological framework support the use of nicotine replacement therapy to reduce health risks?

FURTHER READING

Chalmers, A.F. (1983) *What is this Thing Called Science?* Buckingham: Open University Press.
A highly readable excursion into the nature of scientific research, gently exploding many of the myths about the nature of science.

Davey, B. (1994) 'The nature of scientific research. Biomedical research methods', in McConway, K. (ed.) *Studying Health and Disease*. Buckingham: Open University Press.
A useful summary of the main issues in general scientific and biological research relating to health in particular.

Hubbard, J.L. and Mechan, D.J. (1997) *The Physiology of Health and Illness with Related Anatomy*. Cheltenham: Stanley Thornes.
Targeted at health professionals, this text is clear and concise, and uses British units of measurement. It does not assume a substantial scientific knowledge.

REFERENCES

Cedar, S. H. and Terry, L. (2000) Genes and genealogy. *Family Law*, **30**: 744–7.
Chalmers, A.F. (1983) *What is this Thing Called Science?* Buckingham: Open University Press.
Kuhn, T. (1962) *The Structure of Scientific Revolutions*. Chicago: University of Chicago Press.
Popper, K. (1959) *The Logic of Scientific Discovery*. London: Hutchinson.

Epidemiology

ANNE MULHALL

chapter

2

CONTENTS

Learning outcomes ●●●●●●●●●●●●●●●●●●●●●●●●●

This chapter will enable readers to:

- Define different epidemiological approaches and be aware of their importance to health care
- Understand where epidemiology stands in relation to other disciplines in health care
- Describe the different research designs used by epidemiology
- Gain an appreciation of the concepts of health and sickness as they are used in epidemiology.

OVERVIEW

Epidemiology is the study of how diseases are distributed among different groups of people and the factors that affect this distribution. Accurately recording who in a defined population contracts a disease (the disease rate) also makes it possible to explore factors that might affect disease acquisition. Disease patterns are traditionally studied in relation to time, place and person. For example: Does the disease occur during particular seasons? In certain geographical locations? Age groups? Do those who become sick differ in their lifestyle habits from those who remain healthy? In this way, epidemiology tries to predict conditions (risk factors) that might lead to disease, and thus to identify strategies that might be used to prevent its occurrence. Moreover, once someone has contracted a disease, epidemiology can help to identify prognostic factors, which indicate how quickly or severely the disease may progress. The natural history of diseases (how they develop and progress over time) is thus central to epidemiology. Since it is concerned with rates, epidemiology focuses on populations of people rather than single individuals. The first part of the chapter explores the approach of epidemiology to health care problems and the way in which health and disease are conceptualised in epidemiology. The second part of the chapter describes how epidemiological data are collected and analysed. It concludes with a case study discussing how epidemiology has informed the development of national health strategy.

INTRODUCTION

aetiology – concerns assigning a cause to a given outcome. For example, the aetiology of coronary heart disease might involve smoking, a high cholesterol level, obesity and a stressful lifestyle

Epidemiology (derived from the Greek: *epi* = upon; *demos* = people; *logos* = science) is the science of how often and why diseases occur in different groups of people. It is concerned with the who, what, where, when and how of disease causation (Valenis, 1992). This focus on health and disease in human populations, as opposed to individuals, is central to epidemiological theory and the research methodologies that it uses. Epidemiologists are concerned with the experience of groups, the differences between groups and whether chance might have affected these differences or whether they provide clues to the **aetiology** or cause of disease. Four questions drive the discipline:

- Who becomes sick?
- Why do particular people become sick?
- How effective are the available treatments for the sick?
- How effective are preventive strategies for the healthy?

The focus of epidemiology has been a concern with disease. The study of the distribution of disease – descriptive epidemiology – has been central to public health strategy. It identifies and quantifies ill health problems in communities and assesses the scope for prevention. The assessment of population health is not, however, straightforward. A wide range of data is available to illustrate different aspects of a population's health – the illnesses and diseases experienced, how many people are born and die, and the lifestyles and health behaviours of the population. This chapter argues that, as health is not easily defined, a broader view of epidemiology is needed that uses methodologies incorporating lay perceptions and perspectives. In identifying health problems, a social epidemiology focuses not just on biomedical causes but also on socio-economic factors.

THE CONTRIBUTION OF EPIDEMIOLOGY TO HEALTH STUDIES

For hundreds of years, certainly long before the founding of the discipline, people have been trying to make sense of why disease occurs at certain times, in certain places and in certain people. Some early commentators suggested that supernatural events caused sickness, whereas others, such as Hippocrates, related disease

---

EXAMPLE 2.1

John Snow and the Broad Street pump

During the early 19th century, severe cholera epidemics threatened London, and John Snow, a doctor, became interested in the cause and transmission of the condition. In 1849, he published *On the Mode of Communication of Cholera,* suggesting that cholera is a contagious disease caused by a poison in the vomit and stools of cholera patients. He believed that the main means of transmission was water contaminated with this poison. This differed from the commonly held theory that diseases were transmitted by inhaling vapours or miasmas.

In 1854, 500 people died in the Soho area of London. By plotting the geographical location of each case, Snow deduced that the deaths occurred in people living close to a water pump in Broad Street, yet a workhouse with 535 inmates close to the pump had had only four fatalities. On investigation, Snow found that the workhouse had its own water pump and had not used water from the Broad Street pump. Snow made sure that the handle of the pump was removed, and from then on the number of new cases declined. Although the epidemic was probably self-limiting, this showed the importance of mapping mortality or morbidity.

Snow later proved his theory and clarified the mode of transmission of cholera. Carefully documenting the incidence among subscribers to the city's two water companies, he showed that the disease occurred much more frequently in the customers of one of them, which took its water from the lower Thames where it had become contaminated with London sewage.

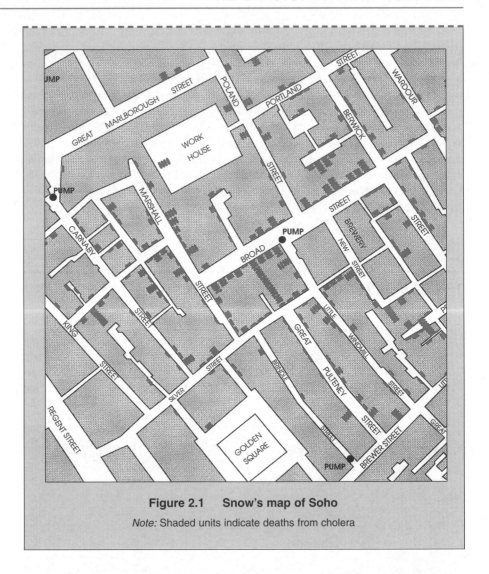

Figure 2.1   Snow's map of Soho

Note: Shaded units indicate deaths from cholera

to lifestyle and environmental conditions. Although the cause of disease was often historically unknown, links between certain conditions (perhaps something to do with the climate or geography) and the occurrence of disease were made.

Until the late 17th century, there was no concept of contagion. Diseases such as diphtheria or smallpox were thought to be caused by changes in the atmosphere. Thomas Sydenham (1624–89) developed the theory of miasma, a vapour that resulted from 'bad air' and spread disease. The invention of the microscope around 1670 allowed living organisms to be studied, but it was not until the mid-19th century that micro-organisms were seen as a cause of disease. The germ theory of causation was vital in the control of infectious diseases.

Much early epidemiological work centred around the control of infectious diseases and involved the initiation, in the mid-19th century, of a public health movement based on the work of sanitary inspectors and engineers. Although the public health movement recognised the link between environmental conditions and health, the motives of reformers such as Edwin Chadwick were not, however, so much to improve the conditions of the poor but to maintain economic and moral stability. With the acceptance of the germ theory of disease, the therapeutic era of public health began. This focused more on treatment than on prevention and emphasised the responsibility of individuals to maintain their own health. The foundation of the National Health Service (NHS) and the professionalisation of medicine further contributed to the emphasis on therapeutic medicine.

In the 1970s, however, this perspective was challenged by McKeown's (1976) observations that immunisation and therapy had had little effect on mortality compared with socio-economic factors. The modern view of disease causation relies on multifactorial explanations. It is now recognised that there may be a particular agent of disease (for example a micro-organism or a dietary substance such as fat). A complex of social factors leads people to behave in particular ways, and these behaviours (for example smoking or a lack of exercise) contribute to disease. The physical environment may also have a bearing on health. Thus a New Public Health movement has emerged that recognises health to be a function of physical, psychological and social environments (Ashton and Seymour, 1991).

> **CONNECTIONS**
>
> Chapter 10 (Health Promotion) discusses different approaches to the promotion of individual and population health including public health work

Such sentiments were enshrined in 1980 in the Black Report (Townsend et al., 1988), which reported the differential health experiences associated with different social classes. The report was largely suppressed by the ruling Conservative government, but the links between social class and health have reemerged under the Labour administration elected in 1997 (Acheson, 1998; DoH, 1997, 1999).

> **CONNECTIONS**
>
> Chapter 4 (Sociology) discusses the evidence of the inverse relationship between social class and health

Although epidemiology and public health have always played a part in the health service, their role has waxed and waned according to prevailing health problems, the ways in which society perceives those problems and the subsequent government policy devised to counteract them. In addition to recognising the importance of socio-economic factors in the genesis of disease, epidemiologists have had to respond to changing problems as the incidence of infectious disease has (at least in the Western world) declined. The simplistic one agent/one disease model had to be abandoned as epidemiology struggled both with more complex problems, such as heart disease and cancer, which have no obvious single cause, and with mental as well as organic disease.

However, over the past 10 years, epidemiology has gained increasing importance as a result of:

- the reorganisation of the NHS precipitated by the Griffiths Report (DHSS, 1983)
- the emergence of the evidence-based health care movement
- the recent acknowledgement that ill health is linked to socio-economic factors.

THE REORGANISATION OF THE NHS

The reorganisation of the NHS in the late 1980s introduced a market economy and general management to health care. Fundamental to these changes, and common to many health care systems in developed countries, was an increasing emphasis on the provision of a service to consumers and a demand for quality care that was cost effective. As part of strategic planning, health authorities

CONNECTIONS

Chapter 6 (Social
Policy) explores the
economic and political
reasons behind the
reforms of the NHS and
many other health care
systems in the late 20th
century

instituted mechanisms to determine the need for health services in their local community and the extent to which that need was being met.

Epidemiology and demography (the study of population size, density, growth and distribution) provide the tools to collect the 'hard' data of statistics that are used to plan services and ascertain quality. All health authorities now collect large data sets of demographic, fertility, mortality and morbidity trends (the Public Health Common Data Set), which can be used to identify geographic variations and local patterns.

THE EMERGENCE OF THE EVIDENCE-BASED HEALTH CARE MOVEMENT

Over the past five years, a strong movement towards the use of more evidence in health care has been promoted by both the government and the professions (DoH, 1993, 1996). It is argued that if health care professionals based more of their decisions on evidence, the quality of care could be both standardised and improved, in some instances also saving costs. There is thus a drive towards increasing clinical effectiveness. For many, such evidence takes the form of research, such as surveys and clinical trials, which produces quantitative data. Many of these designs have a foundation in epidemiology.

The rise of evidence-based health care was strongly influenced by a group of clinicians who advocated the principles of clinical epidemiology (Fletcher et al., 1988; Sackett et al., 1991). In their interactions with clients, most health care professionals go through a process of gathering information about, for example, physical and psychological symptoms, the results of investigations, social circumstances, cultural histories and so on. In medicine, such information is required to answer certain questions – is this person sick?, do I need to do further tests?, what is the optimal treatment for this condition? The answers to these questions form the basis of the subsequent action taken by the doctor. Clinical epidemiology aims to provide a scientific basis for this process of decision-making.

screening – the presumptive
identification of a disease or
condition through the use of
tests (for example blood
tests in newborns to detect
phenylketonuria) or
examinations (for example
the use of chest X-rays to
detect tuberculosis)

EXAMPLE 2.2

Screening for prostate cancer

The question of whether men should be routinely offered a screening test for prostate cancer provides an example of where the science of epidemiology can be applied at the level of individual patient encounters.

There are clearly few advantages to instituting a screening procedure for a condition for which no treatment exists, or in which early treatment is no better than late treatment. From a socio-economic viewpoint, it also is reasonable only to screen for conditions that have a relatively high incidence and that cause a considerable burden of suffering, although any one individual may naturally take a different view on this. The acceptability of screening tests and the potential of reaching those at most risk is also important. It is, for example, well known that those who take up screening for cervical cancer are in fact those least at risk of this disease. Finally, it is important to establish the trustworthiness of any screening test.

The incidence of prostate cancer has risen by 107 per cent between 1970 and 1990. This apparent rise may be due to an increased rate of screening for this disease and/or to the ageing population. There is also, however, controversy over the accuracy of the screening procedure, which consists of a blood test, a rectal examination and an ultrasound scan (Waldman and Osborne, 1994).

In deciding whether a test is trustworthy and suitable for use, doctors must consider the following question: how often does the test produce a false-positive result (when a person would be wrongly classified as having the disease) or a false-negative result (when a person would be wrongly classified as being disease free)? Diagnostic tests are discussed later in the chapter.

There is also an ethical problem of identifying individuals as 'diseased' when their condition in fact causes few problems. Screening for prostate cancer may identify individuals with early disease that may remain unsymptomatic and untroubling. Such individuals may even die 'with' the disease rather than 'of' the disease (Mettlin et al., 1991).

THE LINK BETWEEN ILL HEALTH AND SOCIO-ECONOMIC CONDITIONS

The third reason why epidemiology has gained renewed prominence in the health services of the 1990s is the increasing recognition of the link between ill health and socio-economic status. The early history of epidemiology illustrates how it recognised this association, but with the rise of a powerful medical establishment, the public health function and preventive medicine were upstaged by an emphasis on therapeutics. However, the New Public Health movement renewed an interest in social epidemiology that focuses on the relationship between socio-economic factors and health. More recently, two reports (Acheson, 1998; DoH, 1999) have highlighted the significance of social inequalities and poverty in the genesis of disease and thus emphasised the central role of epidemiology, community medicine and public health. The new social epidemiology goes beyond establishing that associations exist between static socio-economic factors and ill health, to examining why they exist.

EXAMPLE 2.3

Lay epidemiology and the Camelford water supply

This case study illustrates the way in which the scientific evidence of ill health may differ from people's lived experience.

In the UK, the contamination of the water supply in Camelford, Cornwall in July 1988 precipitated the emergence of the locally organised Camelford Scientific Advisory Panel, which undertook its own investigation independent of the governmental inquiry led by Dame Barbara Clayton. This action was precipitated by the divergence of opinion between the conclusions of the scientific inquiry (that persistent effects on health from aluminium contamination were unlikely) and the views of the local population.

At the heart of the dispute lay the claim to validity of the different types of evidence that each party held. The lay epidemiologists of Camelford carefully collected data gleaned from people's experience, whereas Clayton's committee collected objective scientific evidence from toxicological studies and clinical measurements. Each party considered their evidence to be equally valid; unfortunately, however, only one party (that which was legitimised through the government and the adherence to the principles of scientific epidemiology) was in a position significantly to influence the outcome of the event.

However, health for these people was clearly not simply constructed through a narrative of biological dysfunction. The official Clayton Report stated that, 'In our view it is not possible to attribute the very real current health complaints to the toxic effects of the incident, except in as much as they are the consequence of the sustained anxiety naturally felt by many people' (Cornwall and Isles of Scilly DHA, 1989). Thus these health problems were not only denied a 'biological' cause, but also relegated to a community diagnosis of 'sustained anxiety'. As Williams and Popay (1994) note, this explanation of the community's beliefs 'was a way of indicating its unreliability and, therefore, its distance from the standards of scientific discourse'. Yet a recent scientific research study has found in favour of the community's views. This study concludes that the people exposed suffered considerable damage to their cerebral functioning, that was not related to anxiety (Altmann et al., 1999).

Lay epidemiology is the process whereby lay people gather evidence and use experts in their midst to understand the epidemiology of diseases. It is a process often associated with political activism. This pursuit of epidemiological knowledge by lay people has been brought about by a dissatisfaction with the explanations provided by the conventional scientific community. It is often fuelled by environmental concerns or the failure of governmental responses or public inquiries to satisfy ordinary people.

CONCEPTS OF HEALTH AND DISEASE IN MEDICAL EPIDEMIOLOGY

Before we can fully understand the contribution that epidemiology makes to health care, it is necessary to explore how such concepts as health, disease, normality and abnormality have traditionally been conceptualised. For many of those working in health care, epidemiology is a discipline that remains firmly associated with medicine and the methods of natural science. The following definition reflects this link with biology and physiology:

CONNECTIONS

Chapter 1 (Physiology) illustrates the natural science perspective and outlines the basic premises and development of Western medicine

the study of a disease or a physiological condition in human populations and of the factors which influence that distribution... it can be regarded as a sequence of reasoning concerned with biological inferences derived from observations of disease occurrence and related phenomena in human population groups. (Lilienfeld and Lilienfeld, 1980)

Epidemiology has, however, begun to expand to encompass other perspectives that are based on world views and theories drawn from other disciplines within the social sciences.

Health

In medicine and epidemiology, health has been defined as the absence of disease. This is, however, quite a simplistic definition, and the World Health Organization (WHO) (1946) has specified that health is 'a state of complete physical, mental and social well-being and not merely the absence of disease and infirmity'. Even this definition has attracted criticism as commentators search for a broader, more positive concept of health (Seedhouse, 1986). The major problem with this definition is that disease or physiological status does not fully embrace the image of health held by most people. Many other factors – social, psychological, spiritual and environmental – are involved in perceptions of health.

Disease

In medicine, phenomena relating to health and disease must be subjected to testing and verification under objective, empirical and controlled conditions. These objective and verifiable clinical facts form the basis of the doctor's diagnosis. Thus, the diagnosis of disease is largely based on demonstrable physical changes in the body's structure or function. These changes are measured and then compared with a range of normal physiological values. Each disease entity has particular characteristics that identify it. For medicine and epidemiology, therefore, disease implies an abnormality of structure or function, the need for correction and the idea that abnormalities are undesirable (Dingwall, 1976). Objective diagnoses based on physical findings thus pay less attention to the meaning that sickness has for the individual or the different ways in which such meanings are constructed in society. Infertility, for example, may present as an abnormally low sperm count or as blocked fallopian tubes, but the condition of infertility has a far wider definition than this, encompassing psychological, social and cultural dimensions.

CONNECTIONS

Chapter 10 (Health Promotion) considers how health improvement involves exploring and working from people's own concepts of health. Perceptions of positive health may be based on the ability to cope with stress or the existence of strong social support

CONNECTIONS

Chapter 5 (Cultural Studies) discusses the way in which reproduction is presented in popular culture and contributes to the desirability of motherhood

Medical perspectives on normality and abnormality

In its studies of populations, epidemiology becomes concerned with categorising people into groups according to whether they are normal (that is, disease free) or abnormal (that is, diseased). Reference is usually made to particular physical and biochemical parameters, for example blood count, body weight, concentration of liver enzymes, absence of cellular changes and so on, in order to define normality. Each of these characteristics will have a normal range below, or above, which disease may be indicated.

One example is the test for anaemia. If your haemoglobin level were found to be below 12 mg/100 ml, you would be recalled for further measurements and might be recommended an iron supplement. The recognition of normality and abnormality within epidemiology is often based on precise measurements of the type made in the biological and physical sciences. It is important that such measurements are both *valid* (that is, they measure what you think they are

Thinking about...

Can you think of tests or investigations that you have undergone that employed definitions of normality?

measuring) and *reliable* (repeated measurements coming up with the same result). Validity and reliability are much easier to measure when dealing with numerical data, which can be easily compared with a gold standard.

It is a short step, then, to see how, in this sort of system, phenomena that are readily measured and observed, for example serum cholesterol concentration, are attributed greater 'reality' than other phenomena such as nausea or well-being, which are more difficult to measure and for which normal ranges are less likely to have been defined (although scales have been developed to achieve this; see Bowling, 1991).

? **Why might it be difficult to identify and distinguish a 'normal' state?**

Even when epidemiology and medicine confine themselves to using such objective, hard measures, difficulties may arise, for although in some cases there is a clear distinction between the values that are normal or abnormal in a population, more often than not the values for the diseased population overlap with those of the normal population, giving a 'grey' area. Difficulties then arise in trying to determine where the cut-off point between the two categories lies and thus the point above or below which disease may be defined. There may also be controversy between doctors over what the normal range should be. A good example here is that of blood pressure, for which, over the years, the 'normal range' has changed. Furthermore, the normal range may vary across different populations and different age ranges (see Fletcher et al., 1988).

The classification of diseases

By recognising the differences and similarities between cases, epidemiologists are able to classify diseases. They have traditionally based such classifications of disease on the medical model. As we saw above, the medical diagnosis has become centred on science through the use of tests and technological procedures. The work of early scientists such as Pasteur and Koch suggested that each disease had a single, specific and objective cause, which, given the right treatment, could be selectively destroyed (as with the use of antibiotics to destroy infecting micro-organisms). In the medical model, the classification of disease is based on demonstrable physical changes in the body's structure or function. If these deviate from the norm, the patient 'has' a disease.

Each disease possesses certain recognisable characteristics that distinguish it from other diseases. Moreover, such diseases are considered to be universal in form and content, that is, they 'appear' in the same way in different people in different locations and at different times. Hence the WHO produces the International Statistical Classification of Diseases and Health Related Problems (ICD), which is used in most countries to classify and code mortality and morbidity.

Challenging the medicalisation of epidemiology

Other ways of viewing the world provide different insights into epidemiology. Other disciplines such as sociology, anthropology and medical geography have spent much time grappling with the concepts of health and sickness. Talcott Parsons put forward the theory that the sick role is a form of 'deviance' that is legitimised in the social world. People designated as sick are exempted from normal activities and responsibility for their condition, but there is an expectation that the sick will acknowledge that the sick role is undesirable and seek help. The anthropologist Frankenberg (1980) suggests that the social environment or milieu is central to understanding what health and sickness are. He defines disease as a malfunction of structure or function; illness as a person's perception and experience of socially devalued states; and sickness as the social recognition of disease and illness.

What these sociological and anthropological perspectives have in common is their insistence that ill health is not just a malfunctioning of the physical body, but is instead closely affected by societal and cultural factors. In this respect, the views and ideas that lay people have on how, when and why they become sick become important (Mulhall, 1996; Stacey, 1988; Stainton Rogers, 1991).

Since epidemiology is concerned with measuring the rate of health and ill health in populations and determining the reasons for it, it is clearly important that it takes full account of the different ways in which such concepts have been constructed.

> **CONNECTIONS**
>
> Chapter 3 (Health Psychology) discusses the influence of people's attributions (what they believe to be the cause of ill health) on their decisions about their health

 If there are different perspectives on what constitutes health and sickness, how will this affect ideas of abnormality and disease?

The socio-cultural view of abnormality suggests that although disease may be seen as a biological deviation, what is normal and abnormal is a social and moral judgement. Lewis (1993) contends that the diagnosis of abnormality is not confined to the medical domain but is a departure from some 'standard' of normality. He suggests that such standards are set by both individuals and the society in which they exist. 'Normal' then becomes relative to circumstances and individuals – it is not a universal phenomenon that can be applied across all cultures and all occasions.

EXAMPLE 2.4

The social construction of illness

Schizophrenia provides an example of a socially constructed definition of mental illness. Statistics collected for a study in the Republic of Ireland showed that, on one day in 1971, two per cent of males in western Ireland were in a mental hospital. However, through an exploration of community definitions, it can be shown how abnormality and normality are 'constructed' by the community. Quiet and eccentric individuals are tolerated, but those who violate the strong sanctions against expressions of sexuality, aggression and disrespectful subordination to parental or religious authority are perceived to be nonconformists and thus 'prime candidates for the mental hospital'. Thus, a large number of young bachelors had been labelled as mentally ill and institutionalised.

The medical view is that nature produces diseases in constant and distinct ways. Diseases are not entities or things but a particular set of attributes characteristically shown by people who fall ill in this way. Diseases as such do not exist in nature but are produced by the conceptual schemes imposed on the natural world. Thus, some states of the body are valued and others are not, being deemed abnormal. Biological changes are undoubtedly a material fact, but the socio-cultural viewpoint is that it is the significance of these changes that matters.

Sources: Dingwall, 1992; Lewis, 1993; Scheper-Hughes, 1978

This section has illustrated how epidemiology has traditionally used medicine as the basis for its way of knowing about sickness and health – for building up its understanding of these concepts. The idea that diseases are entities defined through the methods and technologies of biology is, however, challenged by the socio-cultural view. If epidemiology focuses only on the malfunctioning of the corporeal body, it is in danger of ignoring other aspects that are important in the generation of ill health. Moreover, it needs to take account of these other viewpoints in order to understand the considerable impact that the environment and politics have on people's health.

THEORETICAL AND METHODOLOGICAL PERSPECTIVES

Epidemiology predominantly uses the conceptual framework of medicine to direct its activities, although other perspectives drawn from the social science disciplines may also be illuminating. When it comes to looking at the practical ways in which epidemiology might contribute to health care, both these perspectives need to be considered. However, since epidemiologists have traditionally based their methods on medicine, rather more examples exist of activities within this sphere of influence.

Using medicine as its conceptual backdrop, epidemiology has been used in a diverse set of ways (Valenis, 1992):

1. determining the natural history of disease
2. identifying risk
3. classifying disease
4. diagnosing and treating disease
5. in the surveillance of health status
6. planning health services
7. evaluating health services.

THE NATURAL HISTORY OF DISEASE

In attempting to determine who, when and why certain people become sick, epidemiologists are interested in the entire natural progression of a disease, whereas many health care professionals, particularly those working in hospitals, are more focused on specific stages of the disease process when the condition has been deemed by the patient to be serious enough to seek their advice. The natural history of a disease is generally described as the course it takes without medical intervention, whereas the clinical course is defined as that which evolves under medical treatment.

The natural history of a disease is useful in prognosis, which involves the prediction of events to come. In other words, it tells sufferers and their carers what they might expect in the future in terms of recovery, remission symptoms and their ability to 'carry on as normal' either now or at some time in the future.

Descriptions of the course of diseases reported in the literature may be susceptible to sampling bias. This is because such accounts are usually derived from specialist centres whose patients may not be representative of the whole spectrum of patients cared for in the primary and secondary settings. Fletcher et al. (1988) provide the example of multiple sclerosis to illustrate this. From the viewpoint of hospitals, multiple sclerosis must appear to be a lethal disease. A prognostic survey conducted in the community (Percy et al., 1971), however, demonstrated that 50 per cent of diagnosed patients were alive 50 years after the onset – the same number as would have been expected to survive even if they did not have multiple sclerosis. Studies of the natural history of a disease must therefore take into account the full spectrum of people who might be afflicted.

Biological and physiological knowledge enables epidemiologists to understand more clearly how diseases are caused and thus hopefully how they might be prevented. Information concerning the early natural history of conditions is essential to the planning of timely interventions and the identification and treatment of high-risk groups.

IDENTIFYING RISK

Risk refers to the likelihood that someone free of a condition but exposed to certain *risk factors* will subsequently acquire that condition. In today's society, we seem never to be able to escape from the idea of risk – the risk of toxic waste, infectious agents, bad driving, food, war, famine, our genetic inheritance.

For infectious diseases, it is quite simple to identify the relationship between the exposure to risk and an adverse outcome. However, in most chronic diseases, such as cancer and heart disease, the relationship between risk and disease is less clear. In these cases, it is difficult for clinicians to develop estimates of risk based on their own limited experience. An individual doctor will perhaps see neither the resulting outcome following an exposure nor enough patients to determine which of many possible risk factors are the most important. It is here that epidemiology, through its study of populations rather than individuals, can provide vital knowledge. Through the use of case control and cohort studies (see below), risk and *prognostic factors* can be determined, which allows screening programmes and health promotion strategies aimed at changing risk behaviours to be established.

> *Thinking about...*
>
> Think about an illness that you and someone you know have both had. Did your illness follow the same course? Did you have the same treatment?

---

risk factors are those that make an individual or population susceptible to a disease or illness. They may be environmental (for example exposure to asbestos), related to lifestyle (for example drinking alcohol) or genetic (for example a familial history of breast cancer). See also prognostic factors

---

prognostic factors are those that may affect the outcome of individuals already known to have a certain condition. See also risk factors

CLASSIFYING DISEASE

Epidemiological data are used for the classification system (the ICD) that is central to modern Western medicine. The ICD was primarily disease oriented and a means of assigning the cause of death, but it now includes a wider range of health problems. It encompasses infectious and parasitic diseases, diseases and their location in the body – malignant neoplasms (cancers), for example, being linked to sites such as the breast or pancreas – as well as a category on the factors influencing health status and contact with the health services.

? **In what situations might the use of the ICD be limited?**

Using the ICD can be problematic because:

- death certificates give no information about contributory conditions such as smoking

- mental health problems are not identified because malfunctioning of the physical body is absent in them

- conceptualisations of disease classifications based on environmental factors and social grouping would greatly enrich the ways in which epidemiology is practised. Draper et al. (1977) provide examples of risk factors for disease being reconceptualised in categories such as housing and basic amenities.

DIAGNOSING AND TREATING DISEASE

Diagnosing what is wrong with people is a central activity in medicine, this often involving the application of diagnostic tests. The interpretation of these tests is actually quite difficult. Figure 2.2 illustrates some properties that clinicians may use to determine the usefulness of diagnostic tests. Test results may present four possible scenarios. Two are correct – a positive test in the presence of disease and a negative test in the absence of disease. Where tests mislead is when they present results that are false positive (that is, a person is wrongly identified as having a disease) or false negative (that is, a person is wrongly identified as being free of the disease). It would not be too serious if a false-positive test indicated that a patient had a urinary tract infection and should be treated with antibiotics. However, if a patient with breast cancer were given a false-negative result, the disease might progress beyond a stage amenable to treatment. In this latter case, we would want a test with high sensitivity that is unlikely to miss cases of disease. We would also, however, need a specific test since it would be very traumatic if people without breast cancer were told that they had this disease. Highly specific tests are unlikely to classify people without the disease as having it. New diagnostic tests should be compared with a gold standard (the best possible assessment of whether the condition is present or not – for example an expensive 'scan') to determine their appropriateness for use in different situations.

How accurate and reliable are diagnostic and screening tests? The 2×2 table below illustrates the relationship between the results of a diagnostic test and the actual presence of disease.

Disease

		Present	Absent	
Results of diagnostic test	**Positive**	True positive a	False positive b	$a + b$
	Negative	False negative c	True negative d	$c + d$
		$a + c$	$b + d$	$a + b + c + d$

Properties of the diagnostic test:

Sensitivity is the proportion of those with the disease who test positive

Sensitivity = $a/(a + c)$

Specificity is the proportion of those who do not have the disease who test negative

Specificity = $d/(b + d)$

Figure 2.2   Screening tests

SURVEILLANCE AND THE PLANNING AND EVALUATION OF HEALTH SERVICES

Surveillance and planning are interrelated. In epidemiology, surveillance involves the collection, analysis and interpretation of data about who is most at risk of contracting a disease, and where and when diseases are most frequently observed. Monitoring conditions in this way can alert health professionals to trends or unusual clusters of events. In many developed countries, infectious diseases must be notified to the appropriate authorities in order that outbreaks may be identified and confined. The surveillance of other conditions such as birth defects may identify possible causal agents. A knowledge of the distribution of disease in communities according to geographical location, age, ethnic origin, socio-economic group and so on is obviously vital to the planning of health care services; epidemiology can provide the tools for such analyses.

The collection and analysis of data does not, however, occur in a social vacuum, and producing knowledge in numerical form does not guarantee its objectivity. Statistics are collected and presented in different ways for all sorts of different reasons and to fit all kinds of different agendas. Whenever you are presented with health information data, some simple questions should be asked:

- Which population do the data represent?
- Is there any missing information?

Thinking about...

Can you think of an example in which data have been manipulated to present a particular picture? Or where data may not be accurately recorded?

- How have categories such as 'child' and 'elderly' been constructed (that is, how are they defined and by whom)?
- Who collected the data and why?
- Do the data attempt to provide evidence to substantiate a particular viewpoint (for example the government's)?

The example provided earlier concerning the contamination of the water supply at Camelford is an example of data manipulation. In this case, the ethnographic data collected by a support group and a scientific advisory group of 'lay' academics were afforded less credence than the 'scientific' data collected through the official inquiry. Similarly, despite Snow's epidemiological studies on the transmission of cholera, the British authorities continued as late as 1885 to insist that cholera was 'non-communicable, non-specific and endemic in Egypt'; the government did not wish to accept that cholera originated in India because this would have disrupted Britain's substantial commercial and trade interests with that country.

THE METHODOLOGIES USED BY EPIDEMIOLOGY

Every discipline goes about its research in a particular way according to the paradigm within which its practitioners work. A paradigm is perhaps best understood as a world view based on a set of values and assumptions that are shared by a particular group. Epidemiology has strong historical links with medicine, practitioners in both these disciplines tending to work in the natural science paradigm. The scientific paradigm is also often called the positivistic paradigm. The main tenets of this view are as follows:

- Scientists believe that the social world and the physical world are orderly and rational
- There are universal laws that predict and explain phenomena
- It is possible to be objective and study the world
- The data collected are usually quantitative.

The assumptions that underpin the positivistic paradigm have certain consequences for research that is conducted through this perspective. Thus natural scientists:

bias – the result of any process that causes observations to differ from their true values in a systematic way (as opposed to chance, which is defined as random variation). Bias may be introduced into a study at its inception (for example when selecting the sample), during its course or during the analysis

- seek cause and effect relationships
- attempt to generalise these relationships to populations other than the one under study
- ensure that researcher *bias* is carefully controlled
- reduce social situations down into smaller parts (perhaps two variables) for study.

Epidemiologists often use research designs that simply observe events as they happen in a population rather than as they might happen in a controlled experiment. As a result, they are much concerned with factors (other than the one under investigation) that might affect the outcome of the study or bias its results. Bias is the result of any process that causes observations to differ systematically from their true values. Think of your bathroom scales: because they are not regularly calibrated, they might consistently tell you that you weigh five pounds less than when you were weighed at the gym! This is a case of *measurement bias*.

Another source of bias may occur when subjects are recruited for a study. Many epidemiological studies compare the experiences or outcomes of two groups, one of which has been exposed to perhaps a risk factor and the other of which has not. Since we are interested only in the effect of that risk factor, it is important that the two groups being compared do not differ in other significant ways that might affect the outcome.

Selection bias occurs when the way in which subjects are selected distorts the outcome of the study. A study might, for example, be interested in finding out whether meditation reduces stress levels. A programme of meditation seminars is offered to the directors of a large City bank. The amount of stress in those who undertake the programme is then compared with that in those directors who chose not to attend. Selection bias may, however, be present if these two groups differ in other respects that may affect the degree to which they suffer stress. For example, those who volunteer for such programmes may be particularly 'health conscious' and be undertaking other strategies such as regular exercise, which might affect their stress level. In other words, the two groups are not comparable with respect to factors that might affect the outcome of the study.

Confounding bias occurs when two factors are associated and the effect of one is confused with the effect of the other. An example is provided in a study of urinary tract infections in patients with catheters (Crow et al., 1986). When analysing the results of this study, it was found that females who were catheterised by doctors suffered fewer urinary tract infections than those catheterised by nurses. This might have led us to believe that nurses were less skilled at catheterisation. However, the data also showed that doctors usually inserted catheters in the operating theatre and that women undergoing an operation were likely to receive antibiotics. These factors – the person doing the catheterisation, the place of catheterisation and the receipt of antibiotics – were therefore confounding, and it was difficult to know which factor really was responsible.

Another factor that may affect the results of epidemiological studies is chance. Chance is random error. Unlike bias, which results in an observation being consistently above or below a value, chance is just as likely to deflect a measurement below as above its true reading. The probability of chance or random error accounting for the results of a study are estimated using statistics (the p-values that you may have seen in research papers relate to this). These two sources of error – bias and chance – are always carefully considered in the design and analysis of epidemiological studies.

EXPERIMENTAL STUDIES

One of the principal aims of epidemiology is to identify cause and effect relationships, for example does asbestos cause small cell lung cancer?

Table 2.1   Cause and effect relationships

Using the following criteria, it is possible to weigh up the evidence from a number of studies to try to decide whether a strong case exists for a particular factor being the cause of a disease even when it has not been possible to undertake experimental studies. Consider the example of sun exposure as a cause of skin cancer:

1. **Plausibility:** does it seem likely, according to what is known about the pathology and natural history of skin cancer, that sun exposure could be a causal factor?

2. **Temporality:** common sense would suggest that a cause needs to precede its hypothesised effect; that is, does exposure to the sun precede skin cancer?

3. **Dose–response:** if an increasing level of exposure leads to an increased incidence of disease, the case for cause and effect is strengthened; that is, are those who are most exposed to the sun (sunbathers or outdoor workers) more likely to get skin cancer?

4. **Reversibility:** if the removal of a risk factor reduces the incidence of disease, it may be its cause; that is, if sun exposure is reduced (through skin protection creams, covering up and not going out, as in Australia), does the incidence of skin cancer drop?

5. **Consistency:** if several studies all come up with the same answer, this provides strong evidence that the relationship is causal

cause and **association** – unlike in the physical sciences, proving a direct link between a certain causal factor and a certain outcome is, in epidemiology, rarely possible. Factors may be found to be associated together but not causally related. For example, the rate of ice cream eating may be associated with the rate of drowning, but eating ice cream does not cause drowning. Another factor – sunshine – accounts for this effect. Eight criteria have been suggested for determining whether two factors are causally related (see Sackett et al., 1991)

A certain factor is sometimes the direct **cause** of a disease, and early epidemiologists who focused on infections certainly had considerable success in pinpointing their cause and thus controlling outbreaks. However, the focus of epidemiology is now firmly on chronic diseases. Most of these have multiple causes, and in their turn these causes may have multiple effects. Heart disease, for example, has been seen in **association** with smoking, stress, obesity and high blood pressure, but smoking also causes chronic obstructive airways disease, bladder cancer and lung cancer. This intricate relationship between several factors, some known and some unknown, has been termed the 'web of causation'.

The best way of establishing cause and effect relationships is through experimental research in which the investigator has a considerable degree of control over what is happening. In simple terms, in experimental studies two groups of participants are assembled, one group receiving an intervention of some kind, perhaps a new drug treatment, the other group receiving nothing and acting as a control. In such studies, researchers have control over who is and who is not exposed to the intervention. Human populations cannot, however, always be easily studied in this way because of logistical or ethical problems. It would not, for example, be ethical to expose groups of people to potential risk factors for a disease. Much epidemiological research is conducted with naturally occurring populations, when it is not always possible to undertake experiments. It is important to assess the evidence from these other types of studies carefully.

Two types of experimental study are used in epidemiology – clinical trials and preventative trials. In a clinical trial, the effect of a specific 'treatment' on people who already have a particular condition is studied. In this sense, 'treatments' may include not only drugs, but also equipment (for example, different wound dressings) and 'procedures' (such as different ways of organising the accident and emergency clinic). Preventative trials investigate the effect of a potential preventative measure in people who do not have the condition in question. A preventative trial might, for example, examine the effect of two different ways of conveying health promotion messages about smoking to teenagers. A schematic diagram of a typical trial is shown in Figure 2.3.

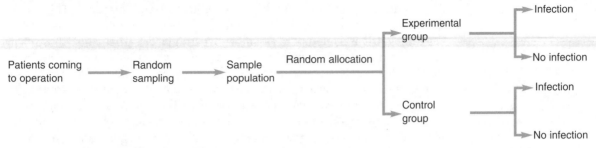

Figure 2.3   Schematic diagram of a randomised controlled trial
(from Mulhall, 1996)

Trials are considered by many to produce very 'strong' (that is, valid and reliable) evidence about cause and effect relationships. This is because the investigator retains control over who does and does not receive the intervention (sometimes called the independent variable).

Consider a study to investigate whether patients washing with an antibacterial soap before an operation suffer fewer post-operative wound infections:

- **Why is it important to have two groups of participants?**
- **Why is it important that the two groups are similar in characteristics (such as age, sex and disease severity)?**
- **What factors could influence the outcome of this study and make it hard to tell whether washing does reduce the incidence of post-operative infections?**

Since in trials we are interested in trying to pinpoint the relationship between just two variables – the intervention and the outcome – it is important to try to minimise the effect of any other factors. For example, if the patients in the control group in Figure 2.3 were younger than those in the experimental group,

Table 2.2   Checklist for assessing the validity of randomised controlled trials

- Is the randomisation of the participants into each group blinded? If clinicians have a choice of which subjects enter which group in the trial, it is highly likely that the two groups that emerge will not be comparable

- Is the assignment of participants to the treatment groups really random? Checking whether the two groups are roughly comparable in terms of various characteristics such as age, sex and so on helps to determine whether the two groups are similar

- Are those assessing outcomes blind to the treatment allocation? If clinicians and/or subjects are aware of which group they are in, this may bias the outcome results

- Are the groups treated identically other than for the named intervention? In all trials, it is important to try to prevent other factors interfering with the outcome of the trial.

they might naturally suffer fewer post-operative wound infections. This would then interfere with the design of the trial and bias its results. To prevent this happening, trialists attempt to assemble two groups of participants whose characteristics (such as age, sex and disease severity) resemble each other very closely. This is achieved by randomly allocating people into either the experimental or the control group, hence the name *randomised controlled trial* (RCT).

One of the most contentious issues surrounding the use of experiments is informed consent – in other words, do people know what they are letting themselves in for when they agree to enter a trial? Although all good trials pay particular attention to this, the gap between the knowledge and language of health care professionals and lay people often militates against the latter really gaining a good understanding. This is well illustrated in a study by Snowdon et al. (1997) that examined informed consent by exploring the parental reaction to a random allocation of their sick babies to treatment or control groups in the UK Collaborative Trial of Extra Corporeal Membrane Oxygenation. The researchers illustrated how the nature of the trial or the trial treatment, particularly the concept of randomisation, was poorly understood by parents. In only 12 out of 21 interviews were they sure that at least one parent was aware of the random nature of the allocation of their baby to standard or trial treatment.

randomised controlled trial – an experimental study in which subjects are randomly allocated to receive or not receive an intervention

CONNECTIONS

Chapter 9 (Ethics and Law) considers the ethics of treatment based on informed consent

OBSERVATIONAL STUDIES

Observational studies involve studying population groups and events as they occur naturally. Thus, epidemiologists might take a group of people who have been exposed through the course of life events to a risk factor, say an occupational exposure to carcinogens, and compare them with another group who have not suffered such exposure to determine whether the exposed group have a higher incidence of cancer.

Epidemiologists undertake three main types of observational research:

● cohort studies
● case control studies
● prevalence studies.

In each of these designs, attempts must be made to recognise, and deal with, the potential differences that might arise between comparison groups.

Cohort studies

Cohort studies are sometimes called longitudinal or prospective studies, indicating that they continue over a period of time and that the participants are usually followed into the future. A cohort is a defined group of people who have a characteristic in common (for example the same disease or the same therapy), who are then followed over time to find out what happens to them. Examples might be the survival rate for Hodgkin's disease, or the improvement in survival for patients with multiple sclerosis who receive interferon: the cohort study would be used to study prognosis in the case of Hodgkin's disease and treatment in the case of multiple sclerosis. Cohort studies are also used to study risk.

Cohort studies provide the next best available evidence when it is not possible to undertake experiments. This is because the design of such studies aims to minimise the effect of the three types of bias (selection, measurement and confounding; see above). There are, however, disadvantages to cohort studies:

- the length of time that may be necessary to conduct the study
- the subsequent costs that will accrue
- the necessity for large-scale studies when the outcome of interest occurs infrequently; (the Framingham heart study (Dawber, 1980) for example, followed 5,000 adults over many years).

As a result of these disadvantages, another type of research design for assessing risk – the case control study – has been developed.

Case control studies

In case control studies, a group of people with the particular condition of interest, for example breast cancer, are assembled (the cases) and compared with an otherwise similar group without the condition (the controls). Thus, in contrast to a cohort study, the cases already have the outcome of interest, a search being made for factors in the past that may explain the outcome. Case control studies are therefore always retrospective. Figure 2.4 outlines a typical case control study.

The advantages of such a design relate to the fact that the investigator identifies cases at the current time. This is simpler and economically cheaper than the situation in the cohort design where one has to observe a large group of unaffected individuals and wait for cases to occur. In other words, the natural frequency of the disease (which may be very low) does not constrain the identification of cases.

Case control studies are more prone to bias than cohort studies. Since the 'case' and 'control' groups are chosen by the investigator, selection bias may occur. It is important that cases and controls have had an equal chance of being exposed to the factor of interest. Furthermore, there is a strong chance of measurement bias, which may occur when cases recall exposure differently from non-cases. Not surprisingly, sick people have generally reflected more than healthy controls on past events (either medical, for example drug history, or non-medical, for example working conditions) that may have affected their condition.

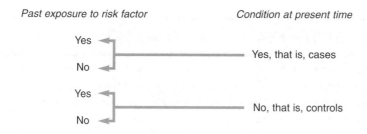

Figure 2.4   Schematic outline for the design of a case control study
(from Mulhall, 1996)

Table 2.3   Common rates used in epidemiology

Crude rates	These refer to the entire population, for example the mortality rate for Greater Manchester, but tell us nothing of the characteristics of the underlying population.
Specific rates	These measure the number of events occurring in a subgroup of the population, for example the mortality rate of female children in social class I in two different districts of Manchester.
Standardised rates	These take account of the structure of a population. This is important when comparing rates because we know that certain characteristics of a population will affect the disease incidence; for example a population with a high proportion of elderly people will have a correspondingly high mortality rate. By determining how many deaths might be expected in a population and then comparing this with how many deaths actually occur, we can gain an idea of whether the experience of the population has been the same as the standard experience. The standardised mortality ratio is the ratio of: $$\frac{\text{number of observed deaths}}{\text{number of expected deaths}} \times 100\%$$ This figure is easy to understand since ratios over 100% indicate an unfavourable 'mortality experience', whereas those below 100% a favourable experience. Coggan et al. (1997) provide a worked example of standardisation.

Prevalence studies

prevalence – the proportion of a defined population that is experiencing a condition over a given period or at a specific point in time (point prevalence). It includes both *old* and *new* cases

The final observational design is the cross-sectional or ***prevalence*** study. In a prevalence study, a defined population is surveyed and its disease status determined at one point in time. This gives us a 'snapshot' at a certain moment of who has and who has not got the condition of interest within a particular population (the point prevalence). This is different from incidence.

incidence –the number of *new* cases that occur in a given population over a period of time

Incidence is the proportion of a group free of a condition who develop it over a given period of time (a day, a year or a decade, for example). It measures the rate at which new cases arise in a population, as opposed to prevalence, which measures the proportion of a population that have the condition at any one point in time. Prevalence studies are particularly useful in planning health care services and informing policy issues.

CASE STUDY – HEALTH CARE PLANNING

Strategic planning is a central activity in health care, but how is it accomplished? Planning for the provision of health services may be viewed as a three-stage process that determines:

1. what the health care 'problems' of a population are

2. how services should be arranged to address these problems

3. how services should be evaluated.

The following case study illustrates the ways in which the methodology of epidemiology is used in health care planning. It shows the importance of a critical reading of data, whose accuracy and reliability must always be questioned. Just because knowledge has been produced in a numerical format does not guarantee its objectivity, all data being socially produced in specific circumstances. Strategic planning based on epidemiological data is dominated by a medical model, as shown in the development of the English national health strategies *The Health of the Nation* (DoH, 1992) and *Saving Lives: Our Healthier Nation* (DoH, 1999).

DEFINING THE POPULATION

The first step to determining the health care problems in any community is the description of the characteristics of the population involved; this is termed 'demography'. A population may be characterised in different ways, for example:

- the percentage in different age groups
- the percentage of males and females
- the percentage who are employed or economically active
- the percentage who live in a particular area
- the percentage who are diagnosed as suffering from a particular disease, for example meningitis.

Sometimes a whole population is studied, using the government 10-yearly census, but more often a sample population is drawn. The General Household Survey, for example, uses a sample of about 12,000 private households in Britain. It is important that the sample represents the whole population, which may be achieved by random selection or selection using relevant characteristics such as age, sex or social class.

Demographers determine the total number of people living in a particular geographical area. The types of question that demographers might pose are:

- How many births occur in a certain geographical area?
- What is the age profile of a particular population?
- Is the proportion of people over the age of 85 years increasing or decreasing?

Demographers can thus calculate such statistics as:

- the age structure
- fertility rate
- mortality rate
- birth rate of the population.

The census, which is coordinated by the Office of National Statistics (ONS, formerly Office of Population, Census and Surveys), is the single most important source of information concerning the size and composition of the population. A census has occurred in Great Britain every 10 years since 1801 with the exception of 1941 (war time).

There are, however, some problems associated with the data it produces. The reliability (or consistency) and accuracy (or 'truth') of the data from the census depend not only on the data collection process, but also on the people who are filling in the forms. Difficulties arise through returns not being completed, particular sources of undercoverage including very young children and the homeless. In addition, certain items of information such as age or occupation may be distorted or too vague for an accurate return to be made. This has important consequences as occupation is used as the basis for the determination of social class, a variable upon which much epidemiological research may be based. If the data from the census are not accurate, long-term population forecasts may be distorted.

DEFINING THE IMPORTANT PROBLEMS: PATTERNS OF MORTALITY AND MORBIDITY

Once the overall structure of the population has been defined, as described above, it is necessary to determine what the major health problems are. What do people die of, and what sorts of condition do they suffer from and for how long? The data will normally be presented as frequency counts and prevalence and incidence rates (see above). The rates are calculated for several years to study trends over time and to examine whether genuine changes are occurring.

Armed with mortality and morbidity rates, epidemiologists are able to search for deviations from the norm. This is achieved by comparing present rates with either previous rates for the same community or current rates in other communities. When a comparison is made between communities, it is very important that a careful matching of the two populations occurs – that like is compared with like. If a comparison with previous rates within the same community is undertaken, any changes in population structure or environmental conditions that might have affected the **mortality rate** must be sought before any conclusions can be drawn. Caution is necessary because such changes may give the impression that the underlying rates have changed when the change may in fact be the result of another factor. The introduction of a new teaching hospital might, for example, attract a greater proportion of severely ill clients to a district, thus elevating the mortality rate for a particular condition.

However, just as with the data collected for the census, caution should be applied when examining mortality and morbidity statistics for although most Western countries have an accurate and reliable system for generating mortality rates, discrepancies and errors may occur once we go beyond the simple recording that a death has occurred. In the UK, the physician who attended the deceased in his or her last illness is required by law to complete a medical certificate of death on which the cause of death must be stated. This is then taken by a qualified informant (usually the closest relative of the deceased) to the local Registrar of Deaths, where other details, including the date and place of death, name, sex, date and place of birth, occupation and place of residence of the deceased, are provided orally by the informant. At

mortality rate – the number of deaths in a population. Thus, the crude mortality rate is the total number of deaths in the population divided by the total population size. Specific mortality rates refer to particular subpopulations, for example the rate of deaths in males of social class I

weekly intervals, the registrar makes a death return to ONS, where the information on the certificates is coded.

Several studies have demonstrated that the cause of death recorded on the certificate may differ from the cause as written in the person's medical notes or the cause as revealed by post-mortem examination. Part of the problem is that the cause of death is ascertained by the doctor and is based purely on clinical judgement as post-mortem examination only occurs in a minority of cases. Discrepancies often occur in the elderly where the precise cause of death may be unclear or multiple causes may be responsible. Coders at the ONS use the ICD issued by the WHO to translate the underlying cause of death into a code. There are, however, occasions on which the diagnosis is vague or an illogical sequence of events is presented; in such cases, the coders resort to a predetermined set of rules to try to disentangle the problem. Errors can clearly occur at this stage.

Errors may also creep in through the provision of information by the qualified informant – the deceased's closest relative. As a death must be registered within five days, this person is probably in a highly emotional state and may provide confused or inaccurate information. Serious errors, particularly relating to the reporting of occupation, are known to occur. The qualified informant may not know precisely what the deceased did or may consciously or unconsciously elevate the deceased's position. In addition, people's last occupation may well not have been what they spent most of their lives doing. These potential discrepancies are important. Data relating mortality to occupation may identify certain workers who are more at risk of dying from certain causes, therefore highlighting occupational exposures that are putting particular groups of workers at risk of certain diseases. Furthermore, because occupation is used to determine social class, inaccuracies may distort the reported differential risk of death among the different social classes. Thus, even with an event as definite as death, some limitations on the accuracy and reliability of the data will be imposed because of its method of collection.

Because of their accessibility and relative completeness, mortality data are often used as the first step in defining a health problem. Historically, however, when acute infectious disease was more important, mortality rates provided a much more accurate reflection of the relative frequency and distribution of particular diseases since people either died quickly or were cured. Today, the most important diseases in the Western world, for example cardiovascular disease, are chronic so mortality data no longer adequately describe the 'health' (or 'disease') of a population. Instead, statistics on illness or morbidity in the population become important.

Data describing morbidity provide information about sickness in communities, whether or not this sickness results in death. The ONS is again responsible in England and Wales for the collection and presentation of these data. Historically, several types of morbidity data have been routinely collected from different population groups. These have included information on hospital inpatients (1949–85), patients attending GPs (1955–56, 1970–71, 1981–82) and 'the general population' in the General Household Survey (every year since 1971). Moreover, statistics are collected routinely on abortions, congenital malformations, cancer, certain infectious diseases, incapacity to work, adverse drug effects, sickness absence and industrial accidents.

Importantly, many of the morbidity data which are collected are based on the use of NHS facilities, often relying on notification from individual practitioners. Therefore, data collected by these information systems may suffer some limitations. For example, any hospital morbidity data relates, by definition, only to people who actually become inpatients. To become an inpatient, people must:

1. consult a medical practitioner and enter hospital

2. suffer from those conditions which merit entry to hospital.

Many people with common and/or serious diseases do not, however, fall into these categories. Similarly, the national morbidity studies of general practice also had their limitations, particularly since the GPs who participated were self-selected rather than a random sample; thus, the data produced might have been biased.

Health statistics derived from self-assessment, such as those collected through the General Household Survey, provide another perspective. This survey collects data on such topics as the occurrence of chronic and acute illnesses, consultations with doctors, smoking habits and medication. Epidemiologists may consider that such data are limited since they rely on self-diagnosis and an individual's memories of events. However, as noted above in the discussion of popular epidemiology, although a lay person's interpretations may not fit neatly into medical disease categorisations, they are equally valid in the determination of the morbidity with which any population is burdened.

needs assessment – this simplistically entails the determination of what any community requires in terms of services and interventions. How and by whom such assessments are structured, organised and monitored may introduce a particular socio-political bias to this process. For example, governmental statistics and policy (such as that contained in *Health of the Nation*) may focus needs assessment on specific areas, to the neglect of others

DEFINING THE IMPORTANT PROBLEMS: *NEEDS ASSESSMENT*

Over the past 10 years, there has been considerable concern and activity given to identifying accurately the health care needs of any given population. This information is certainly essential to the planning of services. It is, however, clear that health strategy occurs at the centre of government and is dominated by an epidemiology based on the medical model.

The national health strategy for England, *The Health of the Nation* (DoH, 1992), and its successor, *Saving Lives: Our Healthier Nation* (DoH, 1999), both selected priority areas for action defined largely by a medical view of what is important. The original strategy selected five key areas for action – coronary heart disease and stroke, cancer, mental illness, accidents and sexual health – although the latter was not included in the later document, becoming instead the focus of a separate strategy.

The following criteria governed the selection of the key areas:

● The area should be a major cause of premature death or avoidable ill health
● Effective interventions should be possible, offering significant scope for improvement in health
● It should be possible to set objectives and targets, and monitor the progress towards them.

Targets concerning health improvement were set for each area. One of the targets for HIV/AIDS and sexual health in 1992, for example, was to reduce the rate of conception among under-16s by at least 50 per cent by the year 2000.

The identification of health care needs and the provision of services to meet those needs is, however, a complex issue. The different groups of government, health care professionals and the public may all have different interests. In this chapter, several potential conflicts have been identified:

- expert versus lay opinion
- intervention versus prevention
- quality of life versus saving life.

Different perspectives can be brought to bear to consider how health care problems are defined. As we have seen, needs as defined by those working in the health services or government may be very different from those seen from the perspective of communities. Rapid appraisal is a technique of needs assessment that uses in-depth qualitative interviews with key informants in the community to identify needs. The data are analysed alongside other sources of qualitative and quantitative data obtained through geographical mapping, observation, censuses and epidemiological techniques. Many projects have recorded a significant difference between needs as identified by the community and by professionals. Moreover, professionals' perceptions of what the community told them they wanted (setting aside what the professionals felt they needed) were, when related to the actual community perspective, alarmingly inaccurate, raising questions about the ability of professionals to elicit or interpret community views (Annett and Rifkin, 1994; Ong and Humphris, 1994).

The English *Health of the Nation* strategy took biomedicine as its framework, the strategies to meet its targets thus adopting this approach. Need was defined solely through the model of clinical medicine. Strategies were devised to reduce risk factors such as smoking and obesity, which are framed within a biomedical and individualistic model of disease. The socio-economic causes underlying ill health, however, went largely unexplored. As Farrant and Russell pointed out in relation to coronary heart disease, 'the alternative model of coronary heart disease aetiology (that is, that rooted in social factors such as poor nutrition and poverty) ultimately challenges orthodox medical practice by locating the point of intervention within the social and political environment' (Farrant and Russell 1985).

This case study has illustrated the framework within which health care problems are identified. There has been a shift from a purely medical perspective to a more holistic model recognising social, environmental, economic and medical factors as important. The publication of the Acheson Report (*Independent Inquiry into Inequalities in Health*, 1998) and the government White Paper *Saving Lives: Our Healthier Nation* (DoH, 1999) recognises that health inequality is widespread and that those who are economically and socially disadvantaged suffer most from poor health. The type of routine data that will be required will therefore extend beyond the current categories of:

- disease incidence and prevalence and survival rates
- service uptake and access

- the lifestyles and beliefs of the population
- mortality rates and years of life lost
- health status, including assessments of pain, social functioning and quality of life.

SUMMARY

- Epidemiology has traditionally relied on a medical model as its basis for theory and practice

- Its key questions are who becomes sick and why particular people become sick. From this, it is possible to identify the health care needs of the population

- It also questions how effective curative and preventative health care services are. From this, more effective strategies for health may be identified

- Epidemiology employs the scientific method of enquiry to answer these questions and uses a variety of large data sets

- Epidemiology is increasingly embracing different perspectives from the social sciences to arrive at a more complete picture of health needs.

QUESTIONS FOR FURTHER DISCUSSION

1. In the past 10 years, epidemiological data have been extensively used as the basis for government policy concerning health service provision, for example *Our Healthier Nation*. How does epidemiology contribute to policies related to clinical effectiveness and clinical governance?

2. Are epidemiological data objective?

3. In what way does a knowledge of the natural history of disease assist in epidemiological studies?

4. How and by whom should health care priorities be determined?

FURTHER READING

Coggan, D., Rose, G. and Barker, D.J.P. (1997) *Epidemiology for the Uninitiated*, 4th edn. London: BMJ Publishing.
  Provides succinct explanations for the novice of the major concepts and research designs used in epidemiology. A quick reference guide.

Fletcher, R.H., Fletcher, S.W. and Wagner, E.H. (1988) *Clinical Epidemiology: The Essentials*. Baltimore: Williams & Wilkins.
  A guide to clinical epidemiology from the perspective of the clinician. Exceptionally clear explanations of, for example, risk, diagnosis, prognosis and their related epidemiological concepts.

Mulhall, A. (1996) *Epidemiology, Nursing and Healthcare*. Basingstoke: Macmillan – now Palgrave.
  This book explores the knowledge base, ideology and practice of epidemiology. It provides an account of traditional medical epidemiology but contrasts this with other approaches to the discipline that are more informed by the social sciences.

Valenis, B. (1992) *Epidemiology and Health Care.* Norwalk, CT: Appleton Lang.
  A comprehensive and detailed text illustrating how epidemiology is used in heath care planning and professional practice.

REFERENCES

Acheson, Sir D. (1998) *Report of the Independent Inquiry into Inequalities in Health.* London: Stationery Office.

Altmann, P., Cunningham, J., Dhanesa, U., Ballard, M., Thompson, J. and Marsh F. (1999) Disturbance of cerebral function in people exposed to drinking water contaminated with aluminium sulphate: retrospective study of the Camelford water incident. *British Medical Journal,* **319**(7213): 807.

Annett, H. and Rifkin, S. (1990) *Improving Urban Health.* Geneva: WHO.

Ashton, J. and Seymour, H. (1991) *The New Public Health,* 3rd edn. Milton Keynes: Open University Press.

Bowling, A. (1991) *Measuring Health: A Review of Quality of Life Measurement Scales.* Buckingham: Open University Press.

Coggan, D., Rose, G. and Barker, D.J.P. (1997) *Epidemiology for the Uninitiated,* 4th edn. London: BMJ Publishing.

Cornwall and Isles of Scilly District Health Authority (1989) *Water Pollution at Lowermoor North Cornwall: Report of the Lowermoor Incident Health Advisory Group* (Chair: Professor Dame Barbara Clayton). Truro: CISDHA.

Crow, R.A., Chapman, R.G., Roe, B. and Wilson, J. (1986) *A Study of Patients with an Indwelling Urethral Catheter and Related Nursing Practice.* Report to the Department of Health. London: DoH.

Dawber, D.R. (1980) *The Framingham Study. The Epidemiology of Atherosclerotic Disease.* Cambridge, MA: Harvard University Press.

DHSS (Department of Health and Social Security) (1983) *NHS Management Inquiry (the Griffiths Report).* DA(83)38. London: DHSS.

Dingwall, R. (1976) *Aspects of Illness.* London: Martin Robertson.

Dingwall, R. (1992) '"Don't mind him, he's from Barcelona". Qualitative methods in health studies', in Daly, J., MacDonald, I. and Willis, E. (eds) *Researching in Health Care. Designs, Dilemmas and Disciplines.* London: Routledge, pp. 161–75.

DoH (Department of Health) (1992) *The Health of the Nation: A Strategy for Health in England.* London: HMSO.

DoH (Department of Health) (1993) *A Vision of the Future. The Nursing, Midwifery and Health Visiting Contribution to Health and Health Care.* London: DoH.

DoH (Department of Health) (1996) *Promoting Clinical Effectiveness: A Framework for Action in and through the NHS.* Leeds: NHSE.

DoH (Department of Health) (1997) *The New NHS: Modern, Dependable.* London: HMSO.

DoH (Department of Health) (1999) *Saving Lives: Our Healthier Nation.* London: Stationery Office.

Draper, P., Best, G. and Dennis, J. (1977) Health and wealth. *Royal Society of Health Journal,* 97.

Farrant, W. and Russell, J. (1985) *Beating Heart Disease: A Case Study in the Production of Health Education Council Publications.* London: Insitute of Education.

Fletcher, R.H., Fletcher, S.W. and Wagner, E.H. (1988) *Clinical Epidemiology. The Essentials.* New York: Williams & Wilkins.

Frankenberg, R. (1980) Medical anthropology and development: a theoretical perspective. *Social Science and Medicine,* **14b**: 197–207.

Lewis, G. (1993) 'Some studies of social causes of and cultural response to disease', in Mascie-Taylor, C.G.N. (ed.) *The Anthropology of Disease*. Oxford: Oxford University Press, pp. 73–124.

Lilienfeld, A.M. and Lilienfeld, D.E. (1980) *Foundations of Epidemiology*, 2nd edn. New York: Oxford University Press.

McKeown, T. (1976) *The Role of Medicine: Dream, Mirage or Nemesis*. London: Nuffield Provincial Hospitals Trust.

Mettlin, C., Lee, F., Drago, J. and Murphy, G. (1991) Findings on the detection of early prostate cancer in 2425 men. *Cancer*, **67**: 2949–58.

Mulhall, A. (1996) *Epidemiology, Nursing and Health Care. A New Perspective*. Basingstoke: Macmillan – now Palgrave.

Ong, B.N. and Humphris, G. (1994) 'Prioritising needs with communities. Rapid appraisal methodologies in health', in Popay, J. and Williams, G. (eds) *Researching the People's Health*. London: Routledge, pp. 58–82.

Percy, A.K., Norbrega, F.T., Okazaki, H., Glattre, E. and Kurland L.T. (1971) Multiple sclerosis in Rochester, Minn. A 60 year appraisal. *Archives of Neurology*, **25**: 105–11.

Sackett, D.L., Haynes, R.B., Guyatt, G. and Tugwell, P. (1991) *Clinical Epidemiology. A Basic Science for Clinical Medicine*, 2nd edn. Boston: Little, Brown.

Scheper-Hughes, N. (1978) Saints, scholars and schizophrenics – madness and badness in Western Ireland. *Medical Anthropology*, Summer (part 3): 59–93.

Seedhouse, D. (1986) *Health: The Foundations of Achievement*. Chichester: John Wiley & Sons.

Snowdon, C., Garcia, J. and Elbourne, D. (1997) Making sense of randomisation: responses of parents of critically ill babies to random allocation of treatment in a clinical trial. *Social Science and Medicine*, **45**(9): 1337–55.

Stacey, M. (1988) *The Sociology of Health and Healing*. London: Unwin Hyman.

Stainton Rogers, W. (1991) *Explaining Health and Illness*. London: Harvester Wheatsheaf.

Townsend, P., Davidson, N. and Whitehead, M. (1988) *Inequalities in Health: The Black Report and the Health Divide*: London: Penguin.

Turshen, M. (1989) *The Politics of Public Health*. London: Zed Books.

Valenis, B. (1992) *Epidemiology and Health Care*. Norwalk, CT: Appleton Lang.

Waldman, A.R. and Osborne, D.M. (1994) Screening for prostate cancer oncology. *Nursing Forum*, **21**: 1512–29.

WHO (World Health Organization) (1946) *Preamble of the Constitution of the World Health Organization*. Geneva: WHO.

Williams, G. and Popay, J. (1994) 'Lay knowledge and the privilege of experience', in Gabe, J., Kelleher, D. and Williams, G. (eds) *Challenging Medicine*. London: Routledge, pp. 118–39.

Health Psychology

JANE OGDEN

CONTENTS

Learning outcomes ●●●●●●●●●●●●●●●●●●●●●●●●●●

This chapter will enable readers to:

- Understand and describe the basic principles of health psychology and how it differs from biomedicine
- Understand why the study of health behaviours is important
- Show an understanding of the role of health beliefs in predicting and potentially changing health behaviours
- Describe the beliefs that people have relating to illness and how these relate to coping
- Illustrate the ways in which health professionals' beliefs may influence their interactions with patients
- Illustrate the role of psychology in the experience of illness, drawing upon theories of pain and pain management
- Illustrate the potential impact of beliefs and behaviour on health, drawing upon the research exploring stress
- Show an awareness of the role of psychology at all stages of becoming and being ill.

OVERVIEW

Psychology focuses on what people believe and how they behave; health psychology explores how these beliefs and behaviours relate to health and illness. This chapter focuses on the beliefs that individuals have relating to health and illness and how these beliefs relate to their health behaviours and subsequently to their health status. This chapter is divided into three parts. The first part explores the contribution of psychology to studying health and illness, describing the background to psychology and highlighting the importance of beliefs concerning both health and illness on the part of both lay people and health professionals. Pain is used as an example of the role of psychology in the experience of illness. The second part then describes the models that have been developed within health psychology, in particular focusing on the structured models of health beliefs and the self-regulatory model of illness behaviour. Stress is used as the example for this section to illustrate the potential impact of psychological factors on illness. Finally, the last part explores how psychology has been applied to cancer as a means of illustrating how psychological factors play a part at all stages of the transition from health to illness.

INTRODUCTION

The roots of psychology date from the beginning of the 20th century and the work of psychoanalysts such as Freud and Jung, as well as behaviourists such as Pavlov and Skinner. The psychoanalysts worked as therapists and developed theories based upon the patients whom they saw. In contrast, the behaviourists used strict experimental approaches and carried out laboratory studies, mostly on animals such as rats and pigeons. The two perspectives appear to be extremely different, but they were based upon the same fundamental questions that remain at the centre of modern-day psychology. Psychologists then and now ask:

- How do people think?
- What causes how people think?
- What changes how people think?
- How do people behave?
- What causes people's behaviour?
- What changes people's behaviour?

These questions form the basis of all the different branches of psychology from biological psychology, with its emphasis on brain chemicals and neurones, to social psychology and its emphasis on individuals and their social world, to cognitive psychology, with its focus on information-processing, problem-solving and language. Health psychology is a relatively new branch of psychology and draws upon the theories and research of its predecessors. Furthermore, although it asks similar questions, it applies these to the study of health and illness. In particular, health psychology asks:

- How do people think about their health and illness?
- How do people behave with regard to their health and illness?
- What impact do such beliefs and behaviours have upon their health and illness?
- What impact do health and illness have upon their beliefs and behaviours?

Health psychology places itself alongside other branches of psychology. However, as it is concerned with health and illness, it is also important to understand its relationship to biomedicine. The biomedical model of medicine was developed in the 19th century and emphasised that man was a part of nature and could therefore be studied in the same way that nature was studied. Health psychology has developed out of the biomedical model.

According to the biomedical model of medicine, diseases either came from outside the body, invaded the body and caused physical changes within the body, or originated as internal involuntary physical changes. Such diseases may be caused by several factors, such as chemical imbalances, bacteria, viruses and genetic predisposition. Within the biomedical model, health and illness are seen as qualitatively different – you are either healthy or ill; there is no continuum between the two. Because illness is seen as arising from biological changes beyond their control, individuals are not seen as being responsible for their illness. The biomedical model seeks to address the manifestations of illness through surgery or drug treatments that aim to change the physical state of the body. According to the biomedical model of medicine, the mind and body function independently of each other, this perspective being comparable to a traditional dualistic model of the mind/body split.

CONNECTIONS

Chapter 2 (Epidemiology) looks at the biomedical model in relation to its influence on the study of disease patterns

THE CONTRIBUTION OF PSYCHOLOGY TO HEALTH STUDIES

During the 20th century, the emergence of psychosomatic medicine, behavioural health, behavioural medicine and, most recently, health psychology has

Figure 3.1   The biopsychosocial model of health and illness
(after Engel, 1980)

CONNECTIONS

Chapter 4 (Sociology) examines the relationship between social factors and ill health, and Chapter 5 (Cultural Studies) explores the links between widely held beliefs and attitudes and health and ill health

posed challenges for the biomedical model. Health psychology suggests that human beings should be seen as complex systems and that illness is caused by a multitude of interacting factors rather than by a single causative factor. Health psychology claims that illness can result from a combination of biological (for example a virus), psychological (for example behaviours and beliefs) and social (for example employment) factors. This approach reflects the biopsychosocial model of health and illness (Engel, 1977, 1980; see Figure 3.1).

Health psychology therefore differs from the biomedical model in several important respects:

- Individuals may be held more responsible, through their behaviours and beliefs, for both the onset of illness and its management and cure
- Psychological factors are not solely a consequence of illness but may also contribute to its onset
- Treatment must be directed to the whole person rather than just his or her physical symptoms.

Health psychology emphasises the role of psychological factors in the cause, progression and consequences of health and illness. Some of the key questions that health psychology tries to explore are:

- What is the role of psychology in the onset and development of illness?
- Should behaviour then be targeted for intervention?
- Can the study of beliefs predict unhealthy behaviour?
- Is it possible to change beliefs?

Thinking about...

Think about the last time you were ill (any illness from a cold to a more serious problem). Brainstorm all the possible psychological factors that could relate to this illness in terms of how you realised you were ill, the cause of the illness, how you coped with the illness and how you became well again

Health psychologists study the role of psychology in all areas of health and illness, including what people think about health and illness, the role of beliefs and behaviours in becoming ill, the experience of being ill in terms of adaptation to illness, contact with health professionals, coping with illness, compliance with a range of interventions, the role of psychology in recovery from illness, quality of life and longevity. Health psychology therefore represents the study of the complex processes involved in the aetiology, impact and progression of illness.

HEALTH BELIEFS AND BEHAVIOURS

It has been suggested that 50% of mortality from the 10 leading causes of death results from individual behaviour. This indicates that behaviour and lifestyle have a potentially major effect on longevity. In particular, Doll and Peto (1981) estimated the contribution of different factors as a cause of all cancer deaths and concluded that tobacco consumption accounts for 30% of all cancer deaths, alcohol for 3%, diet for 35% and reproductive and sexual behaviour for 7%. From this estimate, approximately 75% of all deaths from cancer can be attributed to behaviour. More specifically, lung cancer, which is the most common form of cancer, accounts for 36% of all cancer deaths in men and 15% in women in the UK. It has been calculated that 90% of all lung cancer mortality is attributable to cigarette smoking, which is also linked to other illnesses such as cancer of the bladder, pancreas, mouth, larynx and oesophagus, and coronary heart disease. The relationship between mortality and behaviour is also illustrated by bowel cancer, which accounts for 11% of all cancer deaths in men and 14% in women. Research suggests that bowel cancer is linked to behaviours such as a diet high in total fat, high in meat and low in fibre.

Therefore, **health behaviours** in terms of smoking, drinking alcohol, diet and exercise seem to be important in predicting the mortality and longevity of individuals. Assuming that individuals behave in ways that are in line with how they think, health psychologists have therefore attempted to understand and predict health-related behaviours by studying **health beliefs**. For example, the belief that smoking is dangerous should be associated with non-smoking or smoking cessation; the belief that cervical cancer is preventable should be associated with attendance for cervical screening; the belief that exercise is beneficial should be associated with increased physical activity. Health psychologists thus study what people believe and whether this relates to how they behave. In addition, they explore whether beliefs can be changed and whether any shifts in beliefs predict subsequent changes in behaviour. In particular, individuals have beliefs about:

- *causality and control:* what has contributed to their ill health and whether these factors are controllable
- *risk:* to what extent they feel susceptible to certain diseases or conditions
- *confidence:* whether they feel that there are actions they can take that might affect the condition
- *beliefs about the illness:* what may have caused the illness, how long it might last and what they can do about it.

BELIEFS ABOUT CAUSALITY AND CONTROL

Much work exploring people's beliefs relating to causality and control is based upon Heider's **attribution theory** (Heider, 1958). Attribution theory states that people want to understand what causes events because this makes the world seem more predictable and controllable. Since its original formulation, attribution theory has been developed, differentiations having been made between self-attributions (attributions about one's own behaviour) and other attributions (those made about the behaviour of others). In addition, the dimensions of attribution have been defined as follows:

- *internal versus external* ('My failure to give up smoking is due to my lack of willpower' versus 'Others persuade me to carry on smoking')

CONNECTIONS

Chapter 10 (Health Promotion) looks at strategies that have been used to influence and change health-related behaviours

health behaviour – an act that relates to health, such as eating, drinking or wearing a seat belt

health beliefs – the opinions or thoughts that a person has concerning an object or action, for example the belief that potatoes are fattening

Thinking about...

Think of the last time you changed a behaviour not related to health (for example where you shop, what clothes you buy, how you get to college or work, or how you spend your spare time). Consider all the psychological factors that related to this change in behaviour

attribution theory – attributions are perceived or reported causes of actions, events or feelings. Attribution theory concerns the beliefs that individuals possess about the causes of events

- *stable versus unstable* ('The cause of my failure to give up smoking will always be around' versus 'Next time I might succeed in resisting or avoiding peer pressure')
- *global versus specific* ('The cause of my failure to give up smoking reflects my lack of willpower generally' versus 'I lacked willpower at this specific time')
- *controllable versus uncontrollable* ('The cause of my failure to stop smoking was controllable by me' versus 'It was uncontrollable by me').

Over recent years, attribution theory has been applied to the study of health and health-related behaviour. King (1982) examined the relationship between the attribution of an illness and attendance at a screening clinic for hypertension. The results demonstrated that if the hypertension was seen as external but controllable by the individual, he or she was more likely to attend the screening clinic ('I am not responsible for my hypertension but I can control it'). Bradley et al. (1987) found a relationship between diabetic patients' beliefs about attributions for the responsibility and control of their condition and their choice of treatment. Patients who showed decreased personal control over their diabetes and attributed increased control to doctors were more likely to choose an insulin pump (which provides a continuous dose of insulin) rather than daily injections or other forms of treatment.

locus of control – personality traits to distinguish individuals and their beliefs relating to the factors controlling events – whether themselves, powerful others or chance

The internal versus external dimension of attribution theory has been specifically applied to health in terms of the concept of a health **locus of control**. People differ in terms of the extent to which they can make changes in their lives. Some people believe that what they do and what happens to them is up to them and regard events as personally controllable (an internal locus of control). Others, however, believe that events are largely not controlled by them (an external locus of control). Wallston and Wallston (1982) developed a measure of the health locus of control that evaluates whether individuals:

- regard their health as controllable by them (for example 'I am directly responsible for my health')
- believe that their health cannot be controlled by them but lies in the hands of fate (for example 'Whether or not I am well is a matter of luck')
- regard their health as under the control of powerful others (for example 'I can only do what my doctor tells me to do').

? **How might locus of control be related to an individual's willingness to adopt a more healthy lifestyle?**

People who generally have an external locus of control are less likely to take protective action regarding their health. Part of the work of health professionals may be to encourage them to take more control and set their own targets for change: merely expecting them to follow recommendations from a health professional is unlikely to be effective.

BELIEFS ABOUT RISK

People hold beliefs about their own susceptibility to a given problem and make judgements concerning the extent to which they are 'at risk'. Smokers, for example, may continue to smoke because although they understand that smoking is unhealthy, they do not consider themselves to be at risk of lung cancer. Likewise, a woman may not attend for a cervical smear because she believes that cervical cancer happens only to women who are not like her. People have ways of assessing their susceptibility to particular conditions, and this is not always a rational process. It has been suggested that individuals consistently estimate their risk of getting a health problem as less than that of others. Weinstein (1984) asked subjects to examine a list of health problems and to state 'compared to other people of your age and sex, are your chances of getting [the problem] greater than, about the same, or less than theirs?' The results of this study showed that most subjects believed that they were less likely than others to get the health problem. Weinstein called this phenomenon unrealistic optimism; not everyone can be less likely to contract an illness. Weinstein (1987) suggested that people are likely to dismiss their risk and be unrealistically optimistic if:

- they have a lack of personal experience with the problem
- they believe that the problem is preventable by individual action
- they believe that if the problem has not yet appeared, it will not appear in the future
- the problem is infrequent.

Weinstein (1984) argued that individuals show selective focus by ignoring their own risk-increasing behaviour ('I may drink too much') and focusing primarily upon their risk-reducing behaviour ('but at least I don't drink and drive'). He also argues that individuals tend to ignore others' risk-decreasing behaviour ('My friends all drink sensibly but that's irrelevant'). Individuals may therefore be unrealistically optimistic if they focus on the times when they drink in moderation when assessing their own risk and ignore the times when they do not, in addition focusing on the times when others around them drink to excess and ignoring the times when they are more sensible.

EXAMPLE 3.1

The impact of beliefs and behaviours on health – the example of stress

One of the reasons why stress has been studied so consistently throughout the 20th century is because of its potential effect on the health of the individual. Stress can affect health through either a behavioural or a physiological pathway. Most of the research into the stress–illness link has studied the physiological effects of stress. However, in support of the suggested behavioural pathway (Krantz et al., 1981) and in line with a psychological perspective, some recent research has examined the effect of stress on both specific

CONNECTIONS

Chapter 1 (Physiology) describes the response of the body to stress and physiological reactions

health-related behaviours and more general behavioural change. Research, for example, suggests a link between stress and smoking behaviour in terms of smoking initiation, relapse and the amount smoked. Furthermore, not being able to smoke in a social situation can make the situation more stressful.

Contemporary definitions of stress regard the external environmental stress (for example problems at work) as a stressor, the response to the stressor (for example the feeling of tension) as stress or distress, and the concept of stress as something that involves biochemical, physiological, behavioural and psychological changes. Researchers have also differentiated between stress that is harmful and damaging (distress) and stress that is positive and beneficial (eustress). The most commonly used definition of stress is that of a transactional model stating that stress involves an interaction between the stressor and distress and therefore between people and their environment (Lazarus and Launier, 1978). This approach to stress provides a role for an individual's psychological state and is a departure from more medical perspectives, with their focus on physiology.

Over recent years, theories of stress have emphasised forms of self-control as important in understanding stress. This is illustrated in theories of self-efficacy, hardiness and feelings of mastery. In 1987, Lazarus and Folkman suggested that self-efficacy was a powerful factor for mediating the stress response. Self-efficacy refers to individuals' feelings of confidence that they can perform a desired action. Research indicates that self-efficacy may have a role in mediating stress-induced immunosuppression and physiological changes such as those of blood pressure, heart rate and stress hormone levels. For example, the belief 'I am confident that I can succeed in this exam' may result in physiological changes that reduce the stress response. A belief in the ability to control one's behaviour may therefore relate to whether or not a potentially stressful event results in a stress response.

This shift towards emphasising self-control is also illustrated by the concept of 'hardiness' (Maddi and Kobasa, 1984). Hardiness has been described as reflecting:

● personal feelings of control
● a desire to accept challenges
● commitment.

It has been argued that the degree of hardiness influences an individual's appraisal of potential stressors and the resulting stress response. The term 'feelings of mastery' (Karasek and Theorell, 1990) reflects individuals' control over their stress response. It has been argued that the degree of mastery may be related to the stress response. According to these recent developments, stress is conceptualised as a product of the individual's capacity for self-control. Successful coping and self-management eradicate stress, failed self-regulation results in a stress response, and stress-related illness is considered to be a consequence of prolonged failed self-management.

The relationship between stress and illness is not straightforward, and there is much evidence to suggest that several factors may mediate the stress–illness link. The way in which an individual copes with stress, for example, may reduce stress and subsequently decrease the chance of illness. In addition, increased social support has been related to a decreased stress response and a subsequent reduction in illness. Finally, the degree to which an individual feels in control of the stressor can influence the degree of stress experienced.

Therefore, from a psychological perspective, individuals' states of mind relate to stress and the stress response in terms of their appraisal of the external stressor ('Is it stressful?'), the degree of the stress response to this stressor ('Do I feel stressed?'), their ability to cope with and reduce this response ('It's OK, I can talk this over with my friends') and the degree of any subsequent changes in behaviour ('I think I'll have a cigarette'). Accordingly, each of these factors will in turn determine the extent of any resulting ill health.

 Smoking is a stimulant, yet people use smoking to calm them down when under stress. Why might this be? Do doctors have the right to try and take away a behaviour that helps people to cope with their lives?

BELIEFS ABOUT CONFIDENCE

Individuals also hold beliefs about their ability to carry out certain behaviours. Bandura (1977) has termed this *self-efficacy* to reflect the extent to which people feel confident that they can do whatever it is that they wish to do. A smoker, for example, may feel that she should stop smoking but have very little confidence that she will be able to do so. Likewise, an overweight man may be convinced that he should do more exercise but think that this goal is unlikely to be achievable. These two examples would be said to have low self-efficacy. In contrast, a woman who was motivated to attend for a health check, and felt confident that she could, would be said to have high self-efficacy. Self-efficacy is defined not to reflect a personality trait (that is, this person always has high self-efficacy) but to describe a belief about a particular behaviour at a particular time (that is, this person shows high self-efficacy now in terms of changing this behaviour).

> **self-efficacy** – the belief relating to the degree of confidence an individual has in whether a behaviour can be performed

BELIEFS ABOUT ILLNESS

Illness beliefs have been defined as 'a patient's own implicit common-sense beliefs about their illness' (Leventhal et al., 1980). Such beliefs provide individuals with a framework for coping with and understanding their illness, and for telling them what to look out for if they are becoming ill. There are five cognitive dimensions to these beliefs:

1. *Identity:* what label is given to the illness (the medical diagnosis) and the symptoms experienced (for example, I have a chest infection, 'the diagnosis', with a cough, 'the symptoms').

2. *The perceived cause of the illness:* causes may be biological or psychosocial. People may explain their illness as reflecting different causal models. One person, for example, may believe that 'My chest infection was caused by a virus', whereas another may believe, 'My chest infection was caused by stress and being run down.'

3. *Time line:* beliefs about how long the illness will last, that is, whether it is acute (short term) or chronic (long term) (for example, 'My chest infection will be over in a few days').

4. *Consequences:* perceptions of the possible effects of the illness on an individual's life. The consequences may be physical (for example pain and a lack of mobility), emotional (for example a loss of social contact or loneliness) or a combination of the two (as with, for example, 'My chest infection will prevent me going to college, which will prevent me seeing my friends').

5. *Curability and controllability:* individuals also represent illnesses in terms of whether they believe that the illness can be treated and cured, and the extent to which the outcome of their illness is controllable either by themselves or by powerful others (for example 'If I rest, my chest infection will go away' or 'If I take my medication, my chest infection will go away').

There is some evidence for a similar structure of illness representation in other cultures. Weller (1984) examined models of illness in English-speaking Americans and Spanish-speaking Guatamalans. The results indicated that illness was predominantly conceptualised in terms of contagion and severity. Lau (1995) argued that contagion is a version of the cause dimension (that is, the illness is caused by a virus) and that severity is a combination of the magnitude of the perceived consequences and beliefs about the time line (that is, how will the illness affect my life and how long will it last), dimensions that support those described by Leventhal and his colleagues.

Researchers in New Zealand and the UK have developed the Illness Perception Questionnaire (Weinman et al., 1996). This asks subjects to rate a series of statements about their illness that reflect the dimensions identified by Leventhal et al. The questionnaire has been used to examine beliefs about illnesses such as chronic fatigue syndrome, diabetes and arthritis, and provides further support for the dimensions of illness beliefs.

Individuals thus have beliefs related to both their health and illness. These beliefs influence their behaviours, which may in turn impact upon how healthy they are. The decisions people make are not, however, wholly a product of their beliefs. It is also not only lay people who have such beliefs. Being healthy or ill can bring individuals into contact with a range of health professionals, including GPs, nurses, midwives, hospital doctors and alternative practitioners. These health professionals also have their own beliefs and behaviours.

COMMUNICATION IN HEALTH SETTINGS

The study of health professionals' beliefs developed from the examination of doctor–patient communication and the original focus on compliance.

Haynes et al. (1979) defined **compliance** as 'the extent to which the patient's behaviour (in terms of taking medications, following diets or other lifestyle changes) coincides with medical or health advice'. Compliance has excited an enormous amount of clinical and academic interest over the past few decades, and it has been calculated that 3,200 articles on compliance in English have been listed between 1979 and 1985 (Trostle, 1988).

Compliance is regarded as important primarily because following the recommendations of health professionals is considered to be essential to patient recovery. Studies estimate, however, that about half the patients with a chronic illness such as diabetes or hypertension are non-compliant with their

---

Thinking about...

Think about the last time you did something unhealthy (for example smoked a cigarette, drank too much alcohol or ate too much). How did your views (for example that the behaviour was not really harmful) influence your behaviour?

---

compliance – behaving in line with that which has been suggested, such as taking medication, eating more healthily or attending a health check. Also known as adherence

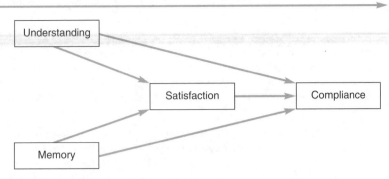

Figure 3.2   Ley's model of compliance

medication regimens and that even compliance for a behaviour as apparently simple as using an inhaler for asthma is poor. Compliance also has financial implications: in the US in 1980, between $396 million and $792 million per year were 'wasted' because of non-compliance with taking prescribed drugs.

 What factors might contribute to a patient's compliance with a medical regimen?

Ley (1988) developed the cognitive hypothesis model of compliance. This claims that compliance can be predicted by a combination of:

● patient satisfaction with the process of the consultation
● understanding the information given
● recall of this information.

Several studies have been carried out to examine each element of the cognitive hypothesis model, which is illustrated in Figure 3.2.

EXAMPLE 3.2

Health consultations

Numerous studies have looked at patients' understanding of what they have been told in a consultation, the extent to which they remember it and whether they feel satisfied with the consultation.

Ley (1988) examined the extent of patient satisfaction with the consultation. He reviewed 21 studies of hospital patients and found that 41% of patients were dissatisfied with their treatment and that 28% of general practice patients were similarly dissatisfied. Studies show that the level of patient satisfaction stems from various components of the consultation, in particular the affective aspects (for example emotional support and understanding), the behavioural aspects (for example prescribing and adequate explanation) and the competence (for example appropriateness of referral, and diagnosis) of the health professional. Ley (1988) has also reported that satisfaction is determined by the content of the consultation and that patients want to know as much information as possible, even if it is bad news. In studies looking at cancer diagnosis, for example, patients showed improved satisfaction if they were given a diagnosis of cancer rather than if they were protected from this information.

Several studies have also examined the extent to which patients understand the content of the consultation. One study by Boyle (1970) examined patients' definitions of different illnesses and reported that, when given a checklist, only 85% correctly defined arthritis, 77% jaundice, 52% palpitations and 80% bronchitis. Boyle further examined patients' perceptions of the location of organs and found that only 42% correctly located the heart, 20% the stomach and 49% the liver. This suggests that the understanding of the content of the consultation may well be low.

Further studies have examined the understanding of illness in terms of causality and seriousness. Roth (1979) asked what patients thought caused peptic ulcers and found a variety of responses, such as problems with the teeth and gums, food, digestive problems or excessive stomach acid. He also examined what individuals thought caused lung cancer and found that although the understanding of the causality of lung cancer was high in terms of smoking behaviour, 50% of individuals thought that lung cancer caused by smoking had a good prognosis.

Researchers have also examined the process of recall of the information given during the consultation. A study by Bain (1977) examined the recall from a sample of patients who had attended a GP consultation and found that 37% could not recall the name of the drug, 23% could not recall the frequency of the dose and 25% could not recall the duration of the treatment. A further study by Crichton et al. (1978) found that 22% of patients had forgotten the treatment regimen recommended by their doctors.

In a meta-analysis of the research into the recall of consultation information, Ley found that recall is influenced by a multitude of factors. Ley argued, for example, that anxiety, medical knowledge, intellectual level, the importance of the statement, the primacy effect and the number of statements affect recall. He concluded, however, that recall is not influenced by the age of the patient, which is contrary to some predictions of the effect of ageing on memory and some of the myths and counter-myths of the ageing process.

 What do these studies suggest about how patient compliance might be improved?

Traditional models of the communication between health professionals and patients have emphasised the transfer of knowledge from expert to lay person. There are, however, several problems with this educational approach, which can be summarised as follows:

● It assumes that the communication from the health professional is from an expert whose knowledge base is one of objective knowledge and does not involve the health beliefs of that individual health professional
● Patient compliance is seen as positive and unproblematic

- Improved knowledge is predicted to improve the communication process
- The approach does not include a role for patient health beliefs.

Doctors are traditionally regarded as having an objective knowledge set that comes from their extensive medical education. If this were the case, it could be predicted that doctors with a similar level of knowledge and training would behave in a similar way. In addition, if doctors' behaviour were objective, it would also be consistent. Considerable variability has, however, been found among doctors in terms of different aspects of their practice. In particular, health professionals have been shown to vary in terms of their diagnosis of asthma, their prescribing behaviour – varying between 15 per cent and 90 per cent of patients receiving drugs – the methods used by doctors to measure blood pressure and their treatment of diabetes (see Marteau and Johnston, 1990).

According to a traditional educational model of doctor–patient communication, this variability could be understood in terms of a differing level of knowledge and expertise: some individuals know more or less than others, and there is a correct way of behaving and a correct diagnosis that experts make successfully, whereas novices make errors. This variability can, however, also be understood by examining the health professionals' own health beliefs.

Patients are described as having lay beliefs that are individual and variable, whereas health professionals are usually described as having professional beliefs that are often assumed to be consistent and predictable. If, however, health professionals vary in the diagnoses that they make, the conclusions that they reach and the treatments that they prescribe, this suggests a role for the health professional's own health beliefs, which may vary as much as the patient's. In particular, these beliefs appear to play a central role in the development of the health professionals' original hypothesis, for example 'This patient looks as if she has a chest infection', 'This patient is anxious but not physically ill', 'This patient wants to tell me something but is embarrassed' or 'This patient could have cancer.'

Health professionals have their own beliefs concerning health and illness, which influence their choice of hypothesis. Some may believe that health and illness are determined by biomedical factors, whereas others may view health and illness as relating to psychosocial factors. A patient suffering from tiredness may be seen by the former as anaemic and by the latter as suffering from stress.

Health professionals will also hold beliefs about the prevalence and incidence of any given health problem. For example, whereas one doctor may regard appendicitis as a common childhood complaint and hypothesise that a child presenting with acute abdominal pain has appendicitis, another may consider appendicitis to be rare and not consider this hypothesis.

Health professionals also have beliefs about the seriousness and treatability of a disease and are particularly motivated to reach a correct diagnosis for serious but treatable conditions. A health professional may, for example, diagnose appendicitis in a child presenting with abdominal pain because appendicitis is both a serious and a treatable condition. There is a high 'pay-off' for a correct diagnosis of such conditions.

Health professionals' existing knowledge of the patient will also influence their original hypothesis. Such knowledge may include the patient's medical history, their psychological state, an understanding of their psychosocial environment and a belief about why the patient uses the medical services.

Thinking about...

Consider the last time
you went to the GP.
Think about the ques-
tions you were asked
and the conclusions that
were reached. What
beliefs do you think the
GP held about you per-
sonally and the problem
that you went with?

In addition, the development of the original hypothesis may be influenced by the health professional's stereotyped views concerning the class, ethnicity or physical appearance of a patient. Furthermore, health professionals' mood, their profile characteristics (such as age and sex) their geographical location and their previous experience may all affect the decision-making process. Therefore, the variability in health professionals' behaviour can be understood in terms of the many pre-existing factors involved in the decision-making process.

In summary, lay people have beliefs about their health and illness. These can take the form of beliefs about cause and control, risk, confidence and the illness in question. However, it is not only lay people who hold such beliefs. Research exploring health professionals' behaviour indicates that their beliefs are just as complex, particularly in areas related to decision-making and diagnosis. Beliefs are therefore central to the experience of being ill in terms of health-related behaviours, beliefs about illness and the beliefs of health professionals. The role of such psychological factors in the experience of illness is illustrated in the research on pain and the role of beliefs and behaviours in both its increase and decrease.

THE EXPERIENCE OF BEING ILL AND THE EXAMPLE OF PAIN

Early models of pain described pain within a biomedical framework as an automatic response to an external factor. From this perspective, pain was seen as a response to a painful stimulus involving a direct pathway connecting the source of pain (for example a burnt finger) to the area of the brain that detected the painful sensation. Although psychological changes ('I feel anxious') were described as resulting from the pain, there was no room in these models for psychology in either the cause or the moderation of pain ('My pain feels better when I think about something else'). Psychology began, however, to play an important part in understanding pain throughout the 20th century. This was based upon several observations:

● It was observed that medical treatments for pain (for example drugs and surgery) were, in the main, useful only for treating acute pain (that is, pain of short duration). Such treatments were fairly ineffective for treating chronic pain (that is, pain which lasts for a long time). This suggested that there must be something else involved in the pain sensation that was not included in the simple stimulus–response models.

● It was also observed that individuals with the same degree of tissue damage differed in their reporting of the painful sensation and/or of a pain response. Beecher (1956) observed soldiers' and civilians' requests for pain relief in a hospital during World War II. He reported that, although soldiers and civilians often showed the same degree of injury, the soldiers requested less medication than the civilians. He found that whereas 80 per cent of the civilians requested medication, only 25 per cent of the soldiers did. Beecher suggested that this reflected a role for the meaning of the injury in the experience of pain: for the soldiers, the injury had a positive meaning as it indicated that their time at war was over. This meaning mediated the pain experience.

The gate control theory of pain

Melzack and Wall (1965) developed the gate control theory of pain, which represented an attempt to introduce psychology into the understanding of pain. This model is illustrated in Figure 3.3. It suggested that although pain still could be understood in terms of a stimulus–response pathway, this pathway was complex and mediated by a network of interacting processes. The gate control theory thus integrated psychology into the traditional biomedical model of pain, not only describing a role for physiological causes and interventions, but also allowing for psychological causes and interventions.

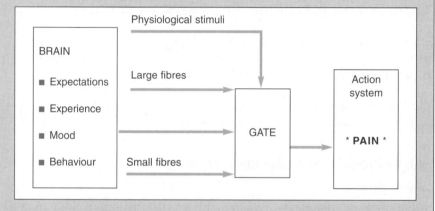

Figure 3.3   The gate control theory of pain

Melzack and Wall suggested that there was a gate existing at spinal cord level, which received input from the peripheral nerve fibres (that is, the site of injury), descending central influences from the brain relating to the psychological state of the individual (in terms of, for example, attention, mood and previous experiences) and the large and small fibres that constitute part of the physiological input to pain perception. They argued that the gate integrates all the information from these different sources and produces an output. This output then sends information to an action system, which results in the perception of pain, the degree of pain relating to how open or closed the gate is. Melzack and Wall suggested that several factors open the gate:

- physical factors, such as injury or activation of the large fibres
- emotional factors, such as anxiety, worry, tension and depression
- behavioural factors, such as focusing on the pain or boredom.

The gate control theory also suggests that certain factors close the gate:

- physical factors, such as medication or stimulation of the small fibres
- emotional factors, such as happiness, optimism or relaxation
- behavioural factors, such as concentration, distraction or an involvement in other activities.

CONNECTIONS

Chapter 1 (Physiology)
examines the contribu-
tion of physiology to
understanding health
and illness and consid-
ers how the perspectives
of physiology and psy-
chology understand pain

● The third observation was phantom limb pain. Between 5 and 10 per cent of amputees tend to feel pain in an absent limb. Their pain can actually get worse after the amputation and continue even after complete healing. Some-times the pain can feel as if it is spreading at the site, often being described as that of a hand being clenched with the nails digging into the palm. Phantom limb pain has no physical basis because the limb is obviously missing. In addition, not everybody feels phantom limb pain, and those who do, do not experience it to the same extent.

The gate control theory was a development from previous theories in that it allowed for the existence of mediating variables and emphasised active percep-tion rather than passive sensation. The gate control theory and the subsequent attempts at evaluating the different components of pain perception reflect a three-process model of pain. The components of this model are:

● physiological processes such as tissue damage
● the release of endorphins and changes in heart rate
● subjective-affective-cognitive and behavioural processes.

The latter two sets of process indicate a central role for psychological factors in pain perception and have been studied as follows.

Subjective-affective-cognitive processes

Learning processes

classical conditioning – a learning process whereby a previously neutral stimulus such as a sound or a smell evokes a response as a result of repeated association with a stimulus

● *Classical conditioning:* research suggests that classical conditioning may have an effect on the perception of pain. As described by theories of associa-tive learning, an individual may associate a particular environment with the experience of pain. For example, if an individual, because of past experience, associates the dentist with pain, pain perception may be enhanced when attending the dentist as a result of this expectation. In addition, because of the association between these two factors, the individual may experience increased anxiety when attending the dentist, which may also increase pain.

operant conditioning – a simple learning process whereby a voluntary response occurs more frequently in a particular situation or in response to a particular stimulus as a result of having previously been rewarded

● *Operant conditioning:* research suggests that there is also a role for operant conditioning in pain perception. Individuals may respond to pain by showing pain behaviour (for example resting, grimacing, limping or staying off work). Such pain behaviour may be positively reinforced (by, for example, sympathy, attention and time off work), which may itself increase pain perception (see the section on Behavioural processes below).

Anxiety

Anxiety also appears to influence pain perception. Fordyce and Steger (1979) have examined the relationship between anxiety and acute and chronic pain, reporting that anxiety has a different relationship to these two types of pain. In terms of acute pain, pain increases anxiety, the successful treatment of the pain then decreasing the pain, which subsequently decreases the anxiety. This can then cause a further decrease in the pain level. Therefore with acute pain, because of the relative ease with which it can be treated, anxiety relates to this pain perception in terms of a cycle of pain reduction.

The pattern is, however, different for chronic pain. With chronic pain, pain increases anxiety, but the treatment of chronic pain is often poorly effective, the pain then further increasing anxiety, which further increases the pain. In terms of the relationship between anxiety and chronic pain, there is thus a cycle of pain increase.

Neurosis

It has also been suggested that personality, in particular neurosis, may be related to pain perception. Hysteria, hypochondriasis and depression have been labelled the neurotic triad. Sternbach et al. (1973) reported that an increase in the neurotic triad is related to an increase in chronic pain and can be related to less sleep, reduced social and work life and feelings of exhaustion. In addition, an increased preoccupation with pain may be associated with increased pain.

Cognitive states

One of the most important factors that influences pain is the cognitive state of the individual. Beecher (1956), in his study of soldiers' and civilians' requests for medication, was one of the first people to examine this and asked the question 'What does pain mean to the individual?' Beecher argued that differences in pain perception were related to the *meaning* of pain for the individual. In Beecher's study, the soldiers benefited from their pain. This has been described in terms of secondary gain, whereby the pain may have a positive reward for the individual.

Behavioural processes

The way in which an individual responds to the pain can itself increase or decrease the perception of the pain. In particular, research has looked at pain behaviours, which have been defined by Turk et al. (1985) as facial or audible expressions (for example clenched teeth and moaning), distorted posture or movement (for example limping or protecting the painful area), negative affect (for example irritability and depression) and the avoidance of activity (for example not going to work or lying down).

It has been suggested that pain behaviours are reinforced by attention, the acknowledgement they receive, and through secondary gains such as not having to go to work. Positively reinforcing pain behaviour may increase pain perception. Pain behaviour can also cause a lack of activity, muscle wastage, a lack of social contact and a dearth of distraction, leading to the adoption of a sick role, which can also increase pain perception.

Pain treatment – a role for psychology?

If psychology is involved in the perception of pain, recent research has suggested that psychology can also be involved in the treatment of pain. There are several methods of pain treatment that reflect an interaction between psychology and physiological factors:

- *Biofeedback* has been used to enable individuals to exert voluntary control over their bodily functions. The technique aims to decrease anxiety and tension and therefore to decrease pain.

- *Relaxation* methods are also used. These aim to decrease anxiety and stress, and consequently to decrease pain.

- *Operant conditioning* is related to an increased pain perception. It can therefore also be used in pain treatment to reduce pain. Some aspects of pain treatment aim positively to reinforce compliance and non-pain behaviour, thereby decreasing secondary gains and pain level.

- A *cognitive approach* to pain treatment involves factors such as attention diversion (encouraging the individual not to focus on the pain) and imagery (encouraging the individual to have positive, pleasant thoughts). Both these factors appear to decrease pain.

- *Hypnosis* has also been shown to reduce pain. However, whether or not this is simply an effect of attention diversion is unclear.

Multidisciplinary pain clinics

Over recent years, multidisciplinary pain clinics have been set up to treat pain and attempt to challenge the factors that cause or exacerbate pain. The goals set by such clinics include factors such as:

- improving physical and lifestyle functioning: this involves improving muscle tone, self-esteem, self-efficacy and distraction and decreasing boredom, pain behaviour and secondary gains

- a decreasing reliance on drugs and medical services: this involves improving personal control, decreasing the sick role and increasing self-efficacy

- increasing social support and family life: this aims to increase optimism and distraction and decrease boredom, anxiety, sick role behaviour and secondary gains.

THEORETICAL AND METHODOLOGICAL PERSPECTIVES

Health psychology draws upon a range of models in its approach. These models help us to understand:

- people's views about the causes of ill health
- the extent to which people feel that they can control their life and make changes
- how people explain their health and ill health, which is crucial to making sense of the strategies that they adopt to promote health, prevent ill health and manage illness.

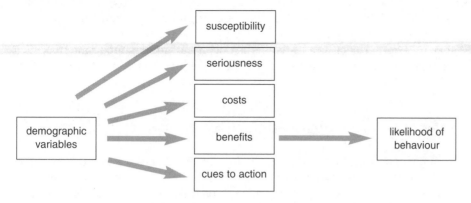

Figure 3.4   The health belief model

THE HEALTH BELIEF MODEL

The **health belief model** (see Figure 3.4) was initially formulated by Rosenstock in 1966, being developed by Becker and colleagues throughout the 1970s and 80s. The health belief model is used to predict people's adoption of preventative health behaviours and in the behavioural response to medical treatment for illness.

The health belief model predicts that behaviour is a result of a set of stable, core beliefs concerning:

● susceptibility to illness (for example 'My chances of having a heart attack are low')
● the seriousness of the illness (for example 'Heart disease is a serious illness')
● the costs involved in carrying out the behaviour (for example 'Eating less will be stressful and boring')
● the benefits involved in carrying out the behaviour (for example 'Eating more healthily will make me feel better')
● cues to action, which may be internal (such as the symptom of breathlessness) or external (such as information in the form of health education leaflets).

Becker and Rosenstock's (1987) revised health belief model includes:

● an assessment of sufficient motivation to make health issues salient or relevant
● the belief that change following a health recommendation will be beneficial to the individual at a level of acceptable cost.

 How might the health belief model be used to predict the likelihood of a smoker giving up?

The health belief model would predict smoking cessation if an individual perceived that she was highly susceptible to lung cancer, that lung cancer was a serious health threat, that the benefits of stopping smoking (for example more money and less odour) were high and that the costs of such action (for example

health belief model – a psychological model suggesting that health behaviour is a function of the perceived benefits and barriers of the behaviour, the perceived susceptibility to a health problem and individual beliefs concerning personal risk, and the perceived seriousness of the problem

potential weight gain or isolation in the peer group) were comparatively low. Furthermore, she is more likely to give up if she is subjected to cues to action that are external, such as a leaflet in the doctor's waiting room, or internal, such as a symptom such as breathlessness perceived (correctly or otherwise) to be related to lung cancer.

THE PROTECTION MOTIVATION THEORY

As a result of some of the criticisms of the health belief model and the emerging focus on self-efficacy (see above), Rogers (1983) developed the protection motivation theory (see Figure 3.5), which expanded the health belief model to include additional factors. The protection motivation theory claims that health-related behaviours are a product of five components:

- self-efficacy (for example 'I am confident that I can attend for a cervical smear')
- response effectiveness (for example 'Having a smear will enable abnormalities to be detected early')
- severity (for example 'Cervical cancer is a serious illness')
- vulnerability (for example 'My chances of getting cervical cancer are high')
- fear (for example an emotional response) in response to education or information.

These components predict behavioural intentions (for example, 'I intend to change my behaviour'), which are related to behaviour. Response effectiveness and self-efficacy relate to coping appraisal (that is, individual self-appraisal), whereas severity, vulnerability and fear relate to threat appraisal (that is, assessing the outside threat). Information, which can be either environmental (such as verbal persuasion or observational learning) or intrapersonal (such as prior experience), influences the five components of the protection motivation theory, giving rise to either an adaptive coping response (that is, behavioural intention) or a maladaptive coping response (for example avoidance or denial).

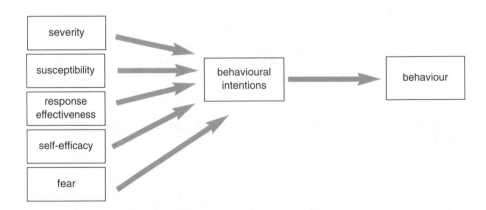

Figure 3.5   The protection motivation theory

How might the protection motivation theory be applied to those thinking about taking up exercise?

Information on the contributory role of a poor fitness level to coronary heart disease would increase individuals' anxiety and their perception of how serious coronary heart disease was (perceived severity) and might also increase their belief that they were likely to have a heart attack (perceived vulnerability/susceptibility). If the individuals also felt confident that they could change their level of physical activity (self-efficacy) and that this change would have a beneficial outcome (response effectiveness) such as a weight loss, they would be more likely to change their behaviour (behavioural intentions). This would be seen as an adaptive coping response to the information. Alternatively, they might not perceive themselves to be unfit and might therefore deny that the information had any relevance to them. This would be seen as a maladaptive coping response.

THE THEORY OF PLANNED BEHAVIOUR

The **theory of reasoned action** (Fishbein and Ajzen, 1975) suggests that people's beliefs related to their social world and the expectations of others who are important to them will affect their behaviour. The theory of reasoned action therefore sees the individual within a social context and, in contrast to the traditional approach in which behaviour is seen as rational, includes a role for values.

The **theory of planned behaviour** (see Figure 3.6) was developed by Ajzen (1988) and represented a progression from the theory of reasoned action. This theory views intentions as 'plans of action in pursuit of behavioural goals'. These intentions are the result of the following beliefs:

- **Attitude** *towards a behaviour:* this is composed of a positive or a negative evaluation of a particular behaviour and the beliefs about the outcome of the behaviour (for example 'Dieting is boring but will improve my health').

- *Subjective norm:* this includes both the perception of social norms and pressures to perform a behaviour, and an evaluation of the individual's motivation to comply with this pressure (for example 'People who are important to me will approve if I stop smoking and I want their approval').

- *Perceived behavioural control:* this reflects individuals' beliefs that they can carry out a particular behaviour. It is derived from internal control factors (for example skills, abilities and information) and external control factors (for example obstacles such as a lack of time, money or opportunity), both relating to past behaviour.

According to the theory of planned behaviour these three factors predict behavioural intentions, which are then linked to behaviour. The theory of planned behaviour also states that perceived behavioural control could have a direct effect on behaviour without the mediating effect of behavioural intentions.

theory of reasoned action – a theoretical model stating that health behaviours are controlled by attitudes and subjective norms (the beliefs of others)

theory of planned behaviour – a revision of the theory of reasoned action that states that behaviour is controlled by attitudes, subjective norms and perceived control

attitude – the feelings an individual has about an object or action. There are three aspects to a person's attitudes to an issue – cognitive (knowledge and information), affective (their emotions, likes and dislikes) and behavioural (their skills and competences)

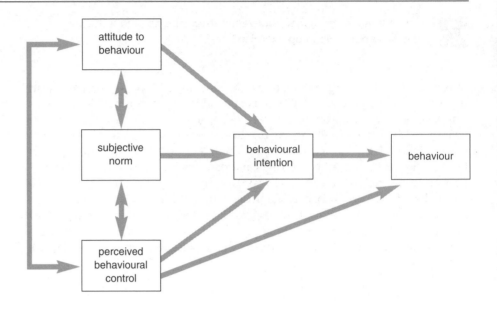

Figure 3.6   The theory of planned behaviour

? How might the theory of planned behaviour be applied to someone who wanted to reduce their drinking?

The theory of planned behaviour would make the following predictions. If an individual believed that cutting down on drinking would make their life more productive and would be beneficial to their health (the attitude to the behaviour), and believed that the important people in their life wanted them to stop (subjective norm), as well as believing that they were capable of reducing or stopping drinking because of their past behaviour and an evaluation of internal and external control factors (high behavioural control), this would predict a high intention to stop drinking (behavioural intention). The model also predicts that perceived behavioural control could predict behaviour without the influence of intentions. For example, if someone believed that they could not stop drinking because they were dependent on alcohol, this would be a better predictor of their behaviour than would their intention to stop drinking.

THE STAGES OF CHANGE MODEL

The stages of change model (also known as the transtheoretical model of behaviour) was originally developed by Prochaska and DiClemente (1982). Unlike other models of beliefs and behaviours, this model does not try to explain what contributes to a decision to change but describes how the change might take place.

Prochaska and DiClemente's model of behaviour change is based on the following stages:

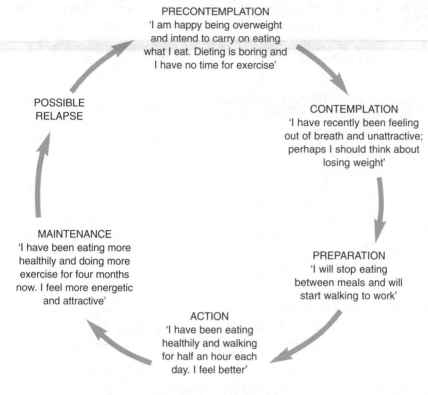

Figure 3.7   Model of behaviour change

1. precontemplation (not intending to make any changes)

2. contemplation (considering a change)

3. preparation (making small changes)

4. action (actively engaging in a new behaviour)

5. maintenance (sustaining the change over time).

The model is cyclic and bi-directional. In other words, an individual may move to the preparation stage and then back to the contemplation stage several times before progressing to the action stage. Furthermore, even when an individual has reached the maintenance stage, he or she may slip back to the contemplation stage over time. Many smokers, for example, contemplate stopping smoking, stop smoking for a while, start smoking again with no intention to stop and then start contemplating cessation again.

An individual may not have an awareness of contemplating, actioning and maintaining change but will at different stages focus on either the costs of a behaviour (for example 'Taking up exercise will mean that I have less time with my children') or the benefits of the behaviour (for example 'Exercise will make me feel fitter').

The stages of change model has been applied to several health-related behaviours, such as smoking, alcohol use, exercise and screening behaviour.

Imagine that you were trying to convince a friend to stop smoking. What beliefs do you think you would have to change in order to be successful? How would you go about doing this? Consider this, bearing in mind the models described above.

THE SELF-REGULATORY MODEL

The above models tend to be used to explore the predictors of health-related behaviours. In contrast, the self-regulatory model is commonly used to examine how individuals adjust to illness (Leventhal et al., 1985; Figure 3.8). In particular, the self-regulatory model suggests that illness and symptoms are dealt with by individuals in the same way as other problems. Thus, if an individual is usually healthy, any onset of illness will be interpreted as a problem, and the individual will be motivated to re-establish their state of health. To do this, an individual needs first to make sense of the problem and then to cope with it.

The stages of the self-regulatory model are described below.

Stage 1: Interpretation

An individual may be confronted with the problem of a potential illness through two channels: symptom perception and social messages.

Symptom perception ('I am feeling breathless')

Symptom perception is not a straightforward process but is influenced by individual difference, mood and cognitions. Pennebaker (1982) argues that individuals vary in the amount of attention that they pay to their internal state. In addition, being more internally focused does not necessarily mean being more accurate in terms of symptom perception. In a study evaluating the accuracy of detecting changes in heart rate, Pennebaker (1982) reported that individuals who were more focused on their internal state tended to overestimate any changes in their heart rate compared with subjects who were externally focused. Being internally focused has also been shown to relate to a perception of a slower recovery from illness. Being internally focused may result in an exaggerated perception of symptom change rather than a more accurate one.

An individual's cognitive state may also influence his or her symptom perception. Ruble (1977) carried out a study in which she manipulated women's expectations of when they were due to start menstruating. She gave subjects an 'accurate physiological test' and told women either that their period was due very shortly or that it was at least a week away. The women were then asked to report any premenstrual symptoms. The results showed that believing that they were about to start menstruating (even though they were not) increased the number of reported premenstrual symptoms. This indicates an association between cognitive state and symptom perception.

The factors contributing to symptom perception can be illustrated by a condition known as 'medical students' disease', described by Mechanic (1962). A large component of the medical curriculum involves learning about the symptoms associated with a multitude of different illnesses. More than two-thirds of

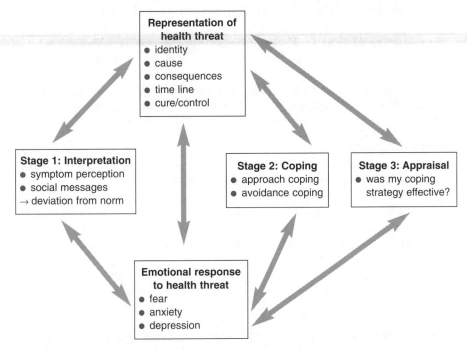

Figure 3.8   Self-regulatory model of illness behaviour

medical students incorrectly report that at some time they have had the symptoms they are being taught about. This phenomenon can perhaps be understood in terms of mood, cognition and social norms. Medical students, for example, become quite anxious as a result of their work load, which may heighten their awareness of any physiological changes, making them more internally focused. In addition, medical students are thinking about symptoms as part of their course, which may result in a focus on their own internal state. Furthermore, once one student starts to perceive symptoms, others may model themselves on this behaviour. Therefore, symptom perception influences how an individual interprets the problem of illness.

Social messages ('The doctor has diagnosed this breathlessness as asthma')

Information about illness also comes from other people, in the form of, for example, a formal diagnosis from a health professional, or a positive test result from a routine health check. Such messages may or may not be a consequence of symptom perception. In addition, information about illness may come from other lay individuals who are not health professionals. Before (and often after) consulting a health professional, people often access their social network – their 'lay referral system' (colleagues, friends and family) – and seek their information and advice. For example, someone with a sore throat may speak to another friend who had a similar condition or may take up a suggestion of a favoured home remedy. Such social messages will influence how the individual interprets the 'problem' of illness.

Individuals may therefore receive information about the possibility of illness through either symptom perception or social messages. This information influences how an individual makes sense of the problem and the development of illness cognitions that will be constructed according to the dimensions of identity, cause, consequences, time line and cure/control (see above). These cognitive representations of the 'problem' will give the problem meaning and will enable the individual to develop and consider suitable coping strategies.

Stage 2: Coping

People cope with illness in many different ways, but, broadly speaking, coping can be considered in terms of two main categories:

- approach coping, such as taking pills, going to the doctor, resting and talking to friends about emotions
- avoidance coping, which involves denial and wishful thinking.

Taylor (1983) examined the ways in which individuals adjust to threatening events including illness and rape. Taylor suggested that coping consists of:

- a search for meaning ('Why did it happen to me?')
- a search for mastery ('How can I prevent it happening again?')
- a process of self-enhancement ('I am better off than a lot of people').

Taylor argued that these three processes are central to developing and maintaining illusions that constitute a process of cognitive adaptation.

Stage 3: Appraisal

Appraisal involves individuals evaluating the effectiveness of the coping strategy to determinine whether to continue with this strategy or try an alternative one.

The model is self-regulatory because its three components (interpretation, coping and appraisal) interrelate in order to maintain the status quo (that is, they regulate the self). Therefore, if the individual's normal state (health) is disrupted (by illness) the model proposes that the individual is motivated to return the balance to normality. This self-regulation involves the three processes interrelating in an ongoing and dynamic fashion.

 Some people are always seriously ill and frequently visit their GP ('I have bronchitis', 'I have tonsilitis', 'I have a migraine') whereas others only have mild complaints ('I have a cough', 'I have a sore throat', 'I have a headache'). How might this relate to the way in which they make sense of their symptoms?

The study of beliefs and behaviour illustrates the role of psychology in the aetiology and progression of illness. This will now be studied through a focus on chronic illness. Although health psychologists study a range of chronic illnesses, including coronary heart disease, AIDS, asthma, multiple sclerosis, chronic fatigue and cancer, this chapter will focus on cancer as it is one of the most common causes of morbidity and mortality in the Western world.

CASE STUDY – CHRONIC ILLNESS, THE EXAMPLE OF CANCER

It has been estimated that up to 85 per cent of all cancers are potentially avoidable. Accordingly, it has been suggested that psychological factors play a role in cancer. The potential role of psychology in understanding cancer is shown in Figure 3.9.

The following factors have been shown to be influential in the initiation and promotion of cancer:

1. *Behavioural factors such as smoking, diet, sexual behaviour and alcohol use.* The relative contribution to cancer from behavioural factors has been estimated as tobacco use 30%, diet 35%, reproductive and sexual behaviour 7% and alcohol 3%.

2. *Stress.* Laudenslager et al. (1983) reported a study that involved exposing cancer-prone mice to stress (shaking the cage). They found that if this stressor could be controlled, there was a decrease in the rate of tumour development. If, however, the stressor was perceived as uncontrollable, this resulted in an increase in the development of tumours. This suggests a role for stress in the initiation of cancer and provides some support for the suggested link between stress and illness described earlier.

3. *Control.* A lack of control over stressors and environmental factors may be related to an increase in the onset of cancer.

4. *Coping styles.* If an individual is subjected to stress, the methods they use to cope with this stress may well be related to the onset of cancer. For example,

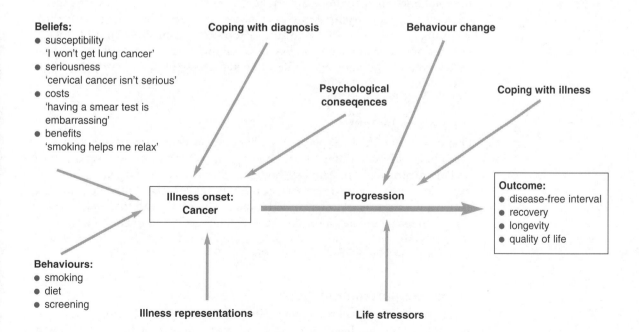

Figure 3.9   The potential role of psychology in cancer

maladaptive, disengagement coping strategies such as smoking and alcohol use may have a relationship with an increase in the incidence of cancer.

5. *Personality*. Temoshok and Fox (1984) have suggested that individuals who develop cancer have a 'type C personality'. A type C personality is described as passive, appeasing, helpless, other focused and unexpressive of emotion. Eysenck (1990) described 'a cancer-prone personality' and suggests that this is characteristic of individuals who react to stress with helplessness and hopelessness, and of individuals who repress their emotional reactions to life events. In 1987, Shaffer et al. carried out a prospective study to examine the predictive capacity of personality and its relationship to developing cancer in medical students over 30 years. At follow-up, they described the type of individual who was more likely to develop cancer as one who had impaired self-awareness and was self-sacrificing, self-blaming and not emotionally expressive. The results from this study suggested that those individuals who had this type of personality were 16 times more likely to develop cancer than those individuals who did not.

The relationship between cancer and personality is, however, not a straightforward one. First, it has been argued that the different personality types predicted to relate to particular types of illness are not distinct from each other, and second that people with cancer do not consistently differ in the predicted direction from either healthy people or people with heart disease (Amelang and Schmidt-Rathjens, 1996).

THE ALLEVIATION OF SYMPTOMS

Psychology also has a role to play in the alleviation of symptoms of cancer and in promoting quality of life. Cartwright et al. (1973) described the experiences of cancer sufferers, varying from very distressing pain, breathing difficulties, vomiting and sleeplessness, to loss of bowel and bladder control, loss of appetite and mental confusion. Psychosocial interventions have therefore been used to attempt to alleviate some of the symptoms of cancer sufferers and to improve their quality of life.

Pain management

One of the main roles of psychology lies in pain management, this occurring through a variety of different pain management techniques (see section above on Pain treatment – a role for psychology?). Biofeedback and hypnosis have, for example, been shown to decrease pain. Turk and Rennert (1981) encouraged patients with cancer to describe and monitor their pain and to develop coping skills, taught them relaxation skills and encouraged them to carry out positive imagery and focus on other things. They reported that these techniques were successful in reducing the pain experience.

Social support interventions

Social support interventions have also been used through the provision of support groups emphasising control and meaningful activities and aiming to reduce denial and hope. It has been suggested that although this intervention may not have any effect on longevity, it may improve the meaningfulness of the cancer patient's life.

Treating nausea and vomiting

Psychology has also been involved in treating the nausea and vomiting experienced by cancer patients. Cancer patients are often offered chemotherapy as a treatment for their cancer, which can cause anticipatory nausea, vomiting and anxiety. Redd (1982) and Burish et al. (1987) suggest that 25–33 per cent of cancer patients show conditioned vomiting and 60 per cent show anticipatory anxiety. Respondent conditioning and visual imagery, relaxation, hypnosis and desensitisation have been shown to decrease nausea and anxiety in cancer patients.

Cognitive adaptation strategies

Research also suggests that quality of life may also be improved using cognitive adaptation strategies. Taylor (1983) used such strategies to improve patients' self-worth, their ability to be close to others and the meaningfulness of their lives. Such methods have been suggested to involve self-transcendence, which has again been related to improvement in well-being and a decrease in illness-related distress.

LONGEVITY

The final question relating to the role of psychology in cancer concerns its relationship to longevity: do psychosocial factors influence survival? Research findings are contradictory, and there is no clear answer to this question. Research has explored the role of cognitive factors and personality in predicting the outcome of cancer treatment, most studies focusing on the impact of life events on longevity. A case control study by Ramirez et al. (1989) that examined the relationship between life stress and relapse in operable breast cancer found that life events rated as severe were related to a first occurrence of breast cancer. Other research, however, finds no relationship between life stress and relapse (Barraclough et al., 1992).

This case study has illustrated the role of psychology in understanding cancer not only in relation to the beliefs and behaviours that may contribute to the onset of cancer, but also in terms of the treatment of symptoms, improving quality of life, the time free from disease and longevity.

> *Thinking about...*
>
> People often say that their symptoms disappear in the waiting room of the GP's surgery. In addition, a headache may go before the pill has been swallowed. Can we really think ourselves well?

SUMMARY

- Health psychologists are interested in how people think about their health and their health-related attitudes and beliefs
- Health psychologists have developed various models to explain the relationship between attitudes, beliefs and behaviours, as well as to predict the decisions that people make
- The study of individual beliefs provides an insight into people's health-related behaviour and how unhealthy behaviours can be changed

- Health psychologists study how people make sense of illness and how these beliefs may contribute to the onset, progression and possible treatment of illness

- Understanding the role of psychological factors may help to reduce the stress and pain associated with being ill.

QUESTIONS FOR FURTHER DISCUSSION

1. Why do people continue to behave in unhealthy ways? Discuss with reference to smoking, diet, exercise or alcohol.

2. Is stress always a bad thing?

3. There is no such thing as physical illness: an illness has a psychological component. Discuss.

4. Why is patient adherence to medical treatment regimes so low? How might it be increased?

FURTHER READING

Bowling, A. (1995) *Measuring Disease*. Buckingham: Open University Press.
Provides a useful overview of the theory behind measuring quality of life and a clear review of the existing scales for assessing health status.

Connor, M. and Norman, P. (1995) *Predicting Health Behaviours*. Buckingham: Open University Press.
Provides a thorough description of the social cognition models and the extent to which they predict health-related behaviour.

Ogden, J. (1996, 2000) *Health Psychology: A Textbook* 1st and 2nd edns. Buckingham: Open University Press.
A comprehensive overview of health psychology covering a range of health psychology areas of research and theory. The current chapter was based upon this book.

Strober, W. and Strober, M.S. (1995) *Social Psychology and Health*. Buckingham: Open University Press.
This book focuses on the aspects of health psychology that draw upon social psychology.

REFERENCES

Ajzen, I. (1988) *Attitudes. Personality and Behaviour*. Chicago: Dorsey Press.
Amelang, M. and Schmidt-Rathjens, C. (1996) Personality, cancer and coronary heart disease: further evidence on a controversial issue. *British Journal of Health Psychology*, **1**: 191–205.
Bain, D.J.G. (1977) Patient knowledge and the content of the consultation in general practice. *Medical Education*, **11**: 347–50.
Bandura, A. (1977) Self efficacy: toward a unifying theory of behavior change. *Psychological Review*, **84**: 191–215.
Barraclough, J., Pinder, P., Cruddas, M., Osmond, C., Taylor, I. and Perry, M. (1992) Life events and breast cancer prognosis. *British Medical Journal*, **304**: 1078–81.
Becker, M.H. and Rosenstock, I.M. (1987) 'Comparing social learning theory and the health belief model', in Ward, W.B. (ed.) *Advances in Health Education and Promotion*. Greenwich, CT: JAI Press, pp. 245–9.

Beecher, H.K. (1956) Relationship of significance of wound to the pain experienced. *Journal of the American Medical Association*, **161**: 1609–13.

Boyle, C.M. (1970) Differences between patients' and doctors' interpretations of common medical terms. *British Medical Journal*, **2**: 286–9.

Bradley, C., Gamsu, D.S., Moses, J.L. et al. (1987) The use of diabetes-specific perceived control and health belief measures to predict treatment choice and efficacy in a feasibility study of continuous subcutaneous insulin infusion pumps. *Psychology and Health*, **1**: 133–46.

Burish, T.G., Carey, M.P., Krozely, M.G. and Greco, F.F. (1987) Conditioned side-effects induced by cancer chemotherapy: prevention through behavioral treatment. *Journal of Consulting and Clinical Psychology*, **55**: 42–8.

Cartwright, A., Hockey, L., and Anderson, J.L. (1973) *Life Before Death*. London: Routledge.

Crichton, E.F., Smith, D.L. and Demanuele, F. (1978) Patients' recall of medication information. *Drug Intelligence and Clinical Pharmacy*, **12**: 591–9.

Doll, R. and Peto, R. (1981) *The Causes of Cancer*. New York: Oxford University Press.

Engel, G.L. (1977) The need for a new medical model: a challenge for biomedicine. *Science*, **196:** 129–35.

Engel, G.L. (1980) The clinical application of the biopsychosocial model. *American Journal of Psychiatry*, **137**: 535–44.

Eysenck, H.J. (1990) The prediction of death from cancer by means of personality/stress questionnaire: too good to be true? *Perceptual Motor Skills*, **71**: 216–18.

Fishbein, M. and Ajzen, I. (1975) *Belief, Attitude, Intentional Behaviour: An Introduction to Theory and Research*. Reading, MA: Addison-Wesley.

Fordyce, W.E. and Steger, J.C. (1979) 'Chronic pain', in Pomerleau, O.F. and Brady, J.P. (eds) *Behavioural Medicine: Theory and Practice*. Baltimore: Williams & Wilkins, pp. 125–53.

Haynes, R.B., Sackett, D.L. and Taylor, D.W. (eds) (1979) *Compliance in Health Care*. Baltimore: Johns Hopkins University Press.

Heider, F. (1958) *The Psychology of Interpersonal Relations*. New York: John Wiley & Sons.

Karasek, R. and Theorell, T. (1990) *Healthy Work. Stress, Productivity and the Reconstruction of Working Life*. New York: Basic Books.

King, J.B. (1982) The impact of patients' perceptions of high blood pressure on attendance at screening: an attributional extension of the health belief model. *Social Science and Medicine*, **16**: 1079–92.

Krantz, D.S., Glass, D.C., Contrada, R. and Miller, N.E. (1981) *Behavior and Health. National Science Foundations Second Five Year Outlook on Science and Technology*. Washington, DC: US Government Printing Office.

Lau, R.R. (1995) 'Cognitive representations of health and illness', in Gochman, D. (ed.) *Handbook of Health Behaviour Research*, Vol. I. New York: Plenum Press.

Laudenslager, M.L., Ryan, S.M., Drugan, R.C., Hyson, R.L. and Maier, S.F. (1983) Coping and immunosuppression: inescapable but not escapable shock suppresses lymphocyte proliferation. *Science*, **221**: 568–70.

Lazarus, R.S. and Folkman, S. (1987) Transactional theory and research on emotions and coping. *European Journal of Personality*, **1**: 141–70.

Lazarus, R.S. and Launier, R. (1978) 'Stress related transactions between person and environment', in Pervin, L.A. and Lewis, M. (eds) *Perspectives in International Psychology*. New York: Plenum Press, pp. 287–327.

Leventhal, H., Meyer, D. and Nerenz, D. (1980) 'The common sense representation of illness danger', in Rachman, S. (ed.) *Medical Psychology*, **2**: 7–30.

Leventhal, H., Prohaska, T.R. and Hirschman, R.S. (1985) 'Preventive health behaviour across the life span', in Rosen, J.C. and Solomon, L.J. (eds) *Prevention in Health Psychology*. Hanover, NH: University Press of New England.

Ley, P. (1988) *Communicating with Patients*. London: Croom Helm.

Maddi, S. and Kobasa, S.G. (1984) *The Hardy Executive. Health Under Stress*. Home-wood, IL: Dow Jones-Irwin.

Marteau, T.M. and Johnston, M. (1990) Health professionals: a source of variance in health outcomes. *Psychology and Health*, **5**: 47–58.

Mechanic, D. (1962) *Students under Stress: A Study in the Social Psychology of Adaptation*. Glencoe, IL: Free Press.

Melzack, R. and Wall, P.D. (1965) Pain mechanisms: a new theory. *Science*, **150**: 971–9.

Pennebaker, J. (1982) *The Psychology of Physical Symptoms*. New York: Springer Verlag.

Prochaska, J.O. and DiClemente, C.C.D. (1982) Transtheoretical therapy: toward a more integrative model of change. *Psychotherapy: Theory Research and Practice*, **19**: 276–88.

Ramirez, A.J., Craig, T.J.K., Watson, J.P., Fentiman, I.S., North, W.R.S. and Rubens, R.D. (1989) Stress and relapse of breast cancer. *British Medical Journal*, **298**: 291–3.

Redd, W.H. (1982) Behavioural analysis and control of psychosomatic symptoms in patients receiving intensive cancer treatment. *British Journal of Clinical Psychology*, **21**: 351–8.

Rogers, R.W. (1983) 'Cognitive and physiological processes in fear appeals and atti-tude change: a revised theory of protection motivation', in Cacioppo, J.R. and Petty, R.E. (eds) *Social Psychology: A Source Book*. New York: Guilford, pp. 153–76.

Rosenstock, I.M. (1966) Why people use health services. *Millbank Memorial Fund Quar-terly*, **44**: 94–124.

Roth, H.P. (1979) 'Problems in conducting a study of the effects of patient compliance of teaching the rationale for antacid therapy', in Cohen, S.J. (ed.) *New Directions in Patient Compliance*. Lexington, MA: Lexington Books, pp. 111–26.

Ruble, D.N. (1977) Premenstrual symptoms. A reinterpretation. *Science*, **197**: 291–2.

Shaffer, J.W., Graves, P.L., Swank, R.T. and Pearson, T.A. (1987) Clustering of person-ality traits in youth and the subsequent development of cancer among physicians. *Journal of Behavioural Medicine*, **10**: 441–7.

Sternbach, R.A., Wolf, S.R., Murphy, R.W. and Akeson, W.H. (1973) Traits of pain patients: the low back 'loser'. *Psychosomatics*, **14**: 226–9.

Taylor, S.E. (1983) Adjustment to threatening events: a theory of cognitive adaptation. *American Psychologist*, **38**: 1161–73.

Temoshok, L., and Fox, B.H. (1984) 'Coping styles and other psychosocial factors related to medical status and to prognosis in patients with cutaeous malignant melanoma', in Fox, B.H. and Newberry, B.H. (eds) *Impact of Psychoendocrine Systems in Cancer and Immunity*. Toronto: C.J. Hogrefe, pp. 258–87.

Trostle, J.A. (1988) Medical compliance as an ideology. *Social Science and Medicine*, **27**: 1299–308.

Turk, D. and Rennert, K. (1981) 'Pain and the terminally ill cancer patient: a cognitive social learning perspective', in Sobel, H. (ed.) *Journal of Behaviour Therapy in Terminal Care*. USA: Ballinger.

Turk, D.C., Wack, J.T. and Kerns, R.D. (1985) An empirical examination of the 'pain-behaviour' construct. *Journal of Behavioral Medicine*, **8**: 119–30.

Wallston, K.A. and Wallston, B.S. (1982) 'Who is responsible for your health? The construct of health locus of control', in Sanders, G.S. and Suls, J. (eds) *Social Psychology of Health and Illness*. Hillsdale, NJ: Laurence Erlbaum, pp. 65–95.

Weinman, J., Petrie, K.J., Moss-Morris, R. and Horne, R. (1996) The Illness Perception Questionnaire: a new method for assessing the cognitive representation of illness. *Psychology and Health*, **11**: 431–46.

Weinstein, N. (1984) Why it won't happen to me: perceptions of risk factors and susceptibility. *Health Psychology*, **3**: 431–57.

Weinstein, N. (1987) Unrealistic optimism about illness susceptibility: conclusions from a community-wide sample. *Journal of Behavioural Medicine*, **10**: 481–500.

Weller, S.S. (1984) Cross cultural concepts of illness: variables and validation. *American Anthropologist*, **86**: 341–51.

Sociology

NORMA DAYKIN

Learning outcomes •••••••••••••••••••••••••••

This chapter will enable readers to:

● identify the key characteristics of sociology as a discipline
● understand key sociological concepts and debate their relevance to health and health care
● understand research evidence exploring the social patterning of health and disease
● debate various theoretical explanations for the social patterning of health and disease
● understand theories and concepts relating to the social impact of health care and the social roles of the health care professions.

OVERVIEW

When we become ill, it sometimes seems that bad luck has singled us out for special attention, yet an extensive body of evidence suggests that health and disease are patterned in complex ways that defy notions of luck or chance, indicating a more systematic process of disease causation. In the first part of this chapter, the social patterning of health and illness is explored. Evidence linking social divisions, such as class, gender and ethnicity, with experiences of health and health care is explored. Finding adequate explanations for the persistence of social inequalities, as well as strategies to eliminate or reduce them, is an important goal of health policy and one to which sociologists can make a distinctive contribution. The second part explores the methodological approaches of sociology to understanding the ways in which people interpret and manage ill health in their lives. The attempts of health professionals to manage and cure ill health have come under sociological scrutiny. In particular, sociologists have looked beyond the altruism often assumed of health professionals to examine the individual, group and social benefits that professional practice may bring. Sociology relies on both evidence and theory. In addition to a critical examination of the available sources of evidence, such as mortality rates, sociology involves the development and testing of theoretical frameworks and perspectives that seek to explain broad patterns of health and illness.

INTRODUCTION

In contrast to disciplines such as biology and psychology, which focus on health at the individual level, sociology examines the social dimensions of health, illness and health care. The sociology of health and illness is concerned with the following key questions:

● What accounts for socio-economic inequalities in health and illness?
● How do social structures, institutions and processes affect the health of individuals?
● What are the characteristics of health care work?
● What is the nature of the doctor–patient relationship?

- How do lay people make sense of health and illness?
- What impact do health care services have on individuals and society?

Sociologists have paid particular attention to the study of social divisions such as **class**, **gender** and **ethnicity**, which seem to exercise a powerful and enduring influence on society even though their form may shift and change. Changes in work and employment, for example, have meant that traditional class divisions no longer seem as significant as they did in the 1950s and 60s. Yet to proclaim the arrival of a classless society seems premature as there is evidence of a continuing and emerging pattern of economic inequality. This in turn indicates the importance of understanding social patterns and divisions, and the influences that shape them.

The ideas and practices surrounding Western scientific medicine have been a central concern within sociology. These ideas are often taken for granted as the basis upon which much health care provision is organised. However, they only emerged alongside the economic and cultural changes brought about by the spread of industrial capitalism during the 18th and 19th centuries (Stacey, 1988). This period was characterised by urbanisation and a changing class structure. The growth of the middle classes provided new markets for health care, which supported the newly established profession of medicine.

These events were underlined by a widespread support for the ideas as well as the practices of medicine. Scientific medicine has, however, always coexisted with a number of rival or alternative approaches. In recent years, the support for such alternatives seems to have grown, an increasing number of people seeking help from complementary therapists as well as, or instead of, medical professionals. Modern medicine is seen as limited in that it draws on the belief that mind and body are separate entities. This notion of Cartesian dualism, named after the philosopher Descartes, is seen as problematic for a number of reasons:

- It leads to a rather mechanistic approach in which illness and disease are treated as a mechanical malfunction
- The approach of scientific medicine is reductionist (that is, it reduces diseases to a single, usually physical, cause).

Such an approach is seen as inadequate for managing conditions that affect an increasing number of people. In the case of repetitive strain injury and myalgic encephalomyelitis, for example, agreement on the existence of physical causes has not been reached.

Health care institutions and their social context have been an important focus of study for sociologists. Social factors such as gender, for example, seem to exert a powerful influence upon the make-up of the various health professions, particularly nursing and medicine. Sociology provides a number of distinctive and well-established approaches to questions about the social patterning of health and disease and the social impact of health care interventions. Recently, in response to wider socio-economic and cultural changes, new debates and perspectives have emerged. Changing experiences of work, the impact of globalisation on economic and cultural life, and changing ideas about gender roles and emerging patterns of family life have all influenced sociological writing. Sociologists have debated whether these changes reflect an intensified late

class – the division and ranking of groups of people according to occupational role, which arose during the growth and development of capitalism. Social class refers to status and power as well as to income

gender – the social meanings and values of the difference between the sexes. Gender refers to socially ascribed traits, characteristics and roles that are seen as belonging to males and females

ethnicity – characteristics of social life, such as culture, religion, language and history, which are shared by groups of people and passed on to the next generation. A term often used instead of 'race', which focuses on physical differences and which has been largely discredited

modern society or herald a new postmodern condition. The debate is reflected in increasing concerns with, for example, identity, consumption, the body and the emotions.

THE CONTRIBUTION OF SOCIOLOGY TO HEALTH STUDIES

The key area which sociology has investigated in relation to health is perhaps the social patterning of health and disease. Explaining patterns of health and illness affecting populations and individuals is a task that is sometimes misunderstood.

Trying to identify the precise aspects of an individual's lifestyle and social background that have caused a particular condition can seem crude and pointless, evoking feelings of responsibility and guilt in the victim and engendering unsympathetic responses from friends, family and professional carers. Sociologists often use epidemiological data not to make predictions about individuals, but to identify the social processes affecting population health, recognising that there will always be exceptions to the rule.

Evidence of health inequalities exists in a number of forms, the most commonly cited being mortality data. These concern death rates, whereas morbidity data illustrate trends in ill health and disease. Mortality data serve as a crude indicator and tell us little about health or quality of life, yet they are often relied upon in health research. This is because it is often difficult to obtain standardised measures of ill health, especially when comparisons are being made between different countries. Data collected by the World Health Organization reveal a number of broad mortality trends:

- First, there is a general trend towards increased life expectancy among many people across the globe. Between 1955 and 1995, life expectancy at birth increased from 48 years to 65 years globally
- More than 50 million people are still living in countries with a life expectancy of less than 45 years
- Ninety-one per cent of deaths occurred in people of 50 years or over in Europe, North America and Scandinavia. In contrast, in the 48 least developed countries, only 26 per cent of deaths occurred in people in this age group.

> ### *Thinking about...*
>
> Can you think of someone you know who never seems to get ill but seems to flout all health advice?

> ### CONNECTIONS
>
> See Chapter 2 (Epidemiology) for more details about data collection and the interpretation of epidemiological data

? **Look at Table 4.1. What are the main differences in the cause of death between developing and developed countries?**

In the developed countries, diseases of the circulatory system are the leading cause of mortality, whereas infectious and parasitic diseases remain the leading cause of death in the developing world. These are not 'exotic' diseases but include conditions such as respiratory infections, tuberculosis and measles, which were a significant cause of mortality in pre-industrial Europe. A number of perspectives have been put forward explaining their decline in the developed

Table 4.1   Causes of death

| | Distribution of death by main causes, by level of development | | | | | |
| | 1985 | | 1990 | | 1997 | |
Cause of death	Developed world (%)	Developing world (%)	Developed world (%)	Developing world (%)	Developed world (%)	Developing world (%)
Infectious and parasitic diseases	5	45	4	44	1	43
Perinatal and maternal causes	1	10	1	9	1	10
Cancer	21	6	21	7	21	9
Diseases of the circulatory system	51	16	48	17	46	26
Diseases of the respiratory system	4	6	3	7	8	5
Other and unknown causes	18	17	23	16	23	9

Source: Data from WHO, 1998

world, although it is widely agreed that an improvement in social conditions and public health measures played an important role (Whitehead, 1997).

The links between poverty and health have been the focus of much sociological research. Poverty has been identified as a significant factor in explaining health trends in developed countries as well as in the developing world. Problems such as circulatory disease and cancer are sometimes perceived to be diseases of affluence, resulting from lifestyle habits such as the excessive consumption of certain foods, tobacco and alcohol. Yet these problems increasingly affect people in the developing world, research within developed countries suggesting that these conditions disproportionately affect those in lower socio-economic groups.

SOCIO-ECONOMIC INEQUALITIES IN HEALTH

As well as examining the differences between rich and poor countries, sociologists have also studied *social inequalities* and their impact on health within developed countries. In the UK, concern about apparently entrenched patterns of health inequality has recently been expressed in government documents such as the public health White Paper (DoH, 1999). This follows a long tradition of research into socio-economic inequalities and health. The debate has centred around the findings of the 1980 Report of the Working Group on Inequalities in Health, chaired by Sir Douglas Black (Townsend et al., 1988). This report examined standardised mortality ratios for different social classes in order to assess the scale of inequality and to monitor changes over time.

In order to measure inequality, the working group adopted the Registrar General's classification of occupational classes. The Registrar General used to classify people into five occupational categories ranging from social class I

social inequalities – inequalities in income, access to resources, power and status that are produced, reproduced and maintained by social processes and institutions

(professional occupations) to social class V (unskilled manual occupations). From 2001, there will be eight categories in order to take account of changes in the labour market, including the rise in the number of self-employed people and the presence of the long-term unemployed.

These classifications, although commonly used, are limited in a number of respects. They have not, for example, adequately reflected the position of women, who have traditionally been classified according to the occupation of a male head of household where one exists. However, the continued use of this approach is justified, for two reasons: occupation is the only socio-economic information that is recorded routinely at the census and at birth and death registration, and occupation is regarded as a powerful determinant of income and life chances (Drever and Whitehead, 1997).

The findings of the Black Report are now well known. These include a marked and persistent difference in mortality rate between the occupational classes, for both sexes and at all ages. A steep class gradient, showing that the risk of death increases with lower social class, was observed for most causes of death. The pattern for respiratory diseases was particularly strong. Babies born to parents in social class V were found to be at double the risk of death in the first month of life compared with the babies of professional-class parents.

The authors concluded that the introduction of the NHS, which aimed to provide free health care to all regardless of income or social status, had not eliminated health inequalities. Furthermore, patterns of relative inequality seemed to have changed little over time despite an overall improvement in life expectancy. In relation to infant mortality, social class differences had actually increased during key periods. Finally, inequalities were also found to exist in the utilisation of health services, working-class people making less use of services and receiving less good care than their middle-class counterparts.

Whitehead (in Towensend et al., 1988) presented updated morbidity data showing that people in the lower social classes experience a higher rate of chronic (long-term) sickness than those in more advantaged groups. Children born to parents in lower-class groups had lower birthweights and other indicators of poor health status. Furthermore, unemployed people and their families were found to suffer poorer mental and physical health than those in employment. Finally, strong regional patterns of health inequality were identified, the highest mortality rates being in Scotland, followed by the north and the north-west regions of England, the lowest rates being in the south-east of England and East Anglia.

The original report received a rather frosty reception by the then Conservative government, which seemed reluctant to embrace the notion of health inequality. More recently, the changing public health agenda has encouraged a renewed focus on socio-economic influences on health. This has been underlined by a concern with widening income inequalities and the growing problems of poverty and homelessness.

The pattern of health inequality identified in the Black Report continued into the 1990s. While the mortality rate for the whole population has declined, the differential between the lowest and the highest group seems to have increased. In the early 1990s, male mortality in social class V was almost three times that in social class I. During the preceding 20-year period, the difference between these groups in mortality from lung cancer, ischaemic heart disease, strokes, accidents and suicide had widened considerably (Drever and Bunting, 1997). Comparing data for 1981 and 1991, Roberts and Power (1996) found that socio-economic inequalities in child injury death rate had also increased during this period.

A recent analysis of data from the General Household Survey has shown that people in the manual social classes are more likely than others to report chronic illness that limits their activities. Socio-economic status is also linked to health-related behaviours such as cigarette smoking and dietary habits. The percentage of smokers among men in the unskilled manual classes is more than two and a half times that seen in professional classes. Similarly, the consumption of fats and sugars increases, and that of fruit decreases, with decreasing income (Bunting, 1997).

These patterns are not confined to the UK but affect many other industrialised countries. Recent data from 11 Western European countries show that the chances of premature death are consistently higher among people with a lower educational level, a lower income level and a lower position in the labour market than for other groups (Kunst et al., 1998). Furthermore, those in lower socio-economic groups report more perceived ill health and a higher rate of long-term disability and long-standing health problems than do other groups (Mackenbach et al., 1997).

Wilkinson (1996) suggests that it is not simply the level of development attained by a particular country that determines its rate of health improvement: the extent of income and status differentials within a given society also seems to influence health outcomes. Hence more egalitarian societies, characterised by a narrow income differential, seem to enjoy a greater improvement in overall life expectancy than more unequal societies at a comparable stage of economic development. It is not clear what could account for this evidence, but it is likely that there is a connection between social stress and our immune response. Unequal societies are characterised by chronic social stress. More equal societies may also be more socially cohesive and have stronger community support, which has been shown to have a positive effect on people's health outcomes.

> *Thinking about...*
>
> How have your own experiences as a user or provider of health care services been influenced by your class position?

Explaining health inequalities

Sociologists are not interested simply in mapping patterns of health inequality: they have also attempted to provide explanations for these patterns. These explanations have important implications for the planning and delivery of health and social services.

 What accounts for the socio-economic patterns of health and disease?

A range of different explanations was debated within the Black Report and in subsequent publications. The debate has centred on four different types of explanation for inequalities in health:

- artefact
- social selection
- cultural
- material/structural.

The artefact explanation

This explanation suggests that the apparent widening of health inequalities is caused by inappropriate methods of measurement (Illsley, 1986). It questions the validity of comparing death rates between social class groupings whose size and composition are changing over time. Economic developments and changes in employment have led to the diminishing size of social class V, which contains traditional unskilled groups such as manual workers and dockers.

In order to overcome the difficulties suggested by the artefact explanation, several studies have adopted alternative methodologies for measuring inequality (Bartley et al., 1998). There would seem to be a persistent inverse relationship between health and socio-economic status regardless of how socio-economic status is measured. Hence the artefact explanation does not seem to provide an adequate explanation for the trends.

The social selection explanation

This explanation suggests that the poorer health status of those in the lower social classes reflects a tendency towards the downward mobility of people with ill health rather than an outcome of class inequality. At the same time, the healthiest members of each socio-economic group may be absorbed into higher groups, leaving those with the greatest number of health problems behind.

Thinking about...
Do you think people with poor health are more likely to be unemployed or have lower-paid jobs?

Longitudinal research, which follows people over a long period in order to identify which emerges first, ill health or downward social mobility, is needed to test this theory. Such research suggests a complex relationship (Bartley et al., 1998). Poor health can often serve to disadvantage people in employment and other areas. However, the selection explanation cannot account for the whole pattern of health inequality, and selection processes themselves may apply differently to different groups. People in more advantageous social positions, with more resources and support, seem to be better able to overcome the effects of early health problems than do those in disadvantaged circumstances.

Cultural explanations

Cultural explanations suggest that the social distribution of ill health is linked to differences in health behaviours such as smoking and alcohol consumption and to different groups' attitudes to their health. The authors of the Black Report did not fully accept that inequalities could be explained with reference to the lifestyles and cultural practices of different groups. The difficulty with such explanations is that they often present lifestyle factors such as smoking and dietary habits as simple choices, ignoring low income as a constraint on choice and therefore 'blaming the victims' for their poor health status.

Materialist/structural explanations

Such explanations focus on the **material** causes of ill health, such as living and working conditions, including factors such as nutrition, housing, transport, environmental and occupational hazards, and stress. These are often seen as arising from the social structure, which is itself a product of the way in which society is organised. These explanations suggest that health inequalities are the result of material deprivation and structural inequality. Relative as well as absolute deprivation is seen to be important. In other words, deprivation is not simply seen as the inability to obtain a defined level of resources necessary to sustain health. Instead, the ability to obtain socially valued resources and to participate in society are also important influences on health.

Subsequent research has explored the links between material and cultural explanations of inequalities in health. Graham (1987), for example, found that smoking among women caring for young children is not a simple cultural choice but serves specific needs arising from the experiences of poverty and deprivation. Smoking can offer a relief to mothers from the emotional pressures of childcare in situations in which there is no alternative means of escape and may be the only thing that women do for themselves in severely constrained situations. It seems increasingly inappropriate to attempt to understand individual behaviour in isolation from its social and material context. While differences in health-related behaviours seem to be consistent with patterns of health inequality, such differences cannot alone provide an explanation for most of the observed differential in health.

This debate on the causes of health inequality continues to influence health policy, each different explanatory framework pointing in a different direction. The Black Report's main recommendations centred on the need to reduce poverty. This was not, however, immediately accepted, public health strategies up until the 1990s emphasising individual health education and lifestyle change in favour of addressing material and structural conditions (DoH, 1992). More recently, the impact of socio-economic inequalities on health has been recognised in public policy (DoH, 1999), although strategies for reducing inequality continue to be debated.

materialism – the theoretical perspective that emphasises the importance of material resources and access to resources such as income and education. This theory focuses on social inequality

CONNECTIONS

Chapter 10 (Health Promotion) explores strategies to reduce health risk behaviours

---

EXAMPLE 4.1

Reducing health inequalities

Twenty years after the Black Report, an Independent Inquiry into Inequalities in Health was set up in 1998. The Acheson Report (named after its chair, Sir Donald Acheson, a former Chief Medical Officer) made 39 recommendations, including the following.

- To raise living standards and tackle low income
  - nearly one in five working-age households has no one in work
  - in 1996/97, four and a half million children were brought up in families with below half the average income

- To improve the health of, and reduce inequalities among, women of childbearing age
  - the life expectancy of a boy whose parents are in the professional or managerial groups is about five years more than one born to parents in a partly skilled or unskilled occupation
  - the mortality rate of the infants of mothers born in Pakistan and the Caribbean is twice as high as the national average

- To promote the material well-being of older people and the maintenance of mobility, independence and social contact
  - the mortality rate of people aged 60–74 living in local authority rented accommodation is 16 per cent above the national average

The first recommendation of the Acheson Report is:

> that as part of health impact assessment, all policies likely to have a direct or indirect effect on health should be evaluated in terms of their impact on health inequalities and should be formulated in such a way that by favouring the less well off they will, wherever possible, reduce such inequalities.

Source: Acheson, 1998

GENDER AND HEALTH

The debate on gender and health has centred on the paradox that although women tend to live longer than men, they seem to experience a higher level of ill health. In most countries, and for most age groups, the ratio of female to male deaths has decreased throughout the latter half of the 20th century, gender difference favouring the female population (WHO, 1998). The current difference in the life expectancy of males and females in the UK is 5 years: women born in the UK in 1994 can expect to live for 79 years compared with a life expectancy of 74 for men (ONS, 1997).

Despite this apparent benefit of longevity, it seems that women experience more ill health than men (Doyal, 1995). The General Household Survey, for example, shows that women consistently report a higher level of chronic and acute sickness than men. The difference is particularly pronounced in relation to mental health, women being one and a half times more likely than men to report having suffered from any neurotic disorder, and nearly twice as many women as men reporting anxiety and depression (Bunting, 1997).

This pattern of gender difference is common in developed countries (Payne, 1998) and means that women are more likely than men to experience a range of conditions that lead to chronic impairment and disability. While ageing does not inevitably lead to ill health and a loss of independence, older women are more likely than older men to suffer from disabling conditions and to need help in performing basic activities such as bathing and shopping (Arber, 1998).

? What do you think accounts for the fact that women live longer yet report more ill health than men?

Explaining gender inequalities in health

Biological explanations

Biological explanations focus on biological differences, in particular the different reproductive roles of men and women, which have an impact on health. Sociologists traditionally tended to reject biologically based notions of gender identity. More recently, however, they have begun to engage more critically with notions of the body, which has led to a more inclusive focus with a willingness to engage with biological discourse.

This shift is also reflected in feminist research, which has begun to explore the interaction between biology and society. Doyal (1995), for example, argues that social factors such as poor nutrition, an unequal access to resources, reproductive risks and unsafe conditions of childbirth make a significant impact on male to female mortality ratios, sometimes enhancing and sometimes reducing the inherent biological advantage that women seem to possess.

Materialist/structural explanations

Such explanations look at the health outcomes for men and women, and at how these may be determined by social factors. Sociologists have drawn attention to differences in the social roles of men and women as well as differences in their access to resources such as income, employment, housing and leisure. Such research has uncovered persistent inequalities that can influence health. For example, segregation in the labour market means that women continue to be concentrated in low-paid employment and in roles such as caring and service work (Doyal, 1995). They also continue to bear the bulk of responsibility for unpaid caring and domestic work (Lloyd, 1999). This means not only that women have less access than men to health-promoting resources, but that women and men may face different hazards and risks in both paid and unpaid work settings.

Cultural explanations and social constructionist accounts

These focus on the way in which gender differences are themselves generated through social processes. Instead of taking notions of gender for granted, the creation of gender differences is seen as a continuous process involving cultural expectations. These expectations include attitudes and behaviours that are approved and associated with masculinity and femininity. 'Masculine' traits traditionally include independence, while femininity implies passivity and dependence. This stereotyping of gender identity has a number of implications for health. Doctors may, for example, be more likely to interpret women's behaviour as indicating mental illness than to perceive men in this way (Payne, 1998). This might partly explain why more women than men are diagnosed with conditions such as depression.

Social constructionist accounts of gender imply that, for individuals, the task of creating and performing an appropriate gender identity is a continuous one, beset with the risk of failure. The implications of these processes for health have been explored in a number of studies.

social constructionism – the theoretical perspective suggesting that all knowledge and discourse (as well as ideology and representations) are socially constructed within a context in which different groups of people have differing interests and priorities, and therefore represent only a partial truth

CONNECTIONS

Chapter 5 (Cultural Studies) examines the cultural construction of gender

Thinking about...

Can you think of an example of where how you feel about your gender may have an impact on your health or health behaviour?

One significant area is that of sexual health: expectations about gender clearly help to shape interaction and the negotiation of sexual activity. They therefore provide the context for, and sometimes constrain, strategies to reduce a number of risks, such as those of unwanted pregnancy and sexually transmitted disease. Research, for example, has found that the explicit pursuit of sexual pleasure is often approved of for males, whereas girls can be stigmatised for displaying sexual knowledge even if this knowledge can protect them from risk (Thomson and Holland, 1994).

Gender affects access to material resources and provides both a context and a set of constraints on people's lives, but this is only part of the picture. Recent research has begun to broaden our understanding of gender in a number of ways:

● Are all women and men affected by gender in similar ways?
● Is masculinity or femininity 'fixed' at birth?
● Is gender associated with particular health behaviours?

To consider the first of these questions, recent research has paid increasing attention to the ways in which women's lives are influenced in different ways by factors other than gender. Research focused on the *differences* between women has examined issues of 'race' and ethnicity as well as sexuality and disability.

Second, the notion that the characteristics of masculinity and femininity are *essential* characteristics inherited at birth has been questioned. Instead, gender roles are seen as being continuously negotiated and not fixed (Cameron and Bernades, 1998). Furthermore, masculinity and femininity may both be associated to a varying degree with individual men and women (Annandale and Hunt, 1990). Research has identified emerging trends in women's health that have arisen as a consequence of the adoption by women of traditional 'masculine' practices. These include cigarette smoking, which seems to be increasing particularly among younger and relatively disadvantaged groups of women (Graham, 1998).

Third, research on gender has begun to examine men's health issues as well as those affecting women. It is suggested that certain notions of masculinity may have a negative effect on men's health. This research distinguishes between different forms of masculinity. It is traditional or hegemonic masculinity, with its emphasis on risk-taking, self-reliance and dominance, that is viewed as potentially dangerous. For example, the desire to be seen as independent, self-reliant and invulnerable can discourage men from seeking help for health problems (Cameron and Bernades, 1998).

Early research on gender and health sought to map out the impact of gender on women's health, relatively little attention being paid to men's health. Many researchers believed that this approach was necessary in order to correct long-standing imbalances that had led to male health concerns dominating research and policy interventions. There is, however, evidence that gender bias continues to affect contemporary research and health policy. Conditions such as coronary heart disease and stroke, for example, are often assumed to be 'male' diseases, and research studies have reflected this assumption by studying male samples and producing treatment programmes that often go untested on women (Doyal, 1995). Yet these conditions account for almost 60 per cent of all adult female deaths in developed countries and are also the major cause of death among women aged 50 years and above in developing countries (WHO, 1998).

'RACE', ETHNICITY AND HEALTH

As well as seeking to cure illness and disease, medicine has been seen as exerting a controlling influence and even contributing to processes of labelling and social exclusion. This can be clearly illustrated by examining the debate on ethnicity, racism and health. Medical discourse has, historically, played a key role in supporting ideas of racialisation. Hence during the 19th century, 'scientific' support was provided for the belief that human beings could be categorised according to a difference in skin colour and other physical characteristics. During slavery, medicine even provided labels such as 'drapetomania', the supposedly pathological desire of slaves to run away from their master (Ahmad, 1993).

While this notion of 'race' is now discredited in academic and scientific circles, the concept of race continues to influence the beliefs of ordinary people and has significant consequences, including social and economic discrimination and the stereotyping of black and minority ethnic patients by health care workers. Not surprisingly, the quest to identify distinctive patterns of health and disease for different ethnic groups arouses scepticism among some critics.

In order to measure these effects without reinforcing racist discourse, some researchers adopt the notion of ethnicity. Ethnicity refers to shared experiences such as religion, language, history and **culture**. Ethnicity applies to white people as well as black people, thereby avoiding the assumption that only the ethnicity of black people needs to be examined. There is, however, an inconsistency in how the terms 'race' and 'ethnicity' are used or defined. In practice, the term 'ethnicity' is often used as a euphemism for 'race', and most studies focus only on ethnic minorities.

culture – may be portrayed as monolithic, implying that all members of society share a common language, religion, traditions and customs. Culture is, however, increasingly pluralistic, different cultures interacting and influencing each other

---

EXAMPLE 4.2

'Race', ethnicity and health

- The evidence linking ethnicity with health is complex and apparently contradictory, the picture being further limited by a number of methodological problems. Studies have, however, shown excess mortality among migrant ethnic minority groups in the UK

- An excess coronary heart disease mortality has been found in people born in the Indian subcontinent, and a relatively high mortality from stroke has been found among people of Afro-Caribbean origin

- In contrast, the mortality rates of common types of cancer, such as breast and lung cancer, appear to be relatively low among people from the Caribbean and the Indian subcontinent, although there is evidence that this pattern may be changing

- A higher rate of infant mortality is found for most migrant groups, a particularly high level being seen among the babies of Pakistan born mothers

- The members of minority ethnic groups perceive their health in poorer terms than do the general population

The Black Report's framework has been used to explain these data. *Artefact* explanations point to the problematic use of country of birth as a measure of ethnicity, half of the UK's ethnic minorities having been born in the UK. Other problems include treating ethnicity and class separately and failing to recognise the heterogeneous nature of ethnic majority populations. *Biological* explanations have been criticised for overestimating the impact of genetic factors on the causation of disease. *Cultural* explanations tend to focus on the apparent negative impact of the dietary, religious and other practices of minority groups, neglecting the positive influences of culture on health.

Material explanations emphasise the direct effects of the socio-economic disadvantage of members of minority ethnic groups. Unemployment and poor housing have been reported as contributing more to poor health than do lifestyle factors such as smoking. Material disadvantage exerts an enduring influence on the health of minority ethnic groups, although social class cannot adequately explain the excess mortality observed in minority ethnic groups.

Racism as an explanation has been used to identify the slowness of health authorities to respond to the needs of minority ethnic groups, for example in providing appropriate screening and counselling services for those with sickle cell disorder and thalassaemia. Public services are also seen as responding more punitively to ethnic minorities than to other groups. Caribbeans, for example, are more likely than other groups to be admitted compulsorily to psychiatric hospital, particularly following an encounter with the police. Many health care workers receive little training in either race or gender awareness. The result may be individual or institutional racism.

Sources: Anionwu, 1993; Balarajan, 1990; Balarajan and Soni Raleigh, 1993; Douglas, 1998; Dunn and Fahy, 1990; Harding and Maxwell, 1997; Peach, 1996; Rudat and Barnes, 1995; Smaje, 1996.

THEORETICAL AND METHODOLOGICAL APPROACHES

Sociology – the study of human social life – involves a conscious distancing of the sociologist from the object of study, whether that involves personal emotions (for example love, bereavement or ill health), social institutions (such as the family, the education system or health care services) or group life (rave culture, or health professionals peer group norms and pressures). Sociological study often involves investigating what appears at first sight to be natural, universal or common sense, only to discover that such behaviours or practices are fundamentally affected by specific social factors and influences.

While health services seem self-evidently beneficial, some have questioned their impact, even arguing that the harm done by modern medicine outweighs the benefits. We can explore this debate by distinguishing between consensus and conflict approaches. Both acknowledge that health professionals, particularly doctors, enjoy a significant amount of power. They can sanction a number of benefits such as employees' sick leave, claimants' eligibility for welfare payments and patients' entitlement to services. They also endorse controlling and restraining actions such as the incarceration of individuals defined as mentally ill.

Consensus approaches accept the necessity of these functions for the smooth running of modern societies. Furthermore, they suggest that members of regulated professions are, because of their extensive training and commitment to ethical conduct, well placed to carry them out. In contrast, conflict perspectives question professional power, highlighting issues of professional domination and social control, and the oppressive impact of some practices.

Recent developments, such as the advancement of nursing and other professions, increased managerialism in the NHS and the growth of complementary therapies, suggest that power, particularly medical power, is not exercised without challenge and resistance. Theorising these trends, recent accounts suggest that traditional approaches may be limited by a rather narrow and mechanistic understanding of power. Rather than being delegated by society or imposed on individuals and groups, power is increasingly viewed as fluid and diffuse, capable of being mobilised in many ways and from a range of sources.

> **Thinking about...**
>
> Which perspective comes closer to your own view of the power of medicine?

FUNCTIONALIST PERSPECTIVES

The sociology of Talcott Parsons (1951, 1975) provides a well-known example of a consensus model. Parsons was concerned to demonstrate the ways in which practices such as medicine contribute to the maintenance of the social order. Illness not only disturbs individual functioning, but is also socially dysfunctional, undermining the values, activities and roles that support productivity and social stability. In order to prevent such a disruption, mechanisms are needed that render illness an undesirable and temporary social state. Parsons identified such a mechanism in the form of the **sick role**, into which people ideally enter when they become ill. The sick role confers both rights and obligations. The rights are:

> **functionalism** – the theoretical perspective that sees institutions and processes as having specific social functions, which may differ from their overt function and which contribute to social continuity and consensus

- an exemption from responsibilities such as work and social obligations, which needs to be legitimised by a physician in order to be valid
- that the sick individuals avoid any blame or responsibility for their condition.

The two obligations are:

- the sick person must want to get better
- the sick person must seek competent help, usually from a trained physician.

> **sick role** – Parsons' theory that ill people enter into the sick role, which confers both rights and obligations. The sick role legitimates and regulates illness and hence minimises the disruption caused by illness

 How adequate is the sick role in accounting for:
1. **someone with food poisoning**
2. **someone with depression**
3. **someone with asthma**
4. **someone who is HIV positive**

Parson's sick role concept has stimulated an important debate on the role of medicine and the nature of medical power. Sociologists have debated the relevance of the concept in relation to contemporary patterns of health and illness.

One of the issues that arises is that access to the sick role may not be enjoyed equally by all. The sick role concept may apply relatively closely to acute illnesses such as influenza, but even in these cases there are some social obligations (such as caring for others) from which exemption may be difficult to gain. In the case of chronic conditions, the rights associated with the sick role concept apply less clearly, and social obligations may be difficult to escape in the longer term. Furthermore, some conditions (for example HIV/AIDS) carry a stigma. This means that assumptions of responsibility and blame may influence how the person is seen and treated by others.

The obligations associated with the sick role concept are also more complex than first appears. Sociologists have pointed out that these obligations render the doctor much more powerful than the patient in professional–client interactions. Functionalists such as Parsons accept the asymmetrical nature of the doctor–patient relationship on the grounds that doctors, as modern professionals, are required to be altruistic. They are also expected to be committed to other professional values such as universalism, collectivism and neutrality. These values are seen as ensuring that a doctor's personal feelings towards a patient do not influence the consultation or treatment offered. The physician is expected to put the welfare of the patient above any personal interest.

The power imbalance between doctors and patients seems, however, less easy to accept if the professional commitment to these values is questioned. A more critical perspective would suggest that society, rather than being made of groups that share equal access to power, is made up of groups with competing interests and unequal influence, and these include professionals, whose interests may conflict with those of patients. From this perspective, the degree of trust that society grants to doctors, evidenced by their high degree of autonomy and the lack of external surveillance of many procedures, is questionable. This position of professional autonomy, it is argued, protects the doctor from scrutiny and exposes the patient to potential abuse.

Hence Parsons' concept of the sick role has been criticised as being naive in relation to issues of power and inapplicable to many instances of ill health, but it continues to be debated. The 'empowerment' model (Crossley, 1998), for example, has developed as an alternative way of conceptualising professional–client relationships. This model suggests that doctors' technical competence may be more limited than traditional beliefs concerning the efficacy of scientific medicine suggest. This can be seen in relation to conditions such as repetitive strain injury or myalgic encephalomyelitis for which there appears to be little medical consensus on the cause of the problem or appropriate treatment, or HIV, in which there is little possibility of a cure. The obligation to seek technically competent help from a physician makes little sense if technical competence is beyond the physician's scope. Instead, the empowerment model seems to enhance the status and authority of the experiential knowledge of the sufferer in the face of doctors' limited capacity to respond to complex chronic conditions.

Crossley warns, however, that the 'empowerment' perspective underestimates the benefits of medicine. Whereas scientific medicine has not been able to provide a cure for many conditions, the medical management of chronic illness is constantly developing. Furthermore, the empowerment model is seen as

CONNECTIONS

Sociologists explore the power involved in doctor–patient consultations. Chapter 3 (Health Psychology) shows how doctors' health beliefs influence the consultation

CONNECTIONS

Chapter 9 (Ethics and Law) considers the ethical issues involved in the self-regulation of the medical profession

offering a weak basis for practice because it lacks any notion of duty or social obligation to accompany the 'rights' associated with chronic illness.

Although the sick role concept has been widely criticised, we have seen that it has provided a useful insight into the experience of illness and the role of medicine. Importantly, it has drawn attention to questions of power, paving the way for a broader debate on the nature of medical authority and the relationship between medicine and social control.

MEDICALISATION AND SOCIAL CONTROL

During the 1960s and 70s, a number of critical perspectives on medical power emerged. These often drew on the **medicalisation** thesis, in which medicine is seen as expanding its social jurisdiction and replacing earlier mechanisms of social control such as religion. While Parson's functionalist model emphasised the benign and productive aspects of medical power, critical perspectives have identified some undesirable social costs of medical expansion.

medicalisation – the process by which medicine has increased its power in society. This includes the use of medical technology and the professional power of doctors to make decisions about social and ethical problems

The medicalisation of society has been seen as taking place at a number of levels (Zola, 1972):

- Medicine has expanded its concerns to encompass areas of life not previously regarded as illness
- Medicalisation has resulted in the concentration of control over technical procedures among doctors
- Doctors' authority has expanded to encompass areas of moral decision-making

Medicalisation involves the pursuit of medical, individual and technical solutions to an expanding range of problems. Where these problems are social in origin, medicalisation can be seen as obscuring their social causes, inhibiting the development of alternative solutions.

CONNECTIONS

Chapter 9 (Ethics and Law) discusses some of the ethical decisions faced by medicine

---

EXAMPLE 4.3

Medicine as a threat to health

In one well-known critique, Illich described medicalisation as a major threat to health. Modern medicine was portrayed as generating *iatrogenic* disease, that is, illness that would not have come about without medical intervention. It was also suggested that society would be better off without professions such as medicine, which encourage dependency rather than self-reliance.

While it seems unethical to suggest that people be denied access to medical treatment, Illich's ideas remain influential. Contemporary journalism often seeks to expose the 'dangers of modern medicine', while the increasing popularity of complementary therapies and self-help sources such as the Internet reveals apparent widespread disillusionment with conventional medical approaches.

Illich's ideas also continue to be debated in academic circles. One critique revisits the concept of iatrogenesis in relation to the negative impact of conventional health care on women. Foster suggests that the benefits of modern medicine are oversold and its harmful effects understated. As patients, women are constrained in their ability to make rational choices, partly because doctors are themselves unaware of many of the risks attached to accepted forms of medical treatment. Furthermore, when doctors are aware of the risks, they may assume that female patients will not be able to cope with the information, and therefore keep their knowledge to themselves.

Sources: Foster 1995; Illich 1975, 1977; McTaggart, 1996

It is important not to overstate the benefits of medical practice, but these theories may understate medicine's benefits; empirical evidence is needed in order to evaluate the impact of different health interventions. Furthermore, these theories imply that attempts to reduce inequalities in health by widening the access to medical intervention are not worthwhile since these will simply extend rather than address the problem. Given that, for many people in the world, access to basic health care is limited, it seems important to emphasise widening access to beneficial practices and resources as well as re-examine questionable aspects of medical practice.

These theories do, however, highlight the impact of medical decision-making and point towards the need for a greater involvement of patients and lay people in such activity. In the face of such challenging claims about medicine, it seems that consumers need to make more and more complex and difficult choices concerning their health care. This theme is explored in the following sections, which examine a number of different approaches to understanding the relationships between medicine, health professions and society.

MARXIST AND POLITICAL ECONOMY PERSPECTIVES

Marxist and political economy perspectives – the theoretical perspective that sees medicine as a tool of capitalism and economic growth. This approach stresses the conflict inherent in capitalism, characterised by opposing classes with different interests

Marxist and political economy perspectives also highlight the negative impact of medical power. However, rather than seeing professionals as the main problem, Marxist theory suggests that professional power is a product of a deeper set of power relations. Political economy perspectives draw on Marxist theory to suggest that the structuring of society around the needs of capitalism as an economic system is the starting point of any analysis of health and health care. This theory suggests that capitalist societies are organised around the generation of profit, which is created by the exploitation of labour power.

Political economy writers such as Doyal (1979) and Navarro (1979) drew broadly on this theory and applied it to health in a number of ways:

● The processes of industrial capitalism cause ill health directly, for example through occupational disease, industrial accidents and the manufacturing and marketing of harmful consumer products

● This burden of disease is disproportionately felt by those in lower socio-economic groups

● Society does not do enough to prevent these problems or promote health because society's resources are channelled towards the maintenance of production over and above the social goal of securing and improving public health.

 Consider the political economy of tobacco. How do you account for its continued manufacture and advertising?

Governments' reluctance to ban the manufacture and advertising of this dangerous product could be explained in terms of the dominance of the interests of tobacco producers over those of other groups and the economic benefits derived by governments from tobacco tax.

The political economy perspective also offers a critique of the role of medical and health services. According to Navarro, doctors are, partly because of their own class position and partly because of their social role, seen often as serving the interests of the dominant class. Hence the role of medicine is seen as helping to minimise disruption to the economic functioning of society, even if this means supporting exploitative and oppressive economic and social relationships.

 How relevant is the view that capitalism is a major threat to population health?

The global nature of capitalism makes it perhaps impossible to identify examples of societies and cultures unaffected by it. However, critics have argued that social processes other than the economic ones emphasised by Marxist writers are equally influential. These include the movement of ideas and discourse. Furthermore, critics have argued that Marxism places too much emphasis on class divisions as the driving force of social change, ignoring the independent impact of other social relations, including gender and ethnicity.

In response to these criticisms, political economy perspectives have taken a broader view than those of traditional Marxism, widening their scope to examine other aspects of power relationships such as gender and ethnicity. Political economy perspectives have exercised a strong influence over the sociology of health and illness, although this influence declined during the 1980s and 90s as new economic and social trends, such as changes in employment, leisure and lifestyle, emerged to challenge core assumptions concerning identity and class. Political economy perspectives may still evolve to meet these challenges. In the meantime, however, their legacy can still be seen, for example in relation to the inequalities in health debate, where material and structural explanations continue to hold sway.

INTERACTIONIST PERSPECTIVES AND THE EXPERIENCE OF ILLNESS

The perspectives discussed so far concentrate on the impact of illness, health and health care on society as whole. Sociologists have also examined the nature and meanings of the illness experience at the individual level, analysing this experience in the context of the interaction between people and exploring its implication for notions of identity and self. This tradition draws on the work of George Herbert Mead (1934), who saw human beings as distinctive in that they are able to reflect on their own thoughts and actions. This approach, sometimes referred to as 'symbolic *interactionism*', emphasises the ways in which people gain a shared understanding of the meanings attached to objects and phenomena, meanings that are not seen as pre-existing or intrinsic. Instead, they emerge from an interpretative process between people in which language is an important element. A nurse's uniform, for example, suggests femininity, caring, altruism and sacrifice – meanings reaffirmed by countless media portrayals.

interactionism – the theoretical perspective that emphasises the meaning of social life. Meanings emerge from social interaction and interpretation and are conveyed via language, labels and signs

Sociologists have applied these insights to the study of changes in identity, which occur when people become chronically ill or impaired. Goffman's work on stigma (1963) provides a well-known example of such an approach. According to Goffman, a person's sense of identity is formed in interaction with others and is strongly influenced by other people's perceptions. These are reflected back to the individual through verbal and non-verbal communication. When someone possesses a distinguishing attribute that is perceived negatively by others, his or her identity is to some extent 'spoiled' by the stigma. People attribute a range of negative characteristics, not necessarily directly related to the original attribute, to the individual. Wheelchair users, for example, are often assumed to be physically and intellectually dependent. Stigma is not just attributed to people on the basis of physical attributes, but can also be attributed as a result of personal and social characteristics such as being gay or lesbian.

Goffman suggested that, once stigmatised, individuals may react in a number of ways. They may attempt to 'pass', maintaining a performance of self in which the stigmatised attribute is disguised or hidden. They may also respond in ways that seem to confirm society's stereotyped views. Alternatively, they may create meanings that turn their experience into a positive one, for example reflecting on the lessons that their experiences have taught them. They may feel that they have grown in wisdom or sensitivity or somehow become a 'better person' because of their circumstances.

Goffman's theory was developed during the early 1960s and reflects the social values and norms of that time. In contemporary society, it seems that a wider range of options is available to stigmatised groups. These include activism and campaigning to transform social attitudes and end discrimination. Examples of this can be seen in the disability rights movement and in the responses of the gay community, which have challenged society's homophobic attitudes, enabling individuals to 'come out' and find solidarity in the gay pride movement.

Interactionist perspectives may be limited in that they do not address the reasons underlying why stigma occurs; they focus attention on the victim rather than examining the reasons for discrimination against particular groups. Nevertheless, they do draw attention to the stress that can accompany stigmatising experiences, including illness and disability. They also highlight the need for coping strategies in response to the challenges to identity that these experiences may represent. As a consequence, interactionist perspectives have had a strong influence on research in medical sociology, much of which is focused on inter-actions between professionals and patients, and the experiences of people with particular conditions.

The contemporary relevance of sociological perspectives on identity and illness has been emphasised by Mike Bury (1997). Increasing life expectancy and technological advances mean that, in contemporary society, an increasing number of people are surviving for a longer period. While growing older does not inevitably lead to poor health, such a trend is also accompanied by an increasing prevalence of chronic conditions. This means that an increasing number of people are likely to find that they cannot sustain the values of inde-pendence and achievement that they may have assumed would carry them through adult life.

Not surprisingly, then, the onset of chronic illness may represent a profound threat to personal identity. Bury (1982) illustrates this through the notion of illness as a *biographical disruption*, illness being not just a physical experience but a social one. It disrupts the patterns of daily life and social relationships, and generates a range of tasks. These may be partly associated with practical needs such as symptom management. However, illness also creates tasks in relation to maintaining a sense of identity and preserving one's cultural competence in the eyes of others.

SOCIAL CONSTRUCTIONIST PERSPECTIVES AND BEYOND

So far we have examined perspectives that examine the impact of social processes on the meanings of phenomena such as health and illness. These perspectives suggest that health and illness cannot be understood completely as fixed and unchanging entities. Instead, the meanings attributed to health and illness states may differ at different historical periods and between different cultures. Within Western medicine, for example, homosexuality is no longer perceived as a disease. At the same time, new diseases and syndromes, such as 'attention deficit disorder' and 'premenstrual syndrome' describe behaviour that would in previous decades have been understood in very different terms.

Sociologists have also explored the formation of ideas about health and illnesses, examining the role of different groups, such as professionals and scien-tists, in the production of discourses of health. These debates have implications for the study of lay perspectives, which may differ significantly from scientific and professional views. There has been a general shift away from approaches assuming that medical science is 'right' and other views 'wrong'. This has been accompanied by a shift away from approaches that seek to use sociological knowledge to identify the deficits in lay people's knowledge in order to offer correctives and to increase compliance with medical advice. Instead, there is a growing recognition that professional and lay views are both socially constructed. This means that they cannot easily be categorised as 'right' or 'wrong' because they both arise from the experiences and circumstances of different groups within society.

CONNECTIONS

Chapter 5 (Cultural Studies) discusses these perspectives in greater detail

The writings of Foucault (1976, 1979) have been studied by sociologists seeking to explore further this process of the social construction of medical knowledge. The notion of the *gaze* has been used to explain the processes that enabled a medical understanding of the body to emerge during the 18th century. This perspective draws attention to the surveillance and control that are exercised through medical practices. Today, the bodies of healthy as well as sick people are seen as being increasingly under surveillance. Medical practice is no longer concerned with just the treatment of disease but has been extended into new areas such as prevention and health promotion. These practices, while apparently beneficial, may have negative consequences. While apparently exercising care, health professionals may also be exercising power and control.

CONNECTIONS

Chapter 10 (Health Promotion) examines the critique that prevention is a form of social control

FEMINIST CRITIQUES OF HEALTH AND MEDICINE

feminism – the theoretical perspective focusing on gender inequality and the role of women in society. This theory stresses the social and historical origins of women's inferior position in society

Another perspective concerned with power and control in relation to health care is that of **feminism**. Although it is not possible to identify a single feminist perspective in sociology, a number of perspectives do share key elements. They are critical of the ideology and practice of Western medicine in terms of its impact on women and its contribution to the maintenance of gender divisions.

During the 1970s and 80s, feminist theory focused on debates between liberal, radical and materialist feminists, but these have since been overtaken by new perspectives and ideas. Feminists from different traditions share some elements of a critique of Western scientific medicine, which is summarised in Example 4.4.

Thinking about...

Do you think that feminism is still a relevant concept in today's society?

EXAMPLE 4.4

Feminist critique of Western scientific medicine

- Medical discourses lend scientific credibility to common beliefs concerning masculinity and femininity. The 19th century view of women as being inherently weak and at the mercy of their reproductive systems helped to justify the exclusion of women from education and employment. Processes of exclusion and demarcation continue to affect relationships between health care professions such as medicine and nursing

- The 19th century medical view of women also shaped the relationship between doctors and their female patients. The legacy of this view can still be seen in doctors' responses to women patients. Hence health problems affecting women, such as depression, are often attributed to biological rather than social causes. It may be difficult for women patients to voice their concerns and make appropriate treatment choices since doctors' knowledge and judgement are often given priority over women's needs

- Contemporary medical practice involves the medicalisation of women's lives, events such as the menopause and pregnancy being viewed as illnesses. As a result, women are subject to medical surveillance and questionable treatment

- Medical power extends into moral judgements as well as clinical decisions affecting women. As powerful 'experts', doctors can police women's behaviour, for example in relation to sexuality and reproduction. They are key gatekeepers in relation to fertility control

- Women form the majority of paid and unpaid carers, yet they remain underrepresented in key areas of medicine and health care management, male dominance continuing to influence health care provision. The exclusion of women from drug trials, for example, means that little is known about the effects of common treatments on women.

Sources: Doyal, 1995, 1998; Foster, 1995; Miles, 1991; Stacey, 1988; Witz, 1992

The degree of convergence in feminist writings on these subjects should not be overstated. Recent accounts have been increasingly concerned with the *differences* as well as the similarities between women. It has been suggested that feminist theories are wrongly presented as being applicable to all women since they have often emerged out of the experiences of a particular group. This results in problems such as ethnocentrism, which has influenced feminist research in health in a number of ways:

- Feminist writings have been criticised for reflecting issues predominantly affecting white women and suppressing black women's ideas (Hill Collins, 1990). Feminists have, for example, often assumed that women's family roles are problematic for their health, the family being seen as a key site of oppression. This neglects the historical experiences of black women, such as the importance of the family as a site of resistance against slavery (hooks, 1991). Furthermore, the feminist concern with reproductive rights has not been broadened to take into consideration the impact of eugenicist social policies on black women (Nasir, 1996). Hence feminist critiques have highlighted ways in which some women are denied access to services such as contraception and abortion, rather than emphasising the way in which the fertility of minority women has been controlled using these services.

- Feminists have focused on labour market inequalities between men and women, yet they have sometimes overlooked differences in the experience of women from different ethnic groups. Racism as well as sexism has had a significant impact on health service workers. In Britain during the period of post-war expansion, the NHS relied upon a supply of black labour from the former colonies. However, black nurses entered predominantly low-paid and low-status employment with worse conditions than their white counterparts. Within the NHS, black and minority ethnic women remain concentrated in low-paid jobs and shift work, and enjoy less access to training than their white counterparts (Douglas, 1998).

- Feminist accounts have identified the controlling aspects of medical practice in relation to sexual behaviour, but they have tended to concentrate on the experience of heterosexual women. Within medical discourse, same-sex desire has often been treated as a symptom of disease, yet little research has explored the impact of medical practice on lesbian women, and, as a result, little is known about key areas of lesbian health (Wilton, 1995, 2000).

Some feminist researchers have responded to these criticisms by including black and minority ethnic women as well as lesbians and disabled women in their research. Others have argued that the use of separate conceptual categories such as race and gender limits the understanding of the overlapping experiences of racism and sexism. This debate remains unresolved and is likely to continue to develop as researchers seek more sophisticated means of representing the experiences of different groups in society.

CASE STUDY – HEALTH AND WORK

This section explores sociological perspectives in relation to a case study focusing upon the links between health and work. Despite the existence of health and safety legislation in many countries, the level of work-related ill health remains high. In Britain in 1995, for example, 2 million people suffered from a work-related illness and around 20 million working days were lost through work-related ill health (DoH, 1999). This burden of occupational ill health is not shared evenly between all groups in society. Instead, work-related ill health reflects existing patterns of social inequality. Hence those in socio-economically disadvantaged groups, who face an increased general burden of disease, are more likely than other groups to work in hazardous employment with poor working conditions. As a consequence, these groups are also likely to experience an increased incidence of occupational ill health.

Explaining the effects of work on health

A number of theoretical approaches can be utilised in order to understand the effects of work on health:

- The social causation approach seeks to explain the origin of work-related ill health, its social distribution and its impact on different groups. This model is similar to the materialist/structural approach developed by the authors of the Black Report (Townsend et al., 1988). It is also the approach adopted by researchers working within a Marxist or political economy perspective.

- The social constructionist perspective is concerned with ideas about risk and hazard. Rather than taking these for granted, social constructionist perspectives suggest that our ability to recognise hazards and respond to notions of risk is mediated through interaction and language. The social constructionist approach builds on the interactionist perspective in sociology, some accounts taking this further to suggest that risks and hazards cannot be said to exist in any real sense at all.

THE SOCIAL CAUSATION OF OCCUPATIONAL RISK

One way of understanding the social causation approach is to think in terms of the social and environmental conditions that determine exposure to risk (Eakin and MacEachen, 1998). While risks may be a fact of life, an exposure to risk is not inevitable but arises here from how work is organised. Changes in production processes, such as the introduction of assembly line methods, can affect the pace and nature of work activities, increasing the wear and tear on the body and leading to stress and ill health. From this perspective, questions relating to who makes the decisions and who controls the work processes and activities seem important.

The social causation approach takes as its starting point the need to understand the underlying conditions of the physical environment. Together with social conditions and power relationships, these determine both who is at risk and the degree of risk. This approach offers a dynamic model that can be used to analyse the health effects of recent changes in employment. These have arisen from a number of global trends including a shift in investment and employment from manufacturing to service industries and the growing influence of large multinational corporations. The impact of these trends on employment in the UK over the past 20 years is summarised below (Church and Whyman, 1997):

- a decline in manufacturing employment: in 1996, only 25 per cent of men were employed in manufacturing compared with 33 per cent in 1981

- a growth in unemployment, particularly in areas formerly dominated by heavy industry

- a fall in the economic activity rate for some groups, including younger people and older men (for whom there has been a corresponding rise in early retirement). In 1996, just under 50 per cent of men aged 60–64 were economically active compared with 80 per cent in 1971

- a rise in the rate of women's participation in the labour force. Among women whose youngest child was not yet at school, just over half were economically active in 1996

- a rise in part-time working, particularly among women, who are six times more likely than men to be in part-time employment

- a growth in 'flexible' employment, including the use of temporary and short-term contracts.

It is important to consider the impact that these profound changes are likely to have on the pattern of work-related ill health. Although their impact will probably be seen over a long-term period, a number of broad trends are likely to emerge, as summarised below:

- Risks may be increasingly globalised and more difficult to control. Low wages and a lack of regulation in third world countries are attractive to large multinational corporations seeking to avoid the restrictions that exist in developed countries. For example, use of asbestos is restricted in Europe and

North America but is increasing in some poor countries, adding to the high level of ill health that already exists in such places (Johanning et al., 1994).

● Globalisation also has negative implications for workers and consumers in developed countries. Global competition, for example, makes it more difficult for these workers to insist on high wages or strong regulatory controls over industry (Greenlund and Elling, 1995). Furthermore, consumers are affected as banned products are exported to poor countries for use in a range of activities, including the production of food destined for European and North American markets.

● Within developed countries, the decline in manufacturing may eventually result in a decline in traditional forms of occupational disease, such as pneumoconiosis among miners. At the same time, new health problems, for example those relating to unemployment, are emerging.

● Changes in working conditions, such as the introduction of new technology, will lead to new occupational health problems or the spread of existing problems to new groups of workers (Watterson, 1999). Journalists and teachers, for example, may increasingly be affected by musculoskeletal problems that have traditionally affected workers in manufacturing industry.

● Women's rising participation in the labour force may increase their exposure to occupational health problems and risks. This exposure may be compounded by an exposure to other types of risk such as domestic hazards (Doyal, 1999). Since these problems have not traditionally been seen as being significant, more sensitive research tools will be needed to explore them (Messing, 1999).

● The growth in 'flexible', often insecure, employment may affect the pattern of risk. Researchers will in future need to pay increased attention to the psychosocial aspects of work and risk (Wilkinson, 1996).

INTERACTIONIST AND SOCIAL CONSTRUCTIONIST PERSPECTIVES ON HEALTH AND WORK

The second group of theories draws on interactionist and social constructionist perspectives. From this viewpoint, occupational risks and hazards are not seen as existing independently of the processes of interaction. In other words, interaction can influence whether risks are perceived in the first instance, as well as how they are understood and whether anything will be done to prevent or worsen them.

Interactionist perspectives are not necessarily incompatible with social causation approaches, but they do adopt a very different starting point for the analysis of work-related ill health. They suggest that the perceptions and meanings surrounding work and risk are just as important as the material risks themselves. The different cultural environments in which work takes place can influence how risks are seen, and therefore addressed or otherwise, by both workers and managers. For example, employees caring for older people in an institution might be aware of a range of risks that arise from their work. A specialist language, relating to concepts such as manual handling, might be utilised to describe these risks. These concepts represent a resource that enables the recognition of risks and risk prevention strategies. For example, hoists and other forms of equipment might be available for use, and protocols might decree that workers should only lift heavy patients if they work in pairs.

In contrast, those caring for older relatives at home are likely to place different constructs on their activity, as such activity is unlikely to be seen as 'work' in the same sense as if it were carried out for payment outside the home. Whereas this group may face very similar physical hazards, the concepts of manual handling are unlikely to be seen as being applicable to carers in this unregulated sector, and risk prevention strategies are likely to be left to the individual to work out for themselves. Finally, competing values, such as love, might result in a pressure to ignore personal risks in order to care for others (Lloyd, 1999).

These differences may also extend to different types of paid employment. Employees in small firms, for example, seem to perceive issues of health and risk differently from those in large companies. Employers and employees in small organisations may feel that they have a close familial relationship. This can result in positive employment experiences, but it can also make it more difficult for workers to refuse to accept dangerous conditions.

The social construction of notions of health, risk and employment can also affect the experiences of individuals within the workplace. In relation to sickness absence from employment, for example, a range of ideas and concepts exist that can result in this being approved behaviour or otherwise. In order not to be seen as 'malingering', it seems that certain conditions have to be met by the employee, and these do not always arise simply from the nature of the health problem or condition.

Research suggests that one of the requirements of being an employee is to maintain a reputation of moral worth: this might mean being seen as honest and reliable. Taking sick leave can affect employers' and colleagues' perceptions of the individual so that sickness can be seriously discrediting. Pinder (1999) found that employees suffering from rheumatoid arthritis adopt a range of strategies to maintain their identity as morally competent workers as well as managing their physical symptoms. Negative judgements on the part of others seemed to be influenced not by the nature of the physical condition but by other factors, such as the culture of the organisation and its wider economic position. Hence rather than seeing sickness, illness and disability as fixed states, this research suggests that we should recognise the fluidity of these conditions.

While interactionist perspectives suggest that the ways in which work hazards and risks are perceived is important, they also accept that work hazards actually exist in a 'real' sense regardless of our ability to recognise and label them. In contrast, postmodern writers take the social constructionist perspective further, claiming that occupational risks and hazards cannot be known or understood outside language. In other words, these phenomena are completely fabricated through discourse (Fox, 1999). This is a challenging perspective as it suggests that there is little to tell us about whether claims concerning work and health are true or false. On the other hand, this perspective highlights the role of researchers and writers in creating knowledge about risk through their work. It demands that researchers in this field become reflexive in their approach, recognising the possible impact of their work on the social construction of knowledge relating to the work environment.

Sociological research on occupational health remains relatively limited, although there are signs that this is changing. Political economy perspectives have tended to dominate this field, perhaps because they attach greater importance to work than other perspectives seem to do. As we have seen, however, the insights of other perspectives are also beginning to be applied to this field, with interesting results.

This case study has provided a brief discussion of the ways in which sociological perspectives might apply to the study of work-related ill health. Although these perspectives differ in significant ways, they each offer a useful vantage point from which to examine the issues.

SUMMARY

- Sociology – the study of human social life – has addressed many issues concerning people's experiences of health and illness, and the organisation of health care services

- A key theme in this area is the social patterning of health, ill health and premature death. Groups with less access to money and other material resources experience poorer health and a higher premature death rate. Societies with more egalitarian structures enjoy better health than more unequal societies

- 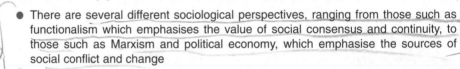There are several different sociological perspectives, ranging from those such as functionalism which emphasises the value of social consensus and continuity, to those such as Marxism and political economy, which emphasise the sources of social conflict and change

- Sociologists have explored the links between medical power and other social stratification variables such as gender and ethnicity

- Sociology involves both the critical examination of data (such as mortality rates) and the testing of theoretical frameworks and propositions.

QUESTIONS FOR FURTHER DISCUSSION

1. The relationship between gender and health seems to be subject to both continuity and change. What are the most important changes currently influencing women's lives, and how might these changes impact on gendered patterns of health?

2. What are the implications of the 'empowerment' perspective for the roles of health professionals and patients? Does this perspective offer an adequate replacement for Parson's 'sick role' concept?

3. Analyse the emergence of HIV/AIDS as a health issue using both social causation and social constructionist approaches.

4. Think back to recent encounters with the medical establishment. Critically analyse these encounters using sociological concepts.

FURTHER READING

Annandale, E. (1998) *The Sociology of Health and Medicine*. Oxford: Polity Press.
A useful recent text. Although slightly more advanced than some introductory texts, this is well worth the effort of reading it.

Daykin, N. and Doyal, L. (eds) (1999) *Work and Health: Critical Perspectives*. London: Macmillan – now Palgrave.
    Contains a number of interesting contributions for those who are interested in research on work-related ill health.

Doyal, L. (1995) *What Makes Women Sick? Gender and the Political Economy of Women's Health*. London: Macmillan – now Palgrave.
    Provides an overview of global trends in women's health as well as a useful insight into contemporary feminist debate.

Gabe, J. (ed.) (1995) *Medicine, Health and Risk*. Oxford: Blackwell.
    For students who are interested in following up recent debates concerning sociological perspectives on risk, this edited collection is a useful starting point.

Gabe, J., Kelleher, D. and Williams, G. (eds) (1995) *Challenging Medicine*. London: Routledge.
    Students interested in debates and critiques of Western scientific medicine should read the contributions in this book.

Stacey, M. (1988) *The Sociology of Health and Healing*. London: Unwin Hyman.
    A classic text that explores the historical development of Western medicine.

Finally, it is important to remember that sociological research often appears in journals before it is described in books. Relevant journals include the *Sociology of Health and Illness*, *Social Science and Medicine*, *Women's Studies International Forum*, *Health Promotion International* and the *International Journal of Health Services*.

REFERENCES

Acheson, D. (1998) *Independent Inquiry into Inequalities in Health: A Report*. London: Stationery Office.

Ahmad, W.I.U. (1993) 'Making black people sick: "race", ideology and health research', in Ahmad, W.I.U. (ed.) *'Race' and Health in Contemporary Britain*. Milton Keynes: Open University Press, pp. 11–13.

Anionwu, E.N. (1993) 'Sickle cell and thalassaemia: community experiences and official response', in Ahmad, W.I.U. (ed.) *'Race' and Health in Contemporary Britain*. Milton Keynes: Open University Press, pp. 76–95.

Annandale, E. and Hunt, K. (1990) Masculinity, femininity and sex: an exploration of their relative contribution to explaining gender differences in health. *Sociology of Health and Illness*, **12**: 24–46.

Arber, S. (1998) 'Health, ageing and older women', in Doyal, L. (ed.) *Women and Health Services. An Agenda for Change*. Buckingham: Open University Press, pp. 54–68.

Balarajan, R. (1990) Ethnic differences in mortality from ischaemic heart disease and cerebrovascular disease in England and Wales. *British Medical Journal*, **302**: 560–4.

Balarajan, R. and Soni Raleigh, V. (1993) *The Health of the Nation: Ethnicity and Health*. London: DoH.

Bartley, M., Blane, D. and Davey Smith, G. (1998) Introduction: Beyond the Black Report. *Sociology of Health and Illness*, **20**(5): 563–77.

Bunting, J. (1997) 'Morbidity and health-related behaviours of adults – a review', in Drever, F. and Whitehead, M. (eds) *Health Inequalities. Decennial Supplement*, Office for National Statistics, Series DS No. 15. London: Stationery Office, pp. 198–223.

Bury, M. (1982) Chronic illness as biographical disruption. *Sociology of Health and Illness*, **4**(2): 167–82.

Bury, M. (1997) *Health and Illness in a Changing Society*. London: Routledge.

Cameron, E. and Bernades, J. (1998) Gender and disadvantage in health: men's health for a change. *Sociology of Health and Illness*, **20**(5): 673–93.

Church, J. and Whyman, S. (1997) 'A review of recent social and economic trends', in Drever, F. and Whitehead, M. (eds) *Health Inequalities. Decennial Supplement*. Office for National Statistics, Series DS No. 15. London: Stationery Office, pp. 29–43.

Crossley, M. (1998) 'Sick role' or 'empowerment': the ambiguities of life with an HIV positive diagnosis. *Sociology of Health and Illness*, **20**(4): 507–31.

DoH (Department of Health) (1992) *The Health of the Nation*. London: HMSO.

DoH (Department of Health) (1999) *Saving Lives: Our Healthier Nation*. London: Stationery Office.

Douglas, J. (1998) 'Meeting the needs of women from black and minority ethnic communities', in Doyal, L. (ed.) *Women and Health Services. An Agenda for Change*. Buckingham: Open University Press, pp. 69–82.

Doyal, L. (1979) *The Political Economy of Health*. London: Pluto Press.

Doyal, L. (1995) *What Makes Women Sick? Gender and the Political Economy of Health*. London: Macmillan – now Palgrave.

Doyal, L. (ed.) (1998) *Women and Health Services. An Agenda for Change*. Buckingham: Open University Press.

Doyal, L. (1999) 'Women and domestic labour: setting a research agenda', in Daykin, N. and Doyal, L. (eds) *Health and Work: Critical Perspectives*. London: Macmillan – now Palgrave, pp. 21–34.

Drever, F. and Bunting, J. (1997) 'Patterns and trends in male mortality', in Drever, F. and Whitehead, M. (eds) *Health Inequalities. Decennial Supplement*. Office for National Statistics, Series DS No. 15. London: Stationery Office, pp. 95–107.

Drever, F. and Whitehead, M. (eds) (1997) *Health Inequalities. Decennial Supplement*. Office for National Statistics, Series DS No. 15. London: Stationery Office.

Dunn, J. and Fahy, T.A. (1990) Police admissions to a psychiatric hospital: demographic and clinical differences between ethnic groups. *British Journal of Psychiatry*, **156**: 373–8.

Eakin, J.M. and MacEachen, M. (1998) Health and the social relations of work: a study of the health-related experiences of employees in small workplaces. *Sociology of Health and Illness*, **20**(6): 896–914.

Foster, P. (1995) *Women and the Health Care Industry. An Unhealthy Relationship?* Buckingham: Open University Press.

Foucault, M. (1976) *The Birth of the Clinic: An Archaelogy of Medical Perception*. London: Tavistock.

Foucault, M. (1979) *The History of Sexuality*, Vol. 1. London: Allen Lane.

Fox, N.J. (1999) 'Postmodern reflections: deconstructing "risk", "health" and "work"', in Daykin, N. and Doyal, L. (eds) *Health and Work: Critical Perspectives*. London: Macmillan – now Palgrave, pp. 198–219.

Goffman, E. (1963) *Stigma*. London: Penguin.

Graham, H. (1987) Women's smoking and family health. *Social Science and Medicine*, **25**(1): 47–56.

Graham, H. (1998) 'Health at risk: poverty and national health strategies', in Doyal, L. (ed.) *Women and Health Services: An Agenda for Change*. Buckingham: Open University Press, pp. 22–38.

Greenlund, K.J. and Elling, R.H. (1995) Capital sectors and worker's health and safety in the United States. *International Journal of Health Services*, **25**(1): 101–16.

Harding, S. and Maxwell, R. (1997) 'Differences in mortality of migrants', in Drever, F. and Whitehead, M. (eds) *Health Inequalities. Decennial Supplement*. Office for National Statistics, Series DS No. 15. London: Stationery Office, pp. 108–121.

Hill Collins, P. (1990) *Black Feminist Thought: Knowledge, Consciousness and the Politics of Empowerment*. London: Routledge.

hooks, b. (1991) *Yearning: Race, Gender, and Cultural Politics*. London: Turnaround.

Illich, I. (1975) *Medical Nemesis*. London: Calder & Boyars.

Illich, I. (1977) *The Limits to Medicine*. Harmondsworth: Penguin.

Illsley, R. (1986) Occupational class, selection and the production of inequalities in health. *Quarterly Journal of Social Affairs*, **2**(2): 151–65.

Johanning, E., Goldberg, M. and Kim, R. (1994) Asbestos hazard evaluation in South Korean textile production. *International Journal of Health Services*, **24**(1): 131–44.

Kunst, A.E., Feikje, G., Mackenbach, J.P. and the EU Working Group on Socioeconomic Inequalities in Health (1998) Mortality by occupational class among men 30–64 years in 11 European countries. *Social Science and Medicine*, **46**(11): 1459–76.

Lloyd, L. (1999) 'The wellbeing of carers: an occupational health concern', in Daykin, N. and Doyal, L. (eds) *Health and Work: Critical Perspectives*. London: Macmillan – now Palgrave, pp. 54–70.

Mackenbach, J.P., Kunst, A.E., Cavelaars, A.E.J.M., Groenhof, F., Geurts, J.J. and the EU Working Group on Socioeconomic Inequalities in Health (1997) Socioeconomic inequalities in morbidity and mortality in Western Europe. *Lancet*, **349**: 1655–9.

McTaggart, L. (1996) *What Doctors Don't Tell You. The Truth about the Dangers of Modern Medicine*. London: Thorsons.

Mead, G.H. (1934) *Mind, Self and Society from the Standpoint of Social Behaviourism*. Chicago: Chicago University Press.

Messing, K. (1999) 'Tracking the invisible: scientific indicators of the health hazards in women's work', in Daykin, N. and Doyal, L. (eds) *Health and Work: Critical Perspectives*. London: Macmillan – now Palgrave, pp. 127–42.

Miles, A. (1991) *Women, Health and Medicine*. Milton Keynes: Open University Press.

Nasir, S. (1996) '"Race", gender and social policy', in Hallet, C. (ed.) *Women and Social Policy: An Introduction*. London: Prentice Hall/Harvester Wheatsheaf, pp. 15–30.

Navarro, V. (1979) *Medicine under Capitalism*. London: Croom Helm.

ONS (Office for National Statistics) (1997) *Population Trends, 87*. Office for National Statistics, London: Stationery Office.

Parsons, T. (1951) *The Social System*. London: Routledge & Kegan Paul.

Parsons, T. (1975) The sick role and the role of the physician reconsidered. *Millbank Memorial Fund Quarterly*, Summer: 257–78.

Payne, S. (1998) '"Hit and miss": the success and failure of psychiatric services for women', in Doyal, L. (ed.) *Women and Health Services. An Agenda for Change*. Buckingham: Open University Press, pp. 83–99.

Peach, C. (ed.) (1996) *Ethnicity in the 1991 Census*, Vol. 2. *The Ethnic Minority Populations of Great Britain*. Office for National Statistics. London: HMSO.

Pinder, R. (1999) 'Zones of danger, zones of safety: disabled people's negotiations around sickness and the sick record', in Daykin, N. and Doyal, L. (eds) *Health and Work: Critical Perspectives*. London: Macmillan – now Palgrave, pp. 161–79.

Roberts, I. and Power, C. (1996) Does the decline in child injury mortality vary by social class? A comparison of class specific mortality in 1981 and 1991. *British Medical Journal*, **313**(7060): 784–6.

Rudat, K. and Barnes, S. (1995) The HEA Health and Lifestyle Survey. *Share Newsletter* **11**: 4–5.

Smaje, C. (1995) *Health, 'Race' and Ethnicity. Making Sense of the Evidence*. London: King's Fund.

Smaje, C. (1996) The ethnic patterning of health: new directions for theory and research. *Sociology of Health and Illness*, **18**(2): 139–71.

Stacey, M. (1988) *The Sociology of Health and Healing*. London: Unwin Hyman.

Thomson, R. and Holland, J. (1994) 'Young women and safer (hetero) sex: context, constraints and strategies', in Wilkinson, S. and Kitzinger, C. (eds) *Women and Health. Feminist Perspectives*. London: Taylor & Francis, pp. 13–32.

Townsend, P., Davidson, N. and Whitehead, M. (1988) *Inequalities in Health. The Black Report/The Health Divide*. London: Penguin.

Watterson, A. (1999) 'Why we still have "old" epidemics and "endemics" in occupational health: policy and practice failures and some possible solutions', in Daykin, N. and Doyal, L. (eds) *Health and Work: Critical Perpectives.* London: Macmillan – now Palgrave, pp. 107–26.

Whitehead, M. (1997) 'Life and death over the millennium', in Drever, F. and Whitehead, M. (eds) *Health Inequalities. Decennial Supplement.* Office for National Statistics, Series DS No. 15. London: Stationery Office, pp. 7–28.

Wilkinson, R. (1996) *Unhealthy Societies.* London: Routledge.

Wilton, T. (1995) *Lesbian Studies: Setting an Agenda.* London: Routledge.

Wilton, T. (2000) *Sexualities in Health and Social Care: A Textbook.* Buckingham: Open University Press.

Witz, A. (1992) *Professions and Patriarchy.* London: Routledge.

WHO (World Health Organization) (1998) *The World Health Report 1998. Life in the 21st Century. A Vision for All.* Geneva: WHO.

Zola, I. (1972) Medicine as an institution of social control. *Sociological Review*, **20**(4): 487–504.

Cultural Studies

SARAH BURCH

CONTENTS

Learning outcomes ●●●●●●●●●●●●●●●●●●●●●●●●●●●

This chapter will enable readers to:

● Understand what is meant by culture and how it can be applied to health
● Understand the five central cultural processes: representation, identity, production, consumption and regulation, and be able to apply them to health
● Gain an overview of the discipline and development of cultural studies, including its theoretical and methodological approaches
● Reflect upon the insights that cultural studies can give to our understandings of health, illness and health care.

OVERVIEW

While health and illness are commonly thought of as biological properties, they can also be seen as being shaped by culture – a system of shared meanings, experiences and practices. Culture is reflected in all the customs and areas of knowledge of social life, including religion, diet, dress, ethnicity and understandings of the body. Cultural studies is a relatively new field that takes a multidisciplinary approach to the study of culture, drawing on insights from anthropology, sociology, communication studies, literature and the visual arts among others. This chapter shows how the different theoretical and methodological perspectives employed by cultural studies can be applied to health. At the heart of the study of culture are five central processes: representation, identity, production, consumption and regulation. These are explored and discussed in relation to health and health practices. Cultural studies can offer insights into health and illness by examining three areas. First, ideas about the body are explored – how it is viewed as being gendered, an object that needs disciplining through health practices, and a site of consumption. Second, representations of health and illness in official health promotion approaches and images within the media and popular culture are examined. Third, understandings of health and illness can vary both within and between cultures. The chapter ends with an extended case study of new reproductive technologies. It relates the five central cultural processes to this area, arguing that assisted conception needs to be understood within the context of ideas relating to nature, technology, motherhood and consumerism.

INTRODUCTION

Culture is a central concept of cultural studies, yet also one of the most contested. Ideas of culture derive from a range of disciplines and perspectives, perhaps the most familiar concept coming to us from the arts and literature, in which culture is seen as representing an elite form of knowledge and artistry. Within cultural studies, however, it is the social dimension of culture that is often seen as most significant. Cultures are systems of shared meanings, representations and practices that comprise the whole of social life. Thus, cultural manifestations may be found in a host of areas, including religious beliefs, ethnic identity, diet, dress, leisure, codes of behaviour and systems of knowledge.

Culture is the way in which we make sense of the world. Helman (1994) provides the following definition:

> To some extent, culture can be seen as an inherited 'lens', through which the individual perceives and understands the world... and learns how to live within it. Growing up within any society is a form of enculturation, whereby the individual slowly acquires the cultural 'lens' of that society.

Every object, action and person is assigned a meaning by us as we try to interpret our encounters and fit them into a unifying framework. The study of culture is thus the study of signification: we examine and deconstruct what certain **cultural practices** or objects signify.

cultural practice – modes of behaviour which reflect and perpetuate culture, such as fashion, food and family relationships

Certain ideas and representations can become dominant in society, particularly if they are disseminated through the mass media. It would, however, be far too simplistic to portray cultural ideals as being unanimously held: culture should not be understood as a homogeneous entity. Within any society, a multiplicity of cultures can operate. All societies are composed of social divisions, various groupings that gain significance based on common denominators of social positioning, such as age, class, sexuality, gender, ethnicity, religious beliefs or geography. The character and extent of these social divisions varies from society to society and across time. Each of these social divisions may have its own culture, which, while not wholly divorced from the mainstream, may have its own distinctive properties.

The study of culture inevitably poses certain questions:

- How do cultures develop and acquire their own particular properties?
- How do certain cultural values and practices become dominant?
- How does culture interact with variables such as socio-economic structure and political ideologies?
- How do cultures affect the lives of individuals?

THE CONTRIBUTION OF CULTURAL STUDIES TO HEALTH STUDIES

Dominant ideas of health and health care are that they are scientific and primarily rooted in biological fact; medicine and health care have tended not to be seen as culturally determined. The exception is research into the health and cultural beliefs of ethnic minority groups in which minority cultures have been represented as faulty for supporting health practices not in keeping with Western norms (Ahmad, 1996). Yet our understanding of what constitutes health and disease, what causes certain conditions, how they should be treated and what experiences of health and illness mean are also based in our culture. How we interpret our **body** or our mental health will be shaped by the world in which we live.

body – the physical body, a concept encompassing not only the experience of living within our bodies, but also the meanings we attach to the body

Culture embraces the whole of our social life and systems of knowledge, including knowledge relating to health and health care. Information on health comes to us via numerous sources apart from the medical profession, such as our families and friends, literature, the media, self-help groups and the Internet. Health is not only a property of our bodies, but also an item of **consumption**. Many products, from sportswear and slimming aids to organic foods and water filters, are marketed as 'healthy' or 'healthier'. These products speak to and shape our notions of health. They not only reflect our current conceptions of health, but also help to create new beliefs and ideas on health. Our health, our illnesses and our lifestyle cannot be divorced from the culture within which we live.

Cultural studies focuses on the importance of culture in defining ourselves, our bodies and our identities. In contrast to Marxist perspectives, which state that culture is produced from economic structures, some cultural studies theorists argue that culture is independent, autonomous and creative. **Structuralists** such as de Saussure (1960) and Lévi-Strauss (1970) focus on the ways in which meaning is socially created, especially through language and linguistic categories and rules. From de Saussure's perspective, while all languages vary, they share the essential quality of ordering the world into interrelated categories. Thus, language orders our conceptual understanding of the world. Lévi-Strauss took this idea of conceptual structure beyond language to include all cultural practices, such as kinship networks, cooking and myths:

> All cultures make sense of the world, and while the meanings that they make of it may be specific to them, the ways by which they make those meanings are not; they are universal. Meanings are culture-specific, but the ways of making them are universal to all human beings. (Fiske, 1990)

For Lévi-Strauss, the fundamental contribution of language was the construction of binary oppositions: the division of the world into two categories that are mutually dependent on one another for their meaning. Thus, hot and cold are binary oppositions that categorise phenomena and rely on their interrelationship to be comprehensible. Health and disease can also be understood as binary oppositions. Those concepts which defy being placed into oppositional categories, possessing characteristics that blur the boundary, are termed 'anomalous categories'. When these categories are seen as being too disturbing to established social knowledge, they become the subject of taboos. Thus, Lévi-Strauss argued that homosexuality was seen as taboo because it undermined gender identity.

Postmodernists argue that, in our post-industrial world, identities and ideas proliferate to create a pluralistic society. Pluralism means that there is a variety of subcultures and groups, each of which has its own validity. Postmodernism rejects the grand **narratives** of perspectives such as Marxism that seek to explain society by reference to a unifying underlying set of ideas (Doyle, 1995). The modernist concept of linear progress is dismissed, as is the search for an ultimate objective truth, such as assuming that societies can be explained solely by their economic organisation or language structure. Within a postmodern world, traditional sources of solidarity and **identity** become dislocated. As family and working structures fragment, we are left without easy certainties. Geographic or social class location, for example, will not be sufficient, or sufficiently unambiguous, to give us a central, lifelong identity.

---

consumption – the way in which cultural artefacts are used or purchased, and the way in which we take meaning from them

structuralism – a term covering theoretical perspectives arguing that the social world is shaped by underlying forces such as economic structure and the role of language

postmodernism – an umbrella term referring to the rejection of modernism, linear progress and essential truths in favour of fragmentation, plural discourses and relativism

narrative – a story that seeks to explain the world, either in the sense of a theoretical perspective or in the sense of personal testimony

identity can be signified by the way in which we consume culture in order to convery a certain image

Postmodernity is characterised by a plurality of **discourses**. At its most extreme, this plurality of discourses can be seen as complete relativism. Thus, within culture, any boundaries between high and low, good or bad, are rejected. All knowledge and practice must be understood within discourse and culture: there is no external or absolute reality that can be known.

discourse – can be used in the sense of language to refer to talk or writing. It can also be used to describe a set of ideas and norms about a topic

CULTURAL PROCESSES

In order to focus on culture in more depth, it is useful to examine some of its key processes. Several writers have attempted to provide frameworks showing the interrelationships between the different components of culture (see, for example, Hall, 1980a; Johnson, 1996). These frameworks are often described as circuits as different processes operate simultaneously and influence each other rather than happening in any particular sequence. This section draws upon the five areas identified by du Gay et al. (1997), which together comprise a circuit of culture:

Thinking about...

What characterises discourses about clubbing?

- representation
- identity
- production
- consumption
- regulation.

Du Gay argues that in order to understand any cultural artefact we must analyse it by means of these five core processes.

Representation

At a basic level, **representation** refers to how cultural artefacts are portrayed. This may well take the form of images. In a broader sense, however, we are talking about the process of **signification**, which relates to the symbolic meanings derived from cultural products. Thus, how something is represented may also refer to how it is discussed, to what language and imagery are employed.

representation – how cultural artefacts are portrayed, discussed and given symbolic meanings

Kitzinger (1995) provides an illuminating discussion on portrayals of AIDS in the media. She argues that representations of people with AIDS draw heavily on extreme and horrific imagery. A common representation is the use of 'before and after' photographs to show how people have been ravaged by their illness. She comments that the pictures echo the use of before and after representations of successful slimmers, although in this case gauntness is associated with death and decay. The photographs, with their accompanying text, reflect trends within medical photography but also appear to be drawing on horror films in their use of shock.

sign – a unit of communication that refers to something else and is understood by others as doing so, for example a gesture

 Is the representation of shocking images likely to encourage a change in behaviour?

Kitzinger (1995) argues that whereas such messages may be interpreted as frightening people into safe behaviour, they also serve to reinforce a moral

dimension that is essentially victim-blaming. At the same time, the images may be so horrific that they become unpalatable. Readers turn the page rather than be confronted with such suffering. In health promotion terms, then, this approach may appear to be counter-productive. Yet for some, such representations may be their main source of knowledge. How health and illness are represented can thus be seen to have consequences for how we understand and respond to these states.

Identity

Culture is, as well as being located in representations, also a site for the construction of identity. The types of films we watch, the clothes we wear, the lifestyles we lead all bestow on us an identity. Our consumption of culture is in part shaped by the identity we wish to convey. Hall and du Gay (1996) argue that identities are constructed within discourses and through difference: 'Throughout their careers, identities can function as points of identification and attachment only *because* of their capacity to exclude' (original emphasis).

 How do a person's clothes and way of talking construct his or her identity?

Not only do we construct our identities through purchase or presentation, but also our actual flesh can form the site for the forging of identity. Soyland's (1997) study highlights the growing incidence of largely irreversible body decorations such as tattoos and piercings. Piercing and scarring the body may seem to many to be the antithesis of health, yet the process of transforming one's body can be seen as a cultural statement of identity. Pain is part of the process of decoration and a necessary hurdle to produce the desired effect: 'The body... is seen as something to be mastered or controlled if the ambition to decorate is to be realised' (Soyland, 1997). The identity derived from being decorated is mingled with a sense of authenticity, that of being genuine as opposed to purely fashionable. Soyland demonstrates that the practice of decoration reveals identity partly at a collective cultural level but principally on a personal basis. Our sense of health is thus linked with our sense of identity.

Production

production – the production of both cultural artefacts and the meanings derived from them

Production is a powerful concept within cultural studies. It is used in two interlinked senses. First, it can refer to the production of cultural artefacts, which from a health perspective might include medical dramas, prescription drugs, academic and clinical textbooks or public health messages. The producers of culture are thus those who create and manufacture a vast range of cultural components. However, the term also refers to the way in which *meanings* are produced. Producers may attempt to 'brand' their products in such a way as to influence how they are received and understood. Thus, the messages produced interact with and influence cultural discourses.

Park (1996) traces the history of marketing practices for products for menstruating women. What is most striking about these products is the way in which they appeal to changing notions of femininity while relating to shifting discourses of health and the body.

> Medical norms of 'good health' in the late nineteenth century excluded women who, by virtue of their cyclicity, were deemed abnormal. Menstruation was a malfunctioning of the human machine and a sign of chronic illness. (Park, 1996)

Thus, menstrual products of the time, by being marketed as 'sanitary towels' reflected this preoccupation with hygiene. Menstruation as a sign of illness meant that products were promoted through the use of medical analogies, companies in the early 20th century utilising the Red Cross symbol as a marker of merit. Cleanliness became seen as women's way of both managing their weak bodies and fulfilling their duties as capable home-makers and, as time progressed, efficient employees. By the middle of the 20th century, changing norms and socio-economic conditions meant that women were expected to overcome any problems associated with menstruation: 'Whereas the Victorian woman was confined to a destiny marked out by her biology, the contemporary, more liberated woman, was supposed to transcend her biology' (Park, 1996).

 What meanings and discourses are conveyed in the modern marketing of sanitary products?

Notions of freedom and liberation are used to market products such as certain brands of 'with wings' pantyliners. Tampons are sold as products that enable women's menstruation to be both undetectable and unconstraining. Advertisements display women swimming or wearing white clothes. For today's woman to be inconvenienced by her period would be a new marker of weakness. Cultural products both *reflect* discourses, such as those of health and femininity, and *contribute* to them by transmitting cultural norms.

Consumption

Consumption and production are intimately linked. Just as in the case of production, consumption has a similar dual meaning. We generally think of consumption as referring to the purchase of goods or the use of services, and this is certainly an important sense of the term. However, it also refers to the consumption of meaning and the ways in which we receive images and messages. When we consume cultural products, we do not simply absorb their intended messages uncritically: instead, we interact with cultural messages in order to produce our own meaning. Thus, the processes of production and consumption cannot be divorced. Bocock (1993) explains that consumption is both a material and a symbolic process: 'Modern consumerism… depends upon its specific set of values becoming acceptable and comprehensible… so that sales of consumer products can be made.'

Thinking about...

In recent years, models
have become increas-
ingly waif-like. How do
these cultural images
represent womanhood,
and what effect, if any,
do you think that they
have on women's
behaviour?

It is often argued that women develop anorexia because they consume images of thin models in the media. Anorexia from this perspective is seen not only as an eating disorder, but also as a 'reading disorder', one that stems from a pathological reading of messages about the body.

Bray (1996) argues that the concept that women are wont to damage themselves through reckless and uncritical reading (both in the literal sense and in the form of receiving and interpreting images) has a long history. Nineteenth-century concerns centred around the damaging effects of popular literature on women's minds and bodies. Today's concerns centre around women's undue suggestibility, with its connotations of hysteria.

Bray situates anorexia within the widespread practice of dieting, in which the concept of metabolism plays a central role, promoting an obsessive translation of food and appetite into units of calories. From Bray's perspective, then, it is too simplistic to understand anorexia as women's incapacity to consume images correctly. Instead, it should be seen as part of a wider cultural emphasis on weight loss in which ideas of calorie-counting, exercise and metabolism combine to regiment the body and its appetites. 'The counting down of this body and that which it consumes is acted out with deathly rigour in anorexia' (Bray, 1996). How we consume images can thus be seen to have consequences for our health. We should not, however, assume that we simply receive images passively and then react to them. More complex processes of interpretation may be involved.

Regulation

Culture and cultural artefacts are seldom given free rein. In any society, rules exist to regulate and control the operation of cultural processes. Whenever we consider a cultural product or act of consumption, we must also consider the conditions that regulate its use or dissemination. *Regulation* can refer to who is allowed to behave in a certain way or use certain products. It can refer to which representations and identities are considered socially acceptable, and it can also cover appropriate places for cultural activities.

regulation – how the
cultural processes are
controlled

> **?** **How do cultures regulate the presentation of the body?**

Bodies are accorded a certain status, which means that there are only certain situations in which they may be uncovered. It is often considered suitable to be undressed in front of a doctor or one's sexual partner, but in other contexts nakedness may be shameful. The extent to which bodies can be uncovered will vary between cultures. Orthodox Hindu women cover the upper body, and women should only venture outside if their bodies are concealed from above the navel to the ankle. Married women are not permitted to be naked even when bathing (Leslie, 1992).

In the case of the regulation of health and health practices, there are many organising principles that can be brought into play. For example, some drugs, such as alcohol or tobacco, have legal status and can be purchased by anyone who is old enough. Alcohol and tobacco may be used for many reasons, such as the relief of stress. However, other drugs that may conceivably be used for the same purpose, such as marijuana, are illegal, and still others may only be prescribed by a doctor. The attempt to produce or control physical and mental symptoms through the use of drugs is subject to processes of cultural control. Those who use illegal drugs will be termed criminals, those who use legal drugs in a way considered to be excessive may be seen as irresponsible, whereas those who use prescription drugs have legitimacy conferred upon them. This legitimacy stems both from being labelled as ill and from the power of the expert prescribing the drug.

EXAMPLE 5.1

Viagra

Viagra illustrates the discourse surrounding sexuality and unacceptable drug use. Viagra has hit the headlines in recent years, marketed as a wonder drug that can relieve impotence. The simplicity of swallowing a pill has been seen as being far more acceptable than the use of previous approaches, which have included appliances, injections and psychotherapy. Viagra has been credited with bringing the formerly taboo subject of impotence into the forum of public debate and acknowledgement.

There have been concerns that men have been able to purchase Viagra privately, without the necessity of having it prescribed by a doctor. The fact that these private purchases have often been conducted via the Internet deepens this alarm. The Internet, whose users are rapidly increasing in number, itself attracts disquiet for purveying cultural products in an unregulated form. Here, the practice of self-medication can be seen as undermining professional power.

This message has been reinforced by numerous headlines and reports documenting deaths or side-effects from the unregulated use of the drug. In the UK, assaults on professional power have also come through the government, which has issued guidelines rationing the use of the drug (DoH, 1999). The outcry from professional organisations such as the British Medical Association has been vociferous (Murray, 1999). While the guidelines are denounced in the name of equity for patients, there is also resentment at what is seen as an unwarranted curbing of clinical freedom.

The limited conditions under which Viagra may be prescribed also suggest another way in which the drug is causing disquiet – they form part of a debate about what constitutes acceptable use. Sexuality and its purpose are being claimed and defined by different discourses. On the one hand, impotence and the failure to participate in penetrative sex are seen as a medical problem, a failure of the body. On the other, sexuality is seen as part of self-expression. This self-expression can, however, be contested if it is seen to be unduly hedonistic. Accounts repeatedly attempt to distinguish between sex as part of a marital relationship, which is perceived as legitimate, and sex which is seen as 'recreational', which is not.

> The Internet... provides access to a mix of information on sildenafil from the responsible material put up on the US Food and Drug Administration and Pfizer websites to a Viagra message board with signposting to pornographic material. The former points to sensible clinically indicated use of sildenafil; the latter to Viagra as a recreational drug, which has already gathered the alternative names 'V' and 'poke'. (Editorial, *Lancet*, 1998)

Sources: DoH, 1999; *Lancet*, 1998; Murray, 1999

CONNECTIONS

Chapters 8 and 9 discuss Viagra from an economic and ethical viewpoint

The interacting cultural processes of representation, identity, production, consumption and regulation may be applied to many health issues. Three key areas that have been well researched are the body, representations of health, and health and illness across cultures.

THE BODY

Our bodies are clearly integral to our understanding of health and disease, forming the terrain on which we experience and interpret states of well-being and illness. Until recently, the body was not considered to be a problematic topic. It was conceived as a biological entity and, as such, the intellectual property of biomedicine.

This can in part be attributed to the predominance of Cartesian dualism within Western science and philosophy: the mind–body separation in which rationality is prized (Bordo 1987, 1993). In general, although the body played an important role within anthropology (Turner, 1991), social science as a whole tended to ignore the body, concentrating instead on people's social roles and conditions. In such a way, the body became almost invisible within social science discourse. Recent years have witnessed a surge of interest in the concept of embodiment and the meanings we attach to our corporeal selves (Frank, 1990).

One of the most significant ways in which the body conveys meaning is by transmitting **gender**. Gendered conceptions of the body are profoundly powerful. In a society that privileges the mind and rationalism, femininity becomes associated with the body and its accompaniments of emotion and irrationality. Thus, a denial of the body can also be seen as a denial of femininity (Davis, 1997). The acceptance of the apparent neutrality of biomedicine has meant that whereas gender roles have frequently been seen as socially constructed, sex – the biological manifestation of males and females – has been taken as a given. Yet this approach has increasingly been challenged, some writers arguing that sex too must be seen as a social construction. Before the Enlightenment, bodies were seen as being of 'one flesh', in which female bodies were held to be simply inverted male bodies (Laqueur, 1990). Hence males and females were both versions of the same sex.

CONNECTIONS

Chapter 1 (Physiology) outlines the ways in which bodily processes are investigated

gender – the social role that is attached to being biologically male or female

CONNECTIONS

Chapter 4 (Sociology) discusses gender and health

? **Why did the view of the body as divided into two sexes emerge in modern society?**

Biological difference was not a central component of the sexual hierarchy before the Enlightenment. With the rise of liberal democracy, which appeared to have the potential to threaten the status quo, the growth of the two-sex model conferred stability by its affirmation of women's different and subordinate role.

Petersen (1998) draws on Laqueur's work in his analysis of the way in which sex differences have been represented in Gray's *Anatomy*. This anatomical text has formed the bedrock of biomedicine since 1858 and is supposedly a culture-free rendition of physiological facts, yet Petersen demonstrates several ways in which its representations reveal an androcentric approach: the male body and its components appear as the norm, whereas the female body appears as deviant in comparison. The most striking example of this hierarchical representation is found in depictions of the sex organs. A developmental description is provided in which female organs are seen as underdeveloped and hence inferior. The comparison is emphasised by the way in which diagrams of the male organs are shown on the left, while female organs are on the right, underlining the primacy of male bodily components. Similarly, Petersen points out that there is a greater concentration on the penis, which is often described using architectural metaphors, while descriptions of the clitoris are less detailed and make more use of botanical metaphors. Thus, throughout a purportedly objective text, anatomical explanations and illustrations are employed in such a way as to position the male body as the point of reference and the female body as an inferior deviation.

The body is, however, not only constructed as gendered, but also a site of consumption as our bodies form a central focus within the upsurge of the interest in lifestyle. What we eat, what we wear and whether we are fit are all cultural markers, locating our identities. Two themes are important here:

- the body that must be disciplined
- the body for which goods and services must be purchased.

Foucault (1975) explores how people voluntarily regulate and discipline their bodies, eager to comply with widespread ideas of what is normal, hygienic and functional. Medicine is a key discourse purporting to tell people which bodily behaviours are normal and which are abnormal. Masturbation, for example, is now generally regarded as normal and acceptable, but for many years it was regarded as unclean and undesirable. The way in which people internalise such discourses means that there is no need for coercive means of control – people learn to regulate themselves.

The emphasis on individualistic models of health, such as the stress on personal responsibility for a healthy diet and fitness, forms another arena of control. Health risks are seen as deriving from the inability to exercise willpower or discipline. Such a view makes few concessions to material factors such as possessing the necessary income with which to service one's body.

While this disciplining of the body may seem to imply a continuous round of self-denial in order to restrain any appetite for excess, it also opens the way for more tangible forms of consumption. The plethora of health and fitness magazines, slimming aids, sportswear and memberships of gyms and health clubs are but a few of the goods and services available in order to assist in the quest for a managed body. Giddens (1991) argues that contemporary society can be characterised as 'high modernity', in which the pace of social change is such that people lack traditional reference points for identity within a fragmented and shifting social order. Instead, the self, or body, becomes a project, the seat of identity and a source of stability, albeit in an ever-changing and unfinished form.

> **CONNECTIONS**
>
> Chapter 10 (Health Promotion) discusses and critiques the individual lifestyle approach to health

REPRESENTATIONS OF HEALTH

One of the most important arenas in which we can observe the cultural properties of health is that of the **media**. Cultural studies makes a valuable contribu-

> **media** – any agents that disseminate information. The term is often used as a shorthand for mass media, which covers agents such as television and newspapers

tion to our analysis of how messages on health are formulated, interpreted and exchanged. Broadly speaking, ideas about health can be conveyed through two channels:

● official channels, which refer to the sphere of public health and health information
● non-official channels, which refer to discourses concerning health within popular culture.

These channels are not discrete but overlap.

Public health and health information

This field encompasses a wide range of health messages. It can refer to concepts of health and illness contained within policy documents, public health initiatives, health promotion initiatives or campaigns by charities to publicise their causes, attract funds and disseminate information. In many ways, public health campaigns resemble advertising: they are designed to sell us an idea of good health and the means of achieving it.

 Why is it more difficult to 'sell' health in a public information campaign than to advertise a commercial product?

The differences between selling health in a public information campaign and advertising a commercial product are summarised in Table 5.1.

Health and popular culture

Health issues appear in popular culture in different ways including:

● press reports, which may be based on official government pronouncements
● medical advisory columns
● television dramas.

The media act as gatekeepers of the public's awareness, reporting material that is deemed to be most interesting, most important or likely to increase circulation or viewing figures. Oinas (1998) presents an analysis of how medical advisory columns promote a medicalised construction of menstruation in response to the letters of teenage girls. The most common response to the letters, most of which required no specialist expertise to answer, was that the young women should go and visit a doctor, either to have a problem solved or for a general check-up. The message conveyed is thus that of an expert monopoly on the body. Magazines act as a bridge between the medical profession and those initially reluctant to consult them.

Health issues are also one of the favourite subjects of dramas, documentaries, films and soap operas. *Casualty* and *ER*, for example, are very popular television programmes, interweaving the lives of medical staff with incidents of health,

Table 5.1 Selling health in a public information campaign and advertising a commercial product

Public information campaign	Commercial marketing of a product
• The aim is to effect fundamental behavioural changes among a large section of the population	• The aim is to effect a small change in behaviour, such as brand-switching, among a section of the market
• The budget is likely to be limited	• The budget may be considerable
• Market research is likely to be limited	• Market research is likely to be detailed
• It may be perceived as unethical to oversell potential gains from following advice	• Exaggerated claims may be made, albeit within legal standards
• The rewards for acquiescence may not be immediate	• The rewards of consumption are perceived as being immediate

illness, accident and death. Much attention has been paid to how the health messages in these programmes are consumed by their viewers. Some analyses have shown that doctors are routinely portrayed in heroic ways whereas nurses are usually nurturing or sexy (Karpf, 1988; Turow, 1989). Bury and Gabe (1994), in contrast, argue that whereas the massive growth in media representations of health and medicine strengthens their influence over consumers, the portrayals are increasingly reflecting shifting and contested power relations.

Health and illness has also always been a powerful subject matter within literature. In recent years, there has been an upsurge in what has been dubbed confessional writing, in which authors explore and detail their encounters with illness.

Books (for example, Diamond, 1999; Moore, 1996; Picardie, 1998) have been assembled of the writings that authors have produced detailing the ways in which they have experienced their encounters with terminal illness. Other authors, such as Wurtzel in her book *Prozac Nation* (1996), have drawn upon their experience of depression and its treatment in such a way as to present the use of anti-depressant medication as a cultural phenomenon. Some see these books as a symbol of self-indulgence, others citing them as a powerful evocation of subjects previously treated as taboo.

Cultural studies, in its examination of the many manifestations of representations of health and illness within society, permits us to explore both the production and consumption of discourse and the generation of meaning. The discipline reveals the way in which health has a cultural currency.

> *Thinking about...*
>
> How do you regard the literature and filming of people's encounters with serious illness and death?

HEALTH AND ILLNESS ACROSS CULTURES

By grounding concepts of health and illness within culture, these concepts become culture specific. The experience of what constitutes health, illness and appropriate treatment will vary between cultures, so health must be understood from *within* cultures. The dominance of biomedicine within Western societies tends to suggest that health and illness are natural, universal phenomena. Understandings can vary both across and within cultures and societies:

- Different interest groups can be seen to share cultures
- Cultural frameworks of understanding may vary between ethnic groups, leading to differing concepts of health and illness.

Professional and lay views

Professional and non-professional groups construct ideas of health, illness and treatment differently. A visible manifestation of this is the massive growth in the number of self-help groups in the West, as discussed by Kelleher (1994). He identifies a variety of ways in which such groups operate, from being focused on members to adopting a more outwardly looking approach that seeks to heighten public awareness, raise funds and reposition specific medical conditions or social groups higher on the political agenda. Self-help groups also vary in their relationship to medical professionals: some operate hand in hand, others occupy a complementary role, and others are more directly challenging.

One recurring feature of self-help groups is their emphasis on the emotional experience of illness, which often lies in stark contrast to the purely clinical factors focused upon by medical professionals. This polarity between biological manifestation and the impact of illness on the sense of self and everyday life represents differing interpretations of the *meaning* of illness.

Medical professionals and lay people may also approach the control of illness differently. Kelleher's (1994) study of the British Diabetic Association found that diabetics who deviated from their prescribed diet were perceived as being non-compliant within the framework of a medical encounter. Yet within self-help groups, the difficulties of managing a dietary regimen and the strategies adopted to cope with this were perceived as positive ways of coping and self-regulation. Kelleher suggests that the fact that patients may rate other factors, such as their social obligations or employment, as being more important than medical compliance, represents a direct challenge to medical authority. Interpretations of illness and strategies for health maintenance thus reflect power struggles within cultures over the 'ownership' and definition of medical knowledge.

The views of different ethnic groups

Different ethnic groups may have varying understandings of health and illness. Members of an ethnic group will, however, not necessarily share a single culture. Research frequently seeks to render problematic the health behaviour of ethnic minorities, portraying the beliefs and practices of ethnic minority groups as flawed.

The following study shows how medical practitioners need to be sensitive to the various ways in which health and illness are interpreted by different ethnic groups. The study also shows how culture should not be separated from the wider social framework. Morgan (1996) researched the different meanings attached to the diagnosis of high blood pressure (hypertension) by white and African-Caribbean patients. Her study was carried out largely in response to concerns expressed by a GP relating to difficulties he experienced in communicating information about hypertension and its treatment regimen to his African-Caribbean patients, a group with a higher than average incidence of the condition.

Morgan found that African-Caribbean patients had a greater tendency not to take prescribed medication, often preferring to use the herbal remedies with which they were already familiar. This group found the commonness of this condition among family and friends to be a reassuring indication of normality, rather than seeing a high incidence as being illustrative of elevated risk. Among both groups, there was a relatively low level of awareness that hypertension and high blood pressure were one and the same thing, several respondents commenting that they understood hypertension to be a nervous condition relating to stress. This reiterates the fact that different groups may understand diseases differently, medical discourse providing forms of knowledge and language that are not universally shared by lay groups.

One factor that did vary between ethnic groups was that African-Caribbeans were more likely to identify strokes as a dangerous outcome, whereas white males highlighted heart conditions. Each group thus identified the risk to which it was most likely to be exposed. African-Caribbeans, however, tended to take a more fatalistic approach, which appeared to increase acceptance and reduce anxiety. Thus, whereas Morgan identifies some differences in perception relating to hypertension between white and African-Caribbean people, she also draws out a number of similarities that characterise lay understanding as opposed to medical interpretation.

While cultural studies as a discipline may not until recently have focused to a great degree specifically on health, there are a vast number of studies of health and culture that have sought to explain 'bad' health and health behaviours in a simplistic manner as a result of culture. What cultural studies can contribute to this debate is a challenge to such notions, highlighting the interplay between culture, resistance, power and inequality within society.

THEORETICAL AND METHODOLOGICAL APPROACHES

Cultural studies is interdisciplinary and draws on a vast framework of knowledge and approaches, including sociology, media studies, philosophy, literature, anthropology and the visual arts. Its outlook is above all that from a *critical* perspective. Cultural studies challenges the boundaries, status and concerns of many more rigidly defined fields of study. Thus, cultural studies can perhaps best be thought of as a 'cross-disciplinary and anti-disciplinary field as well as an intellectual movement' (Alasuutari et al., 1998). It is in some ways perhaps most easily characterised by its preoccupations, which centre around culture and meaning, and the complex power relations that shape them.

Many writers make a different claim for the origins of cultural studies. It has been variously traced back to Victorian observers such as Booth and Mayhew, to early US sociologists (Jenks, 1993) or, less traditionally, to the work in the 1970s of the Kamiriithu Community Education and Cultural Centre in Kenya (Wright,

1998). However, most accounts of the development of cultural studies cite the influence of three seminal figures and their works: Raymond Williams' *Culture and Society* (1961), E.P. Thompson's *The Making of the English Working Class* (1978/1963) and Richard Hoggart's *The Uses of Literacy* (1958) (Hall, 1980b).

These authors, while divergent in their approaches and concerns, were notable for identifying and celebrating working-class culture, thus rejecting the premium placed on 'high' at the expense of 'low' culture. Hoggart became the first director of the Birmingham Centre for Contemporary Cultural Studies, later being succeeded by Stuart Hall. The Centre is often credited as the academic grouping that consolidated the identity of cultural studies, providing the cohesion that supplied the impetus for growth and expansion within universities across the world.

In theoretical terms, the emergent feature in the works of writers such as Hoggart and Williams was that culture began to be seen as a social feature that could not be reduced solely to a materialist base. This signalled a theoretical shift away from more classical Marxist approaches, which saw the whole of social life as a product of the economic structure. Within classical Marxism, social relations, and hence culture, derive from the need to maintain and legitimate the status quo. It is here that the concept of *ideology* becomes central. An ideology can be understood as a system of ideas that seeks to explain the world and how it is ordered. From the classical Marxist perspective, ideological beliefs are often false: they serve to obscure the realisation that society ultimately works in the best interests of the dominant classes.

CONNECTIONS

Chapter 4 (Sociology) discusses Marxism in more detail

EXAMPLE 5.2

Food as culture

food is never 'just food' and its significance can never be purely nutritional. Furthermore, it is intimately bound up with social relations, including those of power, of inclusion and exclusion, as well as cultural ideas about classification (including food and non-food, the edible and the inedible), the human body and the meaning of health. (Caplan, 1997)

The nature of the food we eat can be linked to capitalist processes. Mintz (1997) has traced the phenomenal growth in the use of sugar, identifying its links to imperialism and the growth of capitalism. Sugar comes principally from areas such as the West Indies. The plantations, established on the back of slavery, fuelled capitalist expansion. They both produced goods such as sugar for sale in Europe, generating much profit for their owners, and bought goods from Europe that were required in the setting up and running of the plantations. Sugar rapidly became established as a staple food even though it has little nutritional value. Mintz argues that it provided a quick source of energy for the poor, describing it as a 'proletarian hunger-killer' and a 'drug-food'. As more and more people began to work outside the home in the wake of industrialisation, their diet changed to include food that required less preparation and gave more stimulation.

One of the most powerful ways in which food is intertwined with culture is through the family. The rise in family diversity, brought about through many factors, including a higher divorce rate, cohabitation, lone parenthood and same-sex relationships, has led many to decry the demise of the 'traditional' family: the nuclear, patriarchal model. One way in which this social anxiety is reflected is through the concern that the family meal, in which the whole family sits down to eat together, is under threat. Murcott (1997) argues that the notion that families always ate together in the past is an idealised one: upper-class families, for example, tended to separate adults and children, so that children would eat either in the nursery or at boarding schools away from home. Murcott traces concerns about the decline in the family meal to the earlier part of the 20th century, arguing that this is a recurrent metaphor for the state of the family.

The shared meal has come to signify the ideal family. Symbolic meals, such as Sunday dinner, acquire great importance. The roles that family members take within this meal communicate their subject position. In the UK, the husband carves the meat, displaying his authority and role as provider. The woman is placed in the subject position of wife and mother by cooking a meal, while the children are placed as dependants, the grateful recipients of their parents' care. This family ideal is so widely held that it remains the dominant model. However, it faces continual challenges from the growth in family diversity, so it must try to reassert itself through rituals such as meals.

Food may be divided into categories such as sweet and sour, fresh and decayed, moistened and burned (Lévi-Strauss, 1970). In a similar vein, Douglas (1997) argues that food can be divided into meals versus drinks, or solids versus liquids. She states that both need to be seen as social events. The way in which meals and drinks are used in social settings signifies our relationships:

> Drinks are for strangers, acquaintances, workmen and family. Meals are for family, close friends, honored guests. The grand operator of the system is the line between intimacy and distance. Those we know at meals we also know at drinks. The meal expresses close friendship. Those we only know at drinks we know less intimately. (Douglas, 1997)

Food has traditionally been used as a marker of cultural identity: 'Simple equations such as "we eat meat, they don't", "we eat horse, they don't", "they eat insects, we don't", affirm, in shared patterns of consumption and shared notions of edibility, our difference from others' (James, 1997). Thus, notions of what comprises British food can be seen as ways of identifying and placing oneself in the world, just as we may categorise ourselves as members of communities or workplaces.

However, just as some of these traditional sources of identity begin to break down into multiple possibilities, so British food has become subject to tremendous diversity. We now regularly eat pizza, lasagne, chicken tikka, chilli or chow mein in conjunction with a vast variety of fruit, vegetables or cheeses from all over the world. It would appear that we are moving towards a greater cultural diversity. James points out that a new trend is occurring in British eating habits, namely 'food Creolisation', in which hybrid dishes evolve. However, class differences in the type of food eaten persist, the middle and upper classes tending to shun Creolisation in favour of authentic cooking, either British or foreign. Similarly, the British preoccupation with food as an easily prepared necessity continues. Here we see that food is intimately related to identity and social relations rather than purely nutrition.

Sources: Caplan, 1997; Douglas, 1997; James, 1997; Lévi-Strauss, 1970; Mintz, 1997; Murcott, 1997

Marxist analyses of the social structure remain a strong, if contested, influence upon many writers within cultural studies. Few, however, now subscribe to the idea that all the features, beliefs and ideologies of a society are determined by its mode of production, or economic organisation. This shift away from reductionism is in part derived from the influence of the work of writers such as Althusser and Gramsci.

Althusser (1971) theorised that ideologies and cultures could be seen as having relative autonomy from the economic superstructure, and that all classes participated in the promotion and processes of ideology rather than the dominant class imposing beliefs upon others. Turner (1992) states that cultural studies draws upon Althusser's view that 'key "ideological" apparatuses (the law, the family, the education system, for instance) are every bit as significant as economic conditions'. One of the most pervasive mechanisms of ideology is that of interpellation, also referred to as hailing. This concept refers to the fact that we are continuously placed in our subject positions, such as mothers, older people or patients, by the way in which we are addressed within different forms of communication.

 In what ways are people hailed or reaffirmed as patients within the health care system?

Doctor–patient relationships serve to reinforce the power of the medical professional over the lay person. The use of professional titles, coupled with the use of symbolic clothing such as white coats, serves to confirm the power of the expert. Thus, while this form of ideological practice and perpetuation is more subtle than Marx's concept of oppression, it still involves the collusion of all subjects in ideological dominance.

Gramsci (1971) suggests that for ideologies to become dominant (or hegemonic), they must continually struggle to reassert themselves through winning the consent of both individuals and institutions. When a system of beliefs becomes dominant, this is often achieved by such a high degree of consent that the beliefs become naturalised. The most powerful set of ideas are those which deny their ideological quality by portraying themselves as natural and 'true'. Thus, the biomedical model of health could be described as hegemonic in that it has become so firmly established that we see it as objective and rooted in the natural realm of biology.

Given cultural studies' critical and anti-disciplinary stance, it is perhaps not surprising that it has often come under attack. One often-heard criticism relates to its frequent lack of methodological explicitness and rigour. This criticism has been voiced from both outside and within the field. As cultural studies develops, however, a series of commentators have begun to address this issue (see, for example, McGuigan, 1997).

Given the eclectic, multidisciplinary nature of cultural studies, it inevitably makes use of a wide range of methodologies that originate in a range of different academic fields. Alasuutari (1995) states that: 'Cultural studies methodology has often been described by the concept of *bricolage*: one is pragmatic and strategic in choosing and applying different methods and practices.' In theory, then, all methodologies are appropriate for use. However, given the emphasis that cultural studies places on *meaning*, it tends, maybe unsurprisingly, to focus primarily on qualitative approaches. These approaches can perhaps best be conceived as forming a broad spectrum, ranging from those which focus on people as the direct source of information to those which study texts.

Methods that centre around people may include or combine different forms of observational studies, types of direct questioning such as semi-structured interviewing or less formal means such as the use of narratives or life histories. At the other end of the spectrum, there is the direct study of cultural artefacts or texts. A text can be any cultural product. It can thus include television, film, newspapers, broadcasts, advertisements, pictures or architecture – in fact, any cultural object or feature can be analysed for the meanings it contains. Along the spectrum lie a variety of methodologies that incorporate a range of techniques.

ETHNOGRAPHY

The use of *ethnography* in cultural studies derives principally from anthropology. It stems from the fieldwork tradition in which researchers immerse themselves in the group or community being studied in order to understand its culture from within. Many methods may be employed in the search for understanding, including interviewing, observation and informal conversations. Data may be noted in a number of ways, such as using tape-recordings, but the principal method of collection is through the use of the researcher's notes and observations recorded in a fieldwork diary. One of the aims of ethnography is often termed, following Geertz's influential work (1973), 'thick description'.

ethnography – the study of a society by immersing oneself within it

Two issues immediately become apparent with this method of research. First, there is an ethical question. Observation may be overt or covert. The latter approach seeks to avoid 'contaminating' findings, which may occur if the research subjects know that they are being observed. This method can, however, be characterised as exploitative. Given the time-consuming nature of an extended period of fieldwork, there is also the danger that the findings may in practice be based on sketchy or sporadic observations, a tendency characterised by Murdock (1997) as 'thin descriptions'.

Second, however fully the researchers immerse themselves within the group, there will inevitably be an element of subjective interpretation. In attempting to understand any culture and its practices, the researchers' interpretation will be shaped by their own cultural location. Many critiques of an earlier, more confident and authoritative ethnography have come from feminist writers who have challenged the notion of the traditional research hierarchy by which subjects become objectified (Atkinson and Coffey, 1995). Feminist researchers have been at the forefront of the cultural studies goal of enabling the voice of marginalised groups to be heard; ethnography can be a valuable method in this cause.

EXAMPLE 5.3

Cultural concepts of health

Adelson's study of health beliefs among the Cree of Whapmagoostui in Northern Quebec clearly illustrates the fact that concepts of health must be understood as cultural. She characterises her research as participant observation, including interviews with over 20 per cent of the adults in the community, which took place over a two-year period. Adelson found that there was no direct translation of the term 'health'; the term used by the Cree translates most closely as 'being alive well'. This concept is closely bound to the Cree's specific socio-cultural context:

> 'being alive well' is defined through local beliefs and practices, simultaneously incorporating references to an idealised past and consolidating issues of cultural identity such that contemporary ideals and practices of health are bound to and defined through a history of colonial and post-colonial influences. 'Being alive well' is inseparable from community, history, identity, and ultimately resistance. (Adelson, 1998)

The history of the Cree village studied is one of contact with prospectors, hunters and traders. As for many indigenous people exposed to outside groups, this contact both altered the traditional way of life and introduced new diseases. The community was transformed by contact, modernisation and cultural exchange. In 1989, the community was mobilised by its opposition to a proposal by the Quebec provincial government to initiate a hydroelectric project that would have had an immense impact on the local environment. Although they were successful in their opposition, they face continual challenges in the face of sovereignty disputes. The specific history and conditions of the Cree form a vital context in understanding concepts of health.

The concept of 'being alive well' is distinct from Western biomedical constructions of health. It is possible to be unwell in the Western sense of the word yet still to be in a state of 'being alive well'. This is because the concept of 'being alive well' is located in elements other than pure physiology. It relates more to a way of life associated with practices such as carrying out physical activity, keeping warm and eating traditional Cree foods, which reflects the people's strong relationship with the land and its preservation. The vigour of the land and the Cree themselves is associated with an idealised past, even though life was often very hard, which existed before the 'whiteman' came. The customs and conditions introduced by the 'whiteman' are seen as weakening the sense in which the Cree can 'be alive well'. This study illustrates the ways in which groups can be studied by ethnographic methods in order to bring cultural practices and beliefs alive. Health in this example is both a product of socio-cultural conditions and a marker of cultural identity.

Source: Adelson, 1998

DISCOURSE AND CONVERSATION ANALYSIS

Broadly speaking, a discourse is a series of terms, values, symbols and words that gather about a topic or group. Discourses are permeated and shaped by cultural and ideological connotations. Discourse analysis in the linguistic sense involves analysing patterns and structures of talk in order to reveal the forms and constraints of social interaction. Within this broad approach, the term 'conversation analysis' is often used more narrowly to describe a specific methodology for analysing how language shapes the discussion of two or more parties.

Conversation analysis permits us to go beyond an examination of the content of a conversation or interview in order to examine how both parties interact and construct their subject positions. Any conversation can be analysed for the incidence of patterned regularities of speech that allow the participants to position themselves in relation to one another. We can, for example, examine how men and women talk to one another, how couples structure a narrative when they are relating an event, and how medical consultations establish the relative social positions of doctor and patient. A crucial element of this approach is that it is only the conversation that is subjected to analysis: all other forms of context or background must be excluded. To this end, transcriptions of conversations for the purposes of analysis follow very detailed rules. All speech must be reproduced verbatim, pauses timed to within a tenth of a second, and the points at which interruptions and responses occur precisely noted.

At the heart of conversation analysis is the recognition that conversations tend to follow certain rules. At a basic level, this comprises turn-taking, that is, the way in which participants negotiate the order of utterances. One important feature is that of pairs of utterances, for example question – answer, invitation – acceptance/refusal. Subverting these implicit rules may result in a call for justification or explanation (Alasuutari, 1995). There can also, however, be a significant difference between the type of conversation. An everyday discussion may have different properties from 'institutional talk' such as meetings or lay person–expert interactions. Conversation analysis, then, reveals how structures of power within society operate through the formal, if often unacknowledged, rules of speech engagement. While conversation analysis is a rigorous approach with a carefully detailed focus, it is also possible to combine its insights with a knowledge of broader cultural patterns and relationships.

Ten Have (1991) argues that such talk is asymmetrical and reflects a hierarchical organisation of speech interaction. This is in part the result of inherent power imbalances between the lay person and medical expert. In addition, the talk itself actively produces asymmetry. First, the patient's, rather than the doctor's, problems are the focus. Second, the carrying out of the tasks of the encounter (complaint presentation, examination, diagnosis and treatment) is dominated by the doctor. Ten Have discusses a number of ways in which this asymmetry becomes manifest in talk. For example, the process by which doctors elicit information from patients frames their replies within the structure of questioning, which is often designed to produce brief answers. Patients are not encouraged simply to narrate an account of their illness. Doctors also display their control by questioning without context or justification: they are not required to explain the reasoning behind their questions. Doctors' noncommittal replies reveal nothing of their reaction to responses. Thus, ten Have states that asymmetry is produced by the doctors' role as initiators and by their control of the information they divulge.

> **Thinking about...**
>
> Recall a recent medical encounter that you have had. How was the talking that took place organised and managed?

SEMIOTICS

Semiotics (or semiology) focuses on the study of *signs* contained within texts. Signs are comprised of two components:

> **semiotics** – the analysis of signs contained within cultural texts

- signifiers, which are sounds, words or images
- the signified, which are the concepts represented by signifiers.

Thus a photograph of someone with a stethoscope around her neck (the signifier) would suggest the concept of medical power (the signified). Meaning emerges from the relationship between the signifier and the signified.

Consider well-known advertisements such as that for Marlboro cigarettes. The Marlboro man was depicted as a cowboy riding a horse in open landscape. What is signified by this image?

The Marlboro man immediately brings forth ideas of the Wild West, freedom, masculinity and independence. These images successfully made consumers and potential consumers perceive Marlboro to be a man's cigarette. By contrast, cigarettes such as Kim or Silk Cut, aimed at female consumers, emphasised the 'lightness' or mildness of the cigarette.

When we are part of a culture, we learn and internalise complex and shifting patterns of associations, which can be termed 'codes'. Thus, we develop a way of making sense of the world in which we learn to read off meanings and associations from signs within everyday life. This is not necessarily something we carry out consciously: the process may become instinctive and automatic. However, as these relationships and associations are dynamic and changing, not everyone will work with the same system of codes or understand codes in the same way. This can lead to what has been termed 'aberrant coding': a mismatch of meaning between those who produce cultural artefacts and those who receive them. Thus, a public health message, for example, may fail because its makers use terms or images that do not conjure up the same pattern of associations in the minds of its target group.

EXAMPLE 5.4

Text analysis: *The Silent Scream*

An example of how texts can be deconstructed in order to reveal their cultural meanings can be found in an analysis of the anti-abortion film *The Silent Scream*, which was shown extensively on American television in the mid-1980s. The film, designed to campaign against abortion, seems to have originated in an article in a medical journal by Fletcher and Evans (1983), which suggested, albeit on very limited evidence, that ultrasound images of foetuses could promote maternal bonding and hence reduce requests for termination. *The Silent Scream* was produced in video format and was designed not only for television viewing, but also to be purchased or rented by schools, churches and anyone who wished to view it. The film represents an ultrasound imaging of an abortion being carried out at 12 weeks, with narration provided by Dr Bernard Nathanson. It contains a complex web of imaging, which, it has been argued, needs to be understood as two simultaneous texts: 'a medical text, largely visual, and a moral text, largely verbal and auditory' (Petchesky, 1987).

The visual text centres on hazy ultrasound images of the foetus and operating table, which are portrayed alongside 'teaching' shots of clinical models of a developing foetus. A suction cannula moves towards the foetus, which appears to make some movements, including moving its head backwards. Threaded throughout the film is the image of Nathanson appearing as the narrator, his medical credentials and professional appearance signifying authority. The auditory text consists of music and narrative. Nathanson characterises the foetus as a 'victim' against a soundtrack of organ music that is used to signify a sense of foreboding. The narrative accompanying these images has been likened to a 'medieval morality play'. The suction cannula is described as a 'lethal weapon' that will 'tear the child apart' until only 'shards' are left. The foetus' movements are described as being attempts to get away, only finally to rear back its head in a silent scream.

The interpretation of both the visual imaging and the soundtrack is highly controversial and contested. These include claims that: 12-week foetuses cannot experience pain as they have not yet developed a cerebral cortex; a scream is not possible if there is no air present; movement is the result of reflexes rather than intention; the speed of the film appears to have been altered to suggest rapid movement; and the image is enlarged to imply that the foetus is twice its real size. Yet the use of ultrasound imaging is used to signify incontrovertible scientific authority. Petchesky argues that it is what the film is intended to signify, as a cultural artefact, that is of most importance. The film acquires credibility from its links to the stock of visual images of the foetus that have appeared in Western culture over the preceding years. These links to other texts can be termed inter-textual: meaning is acquired as part of a referential, cumulative process.

The image of the foetus resonates with the cultural significance of photography, which endows pictures with simultaneous truth and mythic properties, yet any photograph can only ever be a selective representation. Foetuses are commonly represented as solitary, autonomous beings, no reference being made to the women's bodies within which they are carried. The images in *The Silent Scream* are characterised as being from the foetus' point of view, yet they represent the camera's gaze.

Sources: Fletcher and Evans, 1983; Petchesky, 1987

CASE STUDY – REPRODUCTIVE TECHNOLOGY

This chapter has examined a number of ways in which health can be understood as a cultural phenomenon. This case study focuses on reproduction as an example of how culture permeates experiences that are firmly constructed as natural and biological within our society. While most societies identify childbirth as a highly significant event, frequently conceptualised as a rite of passage, the web of practices – and hence meanings – that surround it is culturally specific.

Technology and reproduction have become increasingly intertwined, although their relationship is an uneasy and frequently contested one. Much feminist literature has focused on the way in which birth has become a primarily clinical episode, characterised by the passivity of women in the face of the ultimate control over the process wielded by the medical profession (Oakley, 1993). Lupton (1994) argues that the history of the medical profession's involvement in childbirth is one of male usurpation. From around the end of the 17th century, the male-dominated medical profession increasingly took over the responsibility for assisting and regulating childbirth from female midwives. This was, to a large extent, facilitated by the use of technology, ranging from the introduction of forceps, to surgical procedures and present-day foetal monitoring. The portrayal of childbirth as a site of risk and danger requiring high-tech intervention legitimated its appropriation by experts.

Technology's involvement in reproduction is, however, extending. It shapes the process of childbirth and infiltrates the womb of the expectant mother via the distinctive imaging and representation of ultrasound and new reproductive technologies being harnessed to effect conception itself. Many techniques, including in vitro fertilisation, artificial insemination by donor and gamete intrafallopian tube transfer, come under this heading.

While these technologies may at first glance seem to dramatically enhance a woman's range of reproductive strategies, they remain controversial. Although they are often seen as a triumph of science over nature, their success rate is still low. Even though the incidence of a positive outcome is rising, most couples will be unsuccessful (Foster, 1995). The processes can often be costly, painful and intrusive, with no guarantee of becoming a parent. Given these drawbacks, it may seem surprising that women and their partners are willing to undergo such treatment. Seeing reproduction and technology as cultural processes can perhaps begin to illuminate these issues. In order to examine this topic in more depth, we will look at new reproductive technologies from within the five cultural processes identified earlier: representation, identity, production, consumption and regulation.

Representation

Franklin's (1997) study of couples undergoing assisted conception involved analysing representations in the popular media throughout the 1980s and 90s. She found that many of the accounts were very formulaic. The key image of couples embarking on the process was that of being desperate; science is seen as offering hope to those whose courage and desire motivates them to seek techno-logical help. A range of literature, from legislation to medical textbooks, empha-sises the sense of exclusion that may result from being unable to fulfil one's social role. Infertility is characterised as a tragic state, an interruption of one's social progress, a thwart to the natural drives of parenthood. Successful conceptions and pregnancies are often described as miracles, using religious imagery to describe the process of being allowed to be normal and fulfilled. Thus technology is represented not as the antithesis to nature but as its handmaiden.

Identity

The process of conceiving and bearing children is, in our culture, inextricably linked with the expression of femininity. Motherhood is an idealised institution celebrated in myriad ways, from social policies, to merchandising in the form of Mother's Day cards, to iconic representations of mothers in advertising. While men may not be subject to quite the same pressure to have children, fatherhood is still seen as an important role. Being unable to father children may be an affront to received ideas of masculinity, as reflected in derogatory expressions such as 'shooting blanks' to refer to men who are infertile, or panic about the declining sperm count among the male population.

Representations are therefore linked to identities. The identity of parent-hood, particularly motherhood, is one that is prized as a social status. To be denied this identity can be a terrible blow to one's sense of self. To display the willingness to undergo expensive and degrading treatments in order to attain parenthood is not only a means of establishing a valued identity, but also enables one to deflect the charge of selfishness that is often levelled at those who choose to remain childless.

Production

Immediate links can be made between assisted conception and production: new reproductive technologies are services to be purchased in order to secure the product of a baby. The rationing of health care has become more explicit, and health authorities decide which treatments will be available for their populations. Infertility treatment is not routinely provided. As a consequence, the help of reproductive technologies often has to be secured at personal expense. As Foster (1995) notes, health care is an *industry*. Services are designed to speak to the identities to which individuals aspire. Franklin (1997) argues that reproduction becomes perceived as a technological and professionalised commodity. Undergoing the treatment, which can be traumatic, is represented as heroic in order to overcome its potential unpalatability as an experience that must be paid for.

Consumption

Franklin (1997) argues that the decisions of childless couples to purchase reproductive technologies need to be understood against a cultural backdrop of consumerism in a broader sense. The ideologies of the market, self-reliance, consumption and the promotion of choice have been seen as the antidote to the perceived evils of welfare dependency and economic stagnation. Within this context, the ability to reproduce becomes something that can be chosen and purchased if necessary. Couples are consuming not only a health care product, but also the dream of a way of life that has great cultural meaning:

> As self-reliant individuals, seeking to extend conjugality into family and home-ownership, they express a desire for social achievement through biological reproduction. Assisted conception, in these representations, precisely reproduces the core analogies of English kinship, just as it also fulfils the promise of the enterprise culture in the form of widened consumer choice through market deregulation and expansion. (Franklin, 1997)

Regulation

The regulation of the use of new reproductive technologies reveals interesting relationships between nature and culture. All medical interventions are designed to effect changes in the body; hence all can in one respect be termed 'unnatural'. However, being unnatural is a label that is usually only applied to assisted conception when parents, particularly mothers, fall outside the category that society considers normal. There is thus great disquiet when parents regarded as in some way unconventional have a child with the assistance of technology. Doyal (1995) points out that women who are lesbian, single or considered too old are likely to have a problem obtaining treatment. Recent media stories, for example, have expressed outrage at a woman who gave birth in her fifties and at a woman whose child was dubbed a 'virgin birth' as her mother had never previously had intercourse.

Here we see conflicting discourses of motherhood. On the one hand, mothers have a high cultural status. Women are characterised as possessing a maternal instinct, which means that women who choose not to have children are seen as unnatural. On the other hand, women who choose to have children outside the parameters of acceptability are not praised for fulfilling their maternal instinct, instead being castigated as selfish deviants. Women are also meant to be motivated purely by altruism in matters concerning motherhood. Surrogate mothers are allowed to receive only expenses rather than payment for services, while their ability to surrender the child they have carried is viewed with deep suspicion. Similarly, while men may receive a fee for sperm donation, paying women for egg donation is seen as unethical in spite of the fact that it requires surgery. Thomas (1998) comments that:

> Increasingly complex ethical and social dilemmas are created by the fragmentation of motherhood into egg donor, carrying mother and social mother. This raises profound issues about the nature of kinship, the linking of the biological and social spheres and the management of knowledge of the origins of children resulting from assisted conception.

Technology has thus offered women and their partners the opportunity to fulfil the roles that we have dubbed natural within our culture. It also, however, offers the possibility of transgression, and it is this which shapes regulation.

In this brief case study of conception and reproduction, then, we can understand the insight that a cultural studies approach brings. Reproduction, while undeniably a biological event, is given meaning through the web of culture and practices by which we interpret its significance. The desire for children must be understood as taking on specific features within our society. It is intimately linked to constructions of femininity and the status of motherhood. It represents the social expression of marriage as a foundation of the social structure. It stands at the boundaries of nature and culture, science and technology acting as intermediaries. Achieving this dream echoes the discourse of consumerism.

To adopt a cultural perspective does not necessarily deny any role for biological 'facts' in our understanding of health and illness. It does, however, demonstrate that such facts cannot be experienced outside the cultural meanings we attach to them.

SUMMARY

- Health and illness are cultural concepts that convey social and cultural meanings
- The meanings of health and illness are actively produced by people, and meanings vary with social and cultural group norms
- The five key cultural processes of representation, identity, production, consumption and regulation can all be applied to health

- People tend to regulate themselves with regard to health through, for example, their take-up of vaccination, immunisation and screening services

- Modern notions of the body and sexuality are constructed through cultural practices and communications such as advertising, medicalisation and individualism

- There is no one grand narrative such as biology that explains health and illness, but instead many competing discourses.

QUESTIONS FOR FURTHER DISCUSSION

1. How might a cultural studies approach investigate the recent rise of eating disorders such as anorexia and bulimia among young women?

2. What arguments would you use to justify the inclusion of a cultural perspective in the study of health?

3. Alcohol, cigarettes and illegal drugs all pose health problems. How would a cultural perspective account for the different strategies used to address the excessive use of alcohol and cigarette smoking, as well as illegal drug use?

4. Gather a selection of advertisements for alcoholic drinks (in magazines or from television or billboards). How are these products being marketed? At whom are they targeted?

FURTHER READING

Alasuutari, P. (1995) *Researching Culture: Qualitative Method and Cultural Studies*. London: Sage.
A useful and comprehensive account of various methodologies.

Franklin, S. (1997) *Embodied Progress: A Cultural Account of Assisted Conception*. London: Routledge.
A fascinating study if you are interested in reading more about the case study of new reproductive technologies.

Helman, C. (1994) *Culture, Health and Illness*. Oxford: Butterworth Heinemann.
A clear account from the perspective of medical anthropology, which has a longer tradition of analysing health as a cultural phenomenon.

Lupton, D. (1994) *Medicine as Culture: Illness, Disease and the Body in Western Cultures*. London: Sage.
A very interesting text that takes a cultural perspective on health and medicine while drawing on a number of disciplines.

Turner, G. (1996) *British Cultural Studies: An Introduction*, 2nd edn. London: Routledge.
An accessible overview of the discipline and development of cultural studies.

REFERENCES

Adelson, N. (1998) Health beliefs and the politics of Cree well-being. *Health*, **2**(1): 5–22.
Ahmad, W.I.U. (1996) 'The trouble with culture', in Kelleher, D. and Hillier, S. (eds) *Researching Cultural Differences in Health*. London: Routledge, pp. 190–219.

Alasuutari, P. (1995) *Researching Culture: Qualitative Method and Cultural Studies.* London: Sage.

Alasuutari, P., Gray, A. and Hermes, J. (1998) Editorial. *European Journal of Cultural Studies*, **1**(1): 5–11.

Althusser, L. (1971) *Lenin and Philosophy and other Essays*, trans. B. Brewster. New York: Monthly Review Press.

Atkinson, P. and Coffey, A. (1995) 'Realism and its discontents: on the crisis of cultural representation in ethnographic texts', in Adam, B. and Allan, S. (eds) *Theorizing Culture: An Interdisciplinary Critique after Postmodernism*. London: UCL Press, pp. 41–57.

Bocock, R. (1993) *Consumption*. London: Routledge.

Bordo, S. (1987) *The Flight to Objectivity: Essays on Cartesianism and Culture*. Albany: SUNY Press.

Bordo, S. (1993) *Unbearable Weight. Feminism, Western Culture, and the Body*. Berkeley, CA: University of California Press.

Bray, A. (1996) The anorexic body: reading disorders. *Cultural Studies*, **10**(3): 413–29.

Bury, M. and Gabe, J. (1994) 'Television and medicine: medical dominance or trial by media?', in Gabe, J., Kelleher, D. and Williams, G. (eds) *Challenging Medicine*. London: Routledge, pp. 65–83.

Caplan, P. (1997) 'Approaches to food, health and identity', in Caplan, P. (ed.) *Food, Health and Identity*. London: Routledge, pp. 1–31.

Davis, K. (1997) 'Embody-ing theory: beyond modernist and postmodernist readings of the body', in Davis, K. (ed.) *Embodied Practices: Feminist Perspectives on the Body*. London: Sage, pp. 1–26.

de Saussure, F. (1960) *Course in General Linguistics* (trans. Wade Baskin). London: Peter Owen.

Diamond J (1999) *Because Cowards Get Cancer Too*. Vermillion.

DoH (Department of Health) (1999) *Viagra: NHS prescription proposals announced*. Press release 21 January. London: DoH.

Douglas, M. (1997) 'Deciphering a meal', in Counihan, C. and Van Esterik, P. (eds) *Food and Culture: A Reader*. London: Routledge, pp. 36–54.

Doyal, L. (1995) *What Makes Women Sick? Gender and the Political Economy of Health*. Basingstoke: Macmillan – now Palgrave.

Doyle, B. (1995) 'Changing the culture of cultural studies', in Adam, B. and Allan, S. (eds) *Theorizing Culture: An Interdisciplinary Critique after Postmodernism*. London: UCL Press, pp. 174–85.

du Gay, P., Hall, S., Janes, L., Mackay, H. and Negus, K. (1997) *Doing Cultural Studies: The Story of the Sony Walkman*. London: Sage.

Editorial (1998) Viagra's licence and the Internet. *Lancet*, **352**(9130): 751.

Fiske, J. (1990) *Introduction to Communication Studies*, 2nd edn. London: Routledge.

Fletcher, J.C. and Evans, M.I. (1983) Maternal bonding in early fetal ultrasound examinations. *New England Journal of Medicine*, **308**: 282–93.

Foster, P. (1995) *Women and the Health Care Industry: An Unhealthy Relationship?* Buckingham: Open University Press.

Foucault, M. (1975) *The Birth of the Clinic: An Archaeology of Medical Perception*. New York: Vintage Books.

Frank, A.W. (1990) Bringing bodies back in: a decade review. *Theory, Culture and Society*, **7**(1): 131–62.

Franklin, S. (1997) *Embodied Progress: A Cultural Account of Assisted Conception*. London: Routledge.

Geertz, C. (1973) *The Interpretation of Cultures: Selected Essays*. New York: Basic Books.

Giddens, A. (1991) *Modernity and Self-identity*. Cambridge: Polity Press.

Gramsci, A. (1971) *Selections from Prison Notebooks*. London: Lawrence & Wishart.

Hall, S. (1980a) 'Encoding/decoding', in Hall, S., Hobson, D., Lowe, A. and Willis, P. (eds) *Culture, Media, Language*. London: Hutchinson.

Hall, S. (1980b) Cultural studies: two paradigms. *Media, Culture and Society*, **2**: 57–72.

Hall, S. and du Gay, P. (eds) (1996) *Questions of Cultural Identity*. London: Sage.

Helman, C. (1994) *Culture, Health and Illness*, 3rd edn. Oxford: Butterworth Heinemann.

Hoggart, R. (1958) *The Uses of Literacy*. London: Penguin.

James, A. (1997) 'How British is British food?', in Caplan, P. (ed.) *Food, Health and Identity*. London: Routledge, pp. 71–86.

Jenks, C. (1993) *Culture*. London: Routledge.

Johnson, R. (1996) 'What is cultural studies anyway?', in Morley, D. and Chen, K-H. (eds) *Stuart Hall: Critical Dialogues in Cultural Studies*. London: Routledge.

Karpf, A. (1988) *Doctoring the Media: The Reporting of Health and Medicine*. London: Routledge.

Kelleher, D. (1994) 'Self-help groups and their relationship to medicine', in Gabe, J., Kelleher, D. and Williams, G. (eds) *Challenging Medicine*. London: Routledge, pp. 104–17.

Kitzinger, J. (1995) 'The face of AIDS', in Markova, I. and Farr, I. (eds) *Representations of Health, Illness and Handicap*. Geneva: Harwood Academic Publishers, pp. 49–66.

Laqueur, T. (1990) *Making Sex: Body and Gender from the Greeks to Freud*. Cambridge, MA: Harvard University Press.

Leslie, J. (1992) 'The significance of dress for the orthodox Hindu woman', in Barnes, R. and Eicher, J.B. (eds) *Dress and Gender: Making and Meaning*. Oxford: Berg Publishers, pp. 198–213.

Lévi-Strauss, C. (1970) *The Raw and the Cooked: Introduction to a Science of Mythology, I*. London: Jonathan Cape.

Lupton, D. (1994) *Medicine as Culture: Illness, Disease and the Body in Western Cultures*. London: Sage.

McGuigan, J. (ed.) (1997) *Cultural Methodologies*. London: Sage.

Mintz, S. (1997) 'Time, sugar and sweetness', in Counihan, C. and Van Esterik, P. (eds) *Food and Culture: A Reader*. London: Routledge, pp. 357–69.

Moore, O. (1996) *PWA*. Basingstoke: Macmillan – now Palgrave.

Murdock, G. (1997) 'Thin descriptions: questions of method in cultural analysis', in McGuigan, J. (ed.) *Cultural Methodologies*. London: Sage, pp. 178–92.

Morgan, M. (1996) 'The meanings of high blood pressure among Afro-Caribbean and white patients', in Kelleher, D. and Hillier, S. (eds) *Researching Cultural Differences in Health*. London: Routledge, pp. 11–37.

Murcott, A. (1997) 'Family meals – a thing of the past?', in Caplan, P. (ed.) *Food, Health and Identity*. London: Routledge, pp. 32–49.

Oakley, A. (1993) 'Birth as a 'normal' process', in Oakley, A. (ed.) *Essays on Women, Medicine and Health*. Edinburgh: Edinburgh University Press, pp. 124–38.

Oinas, E. (1998) Medicalisation by whom? Accounts of menstruation conveyed by young women and medical experts in medical advisory columns. *Sociology of Health and Illness*, **20**(1): 52–70.

Park, S.M. (1996) From sanitation to liberation?: the modern and postmodern marketing of menstrual products. *Journal of Popular Culture*, **30**(2): 149–67.

Petchesky, R.P. (1987) 'Foetal images: the power of visual images in the politics of reproduction', in Stanworth, M. (ed.) *Reproductive Technologies: Gender, Motherhood and Medicine*. Cambridge: Polity Press, pp. 57–80.

Petersen, A. (1998) Sexing the body: representations of sex differences in Gray's Anatomy, 1858 to the present. *Body and Society*, **4**(1): 1–15.

Picardie, R. (1998) *Before I Say Goodbye*. London: Penguin Books.

Soyland, J. (1997) 'Speaking the decorated body', in Yardley, L. (ed.) *Material Discourses of Health and Illness*. London: Routledge, pp. 217–31.

ten Have, P. (1991) 'Talk and institution: a reconsideration of the "asymmetry" of doctor–patient interaction', in Boden, D. and Zimmerman, D.H. (eds) *Talk and Social Structure*. Cambridge: Polity Press, pp. 138–63.

Thomas, H. (1998) 'Reproductive needs across the lifespan, in Doyal, L. (ed.) *Women and Health Services: An Agenda for Change*. Buckingham: Open University Press, pp. 39–53.

Thompson, E.P. (1978/1963) *The Making of the English Working Class*. London: Penguin.

Turner, B. (1992) *Regulating Bodies: Essays in Medical Sociology*. London: Routledge.

Turner, B.S. (1991) 'Recent developments in the theory of the body', in Featherstone, M., Hepworth, M. and Turner, B.S. (eds) *The Body: Social Process and Cultural Theory*. London: Sage, pp. 1–35.

Turow, J. (1989) *Playing Doctor: Television Storytelling and Medical Power*. New York: Oxford University Press.

Williams, R. (1961) *Culture and Society (1780–1950)*. Harmondsworth: Penguin.

Wright, H.K. (1998) Dare we de-centre Birmingham?: Troubling the 'origin' and trajectories of cultural studies. *European Journal of Cultural Studies*, **1**(1): 33–56.

Wurtzel, E. (1996) *Prozac Nation*. London: Quartet Books.

Social Policy

LIZ LLOYD

CONTENTS

Learning outcomes ●●●●●●●●●●●●●●●●●●●●●●●●●

This chapter will enable readers to:

● Understand the organisation and development of social policies
● Examine the process of social policy-making
● Understand the role of social policies in influencing health
● Assess the contribution of social policy to health studies.

OVERVIEW

The discipline of social policy examines how and why certain issues relating to people's welfare come to be seen as the legitimate focus of state intervention. Social policy also critically examines the consequences, both intended and unintended, of state intervention, regulation and legislation. The first part of the chapter considers the contribution of social policy to Health Studies. It looks at the historical development of social policies, including health policies, identifying key issues such as the extent of state involvement in the provision of welfare and the ways in which changing political ideologies have affected views on this. The second part considers the methods and analytical tools of the social policy discipline. It traces the development of social policy and examines some of the key theoretical and methodological approaches, with a particular focus on the relevance of these for Health Studies. It looks at the policy process, how certain issues become part of the policy agenda and how policies are negotiated, formulated and implemented. The third part is a case study of ageing and health that examines the issues raised earlier in the particular context of older age. Contemporary issues related to ageing and health are considered from the perspective of social policy.

INTRODUCTION

welfare – the conditions necessary to secure the well-being of individuals in any society

Social policy is the study of how the **welfare** of individuals is organised in any society, in particular of the role of the state in relation to the welfare of its citizens. The term 'social policy' is used in two senses. It sometimes refers to a particular kind of decision, such as that relating to education or health. It may also refer to the academic discipline that studies such policies. In order to avoid confusion, the term 'social policy' will in this chapter refer to the academic discipline; otherwise, the plural form, 'social policies' will be used.

The term 'social policies' is conventionally used to describe policy in relation to welfare benefits, unemployment, education, housing, health and social services. All these areas are related and also influenced by other government policies, such as those on transport and the environment, particularly economic policy. In Britain at the beginning of the 21st century, for example, a study of state intervention in health might reasonably include a focus on agricultural policy, given current concerns over the possible health effects of intensive farming methods.

The 20th century saw the development of state welfare and the establishment of a National Health Service in the UK. This has raised certain core questions, which are still relevant today:

1. What is the role of the state and how far should it be involved? Social policy is concerned with examining the ways in which policies and practices in welfare reflect and reinforce dominant values and norms in any society.

2. How should welfare be organised and funded, and how efficient and effective are welfare policies?

3. The normative nature of social policies gives rise to a number of other questions:

   ● How are contemporary social problems identified?
   ● In what circumstances should the state get involved in people's lives?
   ● Who benefits from social policies?
   ● What is the relationship between welfare and broader social divisions?
   ● Whose values do social policies reflect?
   ● What are the broader functions of social policies?

Social policy is therefore informed by ethics, economics and politics.

In other chapters in this book, we have discussed whether a health authority should pay for a child's treatment even if there is a low chance of success; whether NHS services should be based on users' views; and whether people should be forced through legislation and regulation to choose a healthier lifestyle. All these decisions are value judgements. The rising costs of the health service and the increasing demands of an ageing population and new technology provide a challenge to policy-makers. Continued spending on the health service is not just an economic decision but also a political one. The post-war consensus on the role of the welfare state has been challenged.

THE CONTRIBUTION OF SOCIAL POLICY TO HEALTH STUDIES

need – a socially constructed and highly contested concept related to want. It may be publicly expressed by individuals or groups, or be professionally defined (normative needs)

The area of social policy is concerned not just with what the state provides, but also with broader issues of entitlement and responsibility in society. The provision of health care depends on society's views about who is entitled to receive state support and at what level. A core concept is therefore that of **need**.

 How would you define need? Are different people or population groups more in need than others? How do you decide?

social justice – the concepts of rights and fairness in the distribution of resources

The concept of human need is basic to understanding human health and welfare, yet it is a problematic concept. Attempts to define human need have raised questions about whether and to what extent objective, universal standards of need can and should apply. Conversely, it is necessary to consider how historical, geographical and cultural variations on ideas of what constitutes human need can be explained (Doyal and Gough, 1991).

How any society sets about meeting human needs raises further problematic concepts, such as those of **social justice** and **equity**. These refer to criteria of

equity – fairness in treatment between individuals or groups in society. This may not be identical treatment – hence the difference between equality and equity – but may result in greater equality of outcome

fairness – of who 'ought' to get what when resources are being allocated. Criteria of fairness may take into account level of need or be based on some notion of 'deserts' or merit.

This, in turn, raises the question of whether welfare should be regarded as a right. In his classic text *Citizenship and Social Class and other Essays*, Marshall (1950) identifies social rights (as distinct from civil and political rights) as essential to **citizenship** and the full membership of any society. Social rights include economic security, a share in good living standards and cultural heritage. Thus, access to welfare was, for Marshall, a matter of citizen rights. However, the degree of security and the standard of living to which any individual citizen is entitled remain the subject of political and ideological argument. Moreover, how citizens' rights to welfare can be enforced is another difficult issue.

Where a welfare system embraces the idea of rights, how does that influence ideas about individual and social obligations and responsibilities? To what extent is meeting human needs the responsibility of families, communities or the state? Margaret Thatcher, UK Prime Minister in the 1980s, referred to the UK as a 'nanny state', by which she meant the welfare state had taken over functions that were more properly carried out by families, and had encouraged people to neglect their obligations. The concept of 'welfare dependency' was coined to describe those who were perceived to be content to rely on state benefits instead of seeking to provide for themselves.

Welfare systems are capable of enhancing or diminishing individual autonomy. For example, a basic principle of community care policies was that individual needs should be recognised and met in ways that enhanced the individuality and autonomy of service users, in contrast to institutionalised forms of care.

citizenship – the possession of civil, political and legal rights (for example free speech and voting). In social policy, the possession of social rights (for example to economic security) is also regarded as a precondition to citizenship

THE ORGANISATION OF WELFARE

 What do you understand by the term 'welfare'? Whose responsibility is the welfare of others?

There are different views about responsibility for the provision of social welfare. Many people immediately think that the state should provide for the needy. Titmuss (1974) first showed that welfare may be provided by government, by employers or through taxation. The term 'welfare state' is something of a misnomer, however, since there are many different providers of individual welfare. Welfare can be understood as a system that now comprises five main spheres of activity:

- the state
- informal welfare
- the private sector
- the voluntary sector
- occupational welfare.

Consider the example of Alice James, who is 80 years old. She lives alone and has recently had a fractured hip requiring hospital treatment. She has been

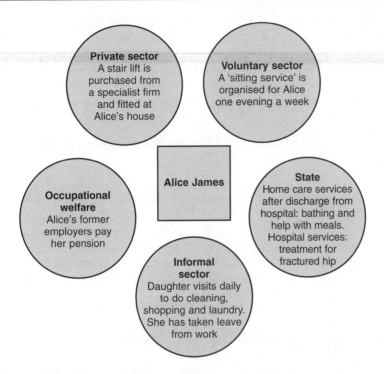

Figure 6.1   Spheres of welfare: the mixed economy

discharged from hospital and has returned home. All five spheres of welfare can be seen to contribute to her welfare.

Figure 6.1 illustrates how these spheres of welfare apply in the case of this one individual, Alice James. These spheres of activity are not clearly definable and separate sectors: there is considerable overlap between them, and the relationship between the sectors is an important area for analysis in social policy. In the case of Alice, for example, her ability to remain at home is likely to depend on services being provided on a more long-term basis in order for her daughter to return to work. However, unless Alice has access to her own financial resources and is able to purchase these for herself, she will be dependent on the state (the local social services department) for help. Of course, if her daughter decides to give up work to care for Alice James, her own financial security in old age is likely to be affected as her contributions to an occupational pension scheme will be stopped. Without the informal care provided by her daughter, Alice will not be able to remain at home. The extent and importance of informal care, which is domestic and private, is often underestimated by the formal sector.

There are many obvious ways in which people benefit from welfare, for example through the receipt of benefits, education and NHS services. It is common to think that people living on the lowest incomes benefit the most from welfare, yet much welfare spending benefits better off people most. Titmuss (1987), for example, describes occupational pensions as the 'concealed multiplier of occupational success' which benefit the middle classes.

The state has a fluctuating relationship with all other sectors in the organisation and management of people's welfare. Take, for example, its regulatory role.

Thinking about...

Consider from your own experience how the different sectors of welfare apply to yourself or to members of your family

In the private sector it has taken on responsibility for regulating tobacco advertising, in the voluntary sector it places controls on the way in which charities raise funds, while in the occupational sector it imposes rules on health and safety at work. State intervention in the informal sector is a highly contentious area. In cases of neglect or violence, intervention is widely accepted and, indeed, expected. At other times, however, the state's role is questioned.

? **Should the state provide financial recompense to carers?**

Financial recompense would be a recognition of the support provided by carers, but it might cloud the caring relationship and make it harder for carers to take on this role. The giving of time, money or expertise is a key element in the provision of welfare. While there is a concern that informal care provides core services that should be provided by the state, informal care is also promoted on the moral grounds that something other than the pursuit of financial gain should be a dominant force in society.

THE CHANGING ROLE OF THE STATE IN WELFARE

Although state activity in welfare involves planning, funding, regulating and providing services, its role has varied. Both values and organisational traditions have influenced the particular form of state welfare. This section outlines the changing roles of different welfare sectors and the socio-economic and political context of welfare.

State involvement in welfare goes back centuries. In 1601, during the reign of Elizabeth I, a Poor Law Act was passed that was intended to control and organise payments from parish funds to destitute people. In 1834, the Poor Law Amendment Act established the Victorian workhouses that became notorious for their treatment of the poor. Under the principle of 'less eligibility', conditions in the workhouses were intended to be harsh and punitive in order to deter people from asking for help. The 'workhouse test' ensured that anybody asking for help had no other means of looking after themselves or their families and that the state was their last resort.

In the late 19th century, the workhouse system was under a great deal of strain, unable to cope with the level of need but also more widely regarded as an unacceptable approach to providing welfare. Problems such as poverty, unemployment, infant mortality, ill health and poor housing conditions led to pressure for state action.

deserving poor – a term used in the 19th century to distinguish between the destitute entitled to state welfare (the deserving poor), and those who could support themselves but did not do so and who thus made claims on the state

Welfare services in the 19th century demonstrate how significantly different values apply in practice. For example, the Charity Organisation Society, which worked with families in poverty, maintained an individualistic approach. It was concerned with identifying '*deserving*' cases among the poor, distinguishing between the 'helpable' and the 'unhelpable'. From a different perspective, campaigners such as Charles Booth and Joseph Rowntree argued that poverty was the outcome of the economic and industrial system rather than of individual idleness or immorality and that social reforms were therefore needed.

In the early 20th century, the liberal government of the British Prime Minister Lloyd George introduced a series of measures, including the first retirement pension in 1908 and a limited health insurance scheme in 1911. After World War I, welfare schemes based on the principle of social insurance were developed. Individual contributions paid from wages into an insurance scheme entitled workers to claim benefits when they were unemployed, sick or retired.

? **Do the principles of 'proving eligibility' and 'social insurance' apply today?**

Both principles are still apparent today. Proving eligibility determines access to benefits such as family credit, which is paid once income has been proved to have fallen below a certain level. The principle of social insurance underpins occupational pensions, the amount paid by these being related to the level of previous contributions.

The early 20th century saw an increased role for the state in public health and sanitary reform. The realisation that epidemic diseases, spread through poor housing conditions and inadequate water and sewage services, affected all layers in society, including the middle classes, was an important factor in promoting and legitimating state intervention. The population as a whole could benefit from the state's increased involvement in public health policies.

> **CONNECTIONS**
>
> Chapter 2 (Epidemiology) and Chapter 10 (Health Promotion) outline the role of the state in public health

BRITAIN BECOMES A WELFARE STATE 1945–50

The post-war period (1945–50) saw the development of Britain's welfare system. The British model differs from that of most of Europe in its approach to social policy and is a distinctive example of a comprehensive and universal welfare system. It reflects the principles of the post-war period and the pragmatic influence of regeneration.

The basic principles underpinning the development of the welfare state in the 1940s were:

- *universalism*
- comprehensiveness
- *collectivism*.

In practice, these principles meant that every citizen should be included within the system of benefits and services, and that the range of services should cater for all their needs.

The principle of collectivism, demonstrated through the levying of taxes to pay for services, represented a major shift from the Victorian position on individual responsibility for welfare. When the National Assistance Act 1948 was passed, Aneurin Bevan, the then Minister of Health, proclaimed, 'At last we have buried the Poor Law'. Establishing welfare services on the basis of rights rather than charity was of fundamental importance at this time. The principle of reducing social and economic inequality was also important. The provision of free education and health care, for example, could be seen as a form of 'social wage' that would compensate for low wages and raise the standard of living of

universalism – benefits and services available to all within a society, regardless of ability to pay

collectivism – the general responsibility of all members of society to meet the needs of individuals, for example services funded through taxation

---

EXAMPLE 6.1

The Beveridge Report

William Beveridge was appointed by the wartime coalition government to review the range of insurance schemes that had developed since the turn of the century. The report he produced in 1942 (Beveridge, 1942) was a plan for a comprehensive reform of social polices in which health care would be universally available and funded from taxation. He identified what he considered to be the major social problems of the day, which he termed the 'Five giants stalking the land': want, ignorance, squalor, disease and idleness.

Beveridge's report formed the basis of the post-war Labour government's welfare state. Key policies included the Education Act 1944, the Family Allowances Act 1945, the National Health Service Act 1946, the National Insurance Act 1946 and the National Assistance Act 1948. These Acts established sickness and unemployment benefits, retirement pensions for men at 65 and women at 60, maternity benefits and widows' benefits. In addition, subsidies to local authorities enabled a programme of council house building, and full employment was made possible by the buoyant economy after the war. The five giants were tackled, albeit not destroyed.

Source: Beveridge, 1942

---

poorer people. Because resources for the new system came from income tax, there was a redistribution of resources from the better off to the poorer, thus reducing the overall economic inequality.

The effect of enlarging the sphere of activity of the state was not to abolish the private and voluntary sectors: private services continued in education, health and pension provision, for example. However, the state became the dominant player in the formal welfare system, the private and voluntary sectors occupying a more peripheral position. Influenced by the ideas of Marshall (1950), there was a widespread consensus across the political parties that a welfare state was desirable in the development of a civilised society.

The NHS established in 1948 was a classic example of the above principles. It was based on the following:

- Health care should be provided according to people's needs rather than their ability to pay. It should, therefore, be free at the point of delivery to ensure that people are not deterred from seeking help when they need it

- Health care should be collectively financed. Like other services developed in the welfare state, the health service should be financed from general taxation

- Health care should be comprehensive; that is, it should cover the whole range of people's health needs in one centrally planned service

- Health care should be universal. As a national service, it should be equally available to all sectors of the population and in all areas of the country. No group should be denied access

- The NHS should be concerned with reducing inequalities in health. The universal provision of a comprehensive service, free at the point of delivery, should reduce sickness and promote equality between the social classes.

In what ways have the principles of universalism, collectivism and comprehensiveness in the NHS been challenged?

Until the 1960s, Britain's welfare state was, alongside New Zealand and Sweden, one of the most developed in the world. The NHS has been financed through National Insurance and general taxation, but there has always been an excess of demand over supply. The assumption that improved health would lead to a reduction in demand for health care was shown to be wrong in the context of medical advances and raised public expectation. There is also concern that some areas and populations gain more from the NHS than others. For example, the debate over 'postcode prescribing', whereby, depending on area of residence, some groups receive NHS treatment for conditions such as infertility, whereas others have to seek private treatment for the same conditions, is of current concern. The recently established National Institute for Clinical Excellence (NICE) is intended to provide expert advice and guidance on what should and should not be provided by the NHS.

The principle of comprehensiveness has not been put fully into practice in the NHS. Consequently, there have always been contested areas, such as dentistry, optical services and chiropody, that are neither fully incorporated into the NHS nor fully privatised. The principle of universal provision has also proved difficult to achieve, regional variations in mortality and morbidity rate remaining a problem. Concern over equity in allocating resources for health led to the establishment in 1975 of the Resources Allocation Working Party. This group developed a formula for allocation based on a 'weighted capitation' basis. This meant that the amount of resources received by various regions was based on population size, adjusted for factors such as age, sex and mortality rate. There were serious difficulties in implementing this formula, especially in the regions that stood to lose out financially, but the formula remained in use until the late 1980s. It was important in reinforcing the principle that a difference in the level of health care should be addressed by the state, but its patchy implementation demonstrates the gap between principles and practice. This is a theme that is explored in the second part of this chapter.

The 1990 reforms to the NHS presented a new approach to the allocation of resources. The aim of the ***internal market*** was to facilitate the flow of funds for treatment. NHS districts were encouraged to trade with each other on a contractual basis, through which the funds followed the patients. There was less emphasis on calculating the amount allocated to the regions and more on encouraging competition between providers so that money would be provided for services rendered.

An expanding system of welfare had, however, little impact on social and health inequalities. In 1977, the Working Group on Inequalities in Health was set up to gather and analyse evidence of health inequalities and to assess the implications of this for policy. Their report (the Black Report, Townsend and Davidson, 1982) was published in 1980, but by then there had been a change of government, and the new Conservative government, led by Margaret Thatcher, largely ignored its findings.

internal market – the introduction of a commercial culture into health services in which different agencies (for example GP practices, hospitals and health authorities) seek to provide or purchase services in managed competition with the intention of increased efficiency

CONNECTIONS

Chapter 4 (Sociology) examines the evidence and explanations for health inequalities

CHALLENGING WELFARE 1980–97

The 1970s saw the end of economic expansion and full employment. Questions were raised about how much welfare could be afforded in times of economic difficulties, and services were cut back. In 1979, the Conservatives were elected to government, under the leadership of Margaret Thatcher. In their view, spending on welfare had gone beyond what the nation could afford. It was argued that the near monopoly position of the state had stifled entrepreneurial activity in welfare and created inefficient and unresponsive bureaucracies. The Conservatives' programme was to 'roll back the state' and stimulate the private market. In addition, it was argued that professional groups such as doctors, social workers and teachers were responsible for driving up the cost of welfare, as each sought to improve its status and extend its influence. An important aspect of Conservative policies was to develop controls over professional groups.

The challenge to state welfare from the political right was not simply based on economic arguments: there were also important ideological challenges. Welfare was characterised as having sapped the moral fibre of the nation and created a culture of dependency. Thatcher herself made references to 'the nanny state', implying that people had become complacent about their responsibility to provide for themselves because they could rely on the state to look after them. In other words, there should be an emphasis on individual responsibility and obligation rather than on rights.

In many ways, the NHS epitomised all that the Conservative government deplored in the welfare state. As they saw it, the NHS was a large and inefficient bureaucracy. Poor management systems had created funding problems, and professionals had too much power and autonomy. In addition, because the NHS was there, people had stopped taking responsibility for their own health or for looking after their own families. On the other hand, the NHS was (and remains) a highly popular institution with all classes of people, and the government had to take this into consideration.

During the 1980s, reforms of the NHS focused on promoting efficiency. Following the 1983 Griffiths Report (DHSS, 1983) into management in the NHS, attempts were made to create a more business-like culture through recruiting general managers, clarifying lines of accountability and improving productivity. Another strategy was to introduce competitive tendering for a range of ancillary services, such as laundry and catering. The government also stimulated private health care provision in order to challenge the monopoly position of the NHS and increase consumer choice.

By the late 1980s, a fundamental restructuring of the welfare state was underway. This was reflected in major changes in the health services. The scope and pace of reforms to the NHS increased dramatically after a government review in 1988. The government White Papers *Working for Patients* (Secretaries of State for Health, 1989) and *Caring for People* (Secretaries of State for Health et al., 1989) were published in 1989, leading to the NHS and Community Care Act 1990. Reforms to the NHS were implemented in 1991 and community care reforms in 1993.

After the 1990 Act, the NHS was reorganised, and the functions of purchasing and providing health care were separated, an arrangement that became known as the internal market:

CONNECTIONS

Chapter 7 (Organisation and Management) outlines the political, economic and social factors influencing the development of the NHS in Britain

Thinking about...

In your view, does the existence of a free health service take away people's willingness to 'look after themselves'?

CONNECTIONS

Chapter 7 (Organisation and Management) discusses the change in the NHS from an administered service to a managed one

- The large public hospitals became self-governing Trusts, whose business was to provide health care services
- Health authorities and fundholding GPs were given funds from the Department of Health (DoH) to purchase health care on behalf of their patients.

Reforms in community care occurred in parallel to those in the NHS after 1990. Local social services departments were designated as purchasers and required to develop a mixed economy of care at the operational, or provider, level. The reorganisation of community care was also intended to promote efficiency through stimulating competition in the private and voluntary sectors as well as through encouraging unpaid care in the community. As one government document put it at the time:

> The primary sources of support and care for elderly people are informal and voluntary. These spring from the personal ties of kinship, friendship and neighbourhood ...Care in the community must increasingly mean care by the community. (DHSS, 1981)

At the same time, care in the community had been a long-standing aim of those who wanted to see an end to large institutions for older and disabled people and those with mental health problems and learning difficulties. Community care was therefore regarded simultaneously as a liberating idea that would restore civil rights and dignity to these groups of people and a means of cutting the cost of welfare.

The internal market in the NHS reflects broader organisational changes that have become known as 'post-Fordist'. Basically, this involves a separation of organisations into strategic and operational sections:

1. The DoH sets overall strategic aims for the health service, and local health authorities must develop their purchasing plans within the guidelines set by central government. At the next level, health authorities develop local strategic plans and purchase health care from operational provider units. Purchasing involves a contractual relationship between purchaser and provider, and it is this relationship which ensures that the strategic aims of the health authority are carried out.

2. Providers need to secure contracts in order to survive and will therefore need to comply with the aims of the health authorities. The separation of purchasing and providing functions was intended to inject competition into the system to stimulate efficiency.

CONNECTIONS

Chapter 7 (Organisation and Management) examines the different theoretical perspectives on organisational management

Le Grand and Bartlett (1993) describe the NHS after 1990 as a 'quasi-market'. In any market, there has to be a commodity for sale and, in the post-1991 NHS, health care was treated as a commodity. The NHS was not, however, a market in the true sense of the word because it was still financed from taxation, and the health service remained in public ownership. Another term used to describe the 1990 reforms is 'managed competition', indicating that although there were to be business-like systems in place, the state remained in control of the overall strategy for health care.

Opinion is divided over whether the 1990 reforms to health services have actually brought about greater efficiency. It has been difficult to assess whether services are more efficiently run because the cost of the reorganisation itself was so great. In addition, there is now a greater number of managerial and administrative staff in the health service than there was prior to the reforms. The process of contracting has proved to be very expensive too. On the other hand, financial audits of health care have generated a greater awareness of the cost of health care, and professional groups are more cost conscious.

SOCIAL POLICIES FROM 1997

mixed economy of welfare – the provision of welfare through a mixture of state, private, voluntary and informal services. Sometimes referred to as welfare pluralism

The election of the New Labour government in 1997 introduced the notion of a 'third way', which draws on both the welfare system and the market approach. The *mixed economy* continues, and the government is committed to strict limits on public spending, but there is an apparent difference in terms of the value base of welfare. New Labour has, for example, developed 'social inclusion' policies, which, in theory at least, are concerned with the civic status of marginalised people, particularly those not in paid employment.

 In what ways could it be said that the UK government is reintroducing the original principles of the NHS?

The two White Papers (DoH, 1997, 1999a) signify a re-emergence of some of the original aims of the NHS, such as the commitment to a national service in which regional variations are removed and the commitment to reducing health inequalities. The Acheson Report, published in 1998 (Acheson, 1998), provided further evidence of continuing inequality in health and access to health care, and the government has committed itself to tackling these. The idea of clinical excellence is also linked to equality. Clinical standards, promoted through NICE, are established centrally so that regional variations are removed and geographical inequality addressed.

However, the 'third way' also holds on to some aspects of the internal market and Conservative policies. There is, for example, a strong emphasis on ensuring

Table 6.1   Changes to welfare from 1997 to the present

Key policy goals of the UK Labour government are embodied in two White Papers:

- *The New NHS: Modern, Dependable*, published in December 1997 (DoH, 1997)

- *Saving Lives: Our Healthier Nation*, published in July 1999 (DoH, 1999a)

These set out the following policies:

1. Primary Care Groups and Trusts will work with local authorities (including social services departments) in order to develop more integrated services

CONNECTIONS

Chapter 10 (Health Promotion) looks at the national strategy for public health

2. Health Improvement Programmes establish local strategies for implementing national targets for health and health care

3. Standards of professional practice are to be monitored through a new National Institute for Clinical Excellence

value for money. In addition, although the NHS continues to be funded through taxation, the Labour government is committed to continuing the Private Finance Initiative, through which private capital is invested in the NHS.

The focus on primary health care is maintained and enhanced through the development of Primary Care Groups. Primary Care Trusts take the reorganisation of primary care a stage further in that they begin to take on the purchasing functions of the health authorities. In theory at least, the development of Primary Care Trusts should mean that decision-making on health services is made at the local level, closer to the public who use the services.

> *Thinking about...*
>
> In your view, is it appropriate that new hospital building is carried out by private enterprise and 'leased' to the government for the NHS?

CURRENT HEALTH ISSUES ON THE SOCIAL POLICY AGENDA

The question of how health care should be funded and how comprehensive services should be continues to be a thorny problem for policy-makers. Public expectations of health services continue to rise as medicine develops new techniques and treatments to which the public demands fair and equitable access. In more recent years, this has become an issue for public debate, and it is likely to continue. Concerns have, for example, recently been raised about the level of availability of dental services in the NHS.

The needs of older people and others with chronic disorders have raised questions on what constitutes health care. In particular, problems remain concerning the boundary between health and social care. This is particularly acute for service providers and, more importantly, service users because health care is free at the point of delivery while social care is subject to charges. This issue impedes the development of integrated care. In Part III of this chapter the case study considers this issue in relation to health care for older people.

Rationing is not simply a consequence of the health service reforms of the 1990s, but is also a consequence of professional judgement. GPs make decisions

---

EXAMPLE 6.2

Analysing health care rationing: the case of Betaferon

In 1997, the results of a study by the King's Fund into the availability of the drug Betaferon were published (King's Fund, 1997). Betaferon is effective in alleviating the symptoms of multiple sclerosis: it is not a cure, but it can play an important role in the management of this chronic and degenerative disorder. Betaferon is, however, an expensive drug.

Evidence from the King's Fund research showed that health authorities in the North Thames Region varied considerably in their willingness to purchase Betaferon. Thus, some people with multiple sclerosis were prescribed the drug whereas those in a neighbouring health authority were not. The research also indicated that purchasers of health care felt pressurised into avoiding explicit rationing because of the damage that this might have on their relationship with local people. The latest advice from the National Institute for Clinical Excellence (NICE) is that, although Betaferon reduces the relapse rate by half, it does not halt or delay the progression of the disease. NICE therefore does not advocate the prescription of Betaferon for people with multiple sclerosis.

CONNECTIONS

Chapter 8 (Health Eco-
nomics) discusses
examples of setting pri-
orities and health care
rationing

A number of issues concerning welfare are raised by this example:

● The NHS was founded on the principle of equity, but rationing contributes to inequality

● A national service may vary at the local level

● Public perceptions of policies and practices need to be taken into account in understanding the policy process. How people experience policies in practice may not
accord with the way in which policies are presented.

Source: King's Fund, 1997

about which of their patients are referred for specialist services, such decisions
being influenced by a range of factors, including the doctor's own ideas, beliefs
and interpretation of need. Research on access to renal dialysis and other kidney
treatments, for example, demonstrates that older people are systematically
discriminated against through decisions not to refer them for specialist treatment (Allsop, 1995; New and Mays, 1997). Analysing the policy process also
enables us to understand the relationship between the process of individual
policies and the broader social environment, which reflects and reinforces
existing social inequalities.

Policy-making and implementation are part of a political process that is influenced by pragmatism and expediency (for example getting elected) as well as
ideology. This historical outline has shown how ideas concerning the role of the
state reflect views on the causes of social problems and the relative responsibilities of individuals, families and the state.

THEORETICAL AND METHODOLOGICAL APPROACHES

THE DEVELOPMENT OF THE DISCIPLINE

The discipline of social policy has, from the outset, been inextricably linked with
the processes of policy-making and practice in welfare provision. At the beginning of the 20th century, there was an upsurge of interest in the education and
training of occupational groups in public sector welfare services. Because there
were no texts written at the time, academic courses relied on casework records,
including those of the Charity Organisation Society, as sources of data. Other
sources included government statistics, census data and official reports.

Empirical research data, such as those produced by Booth (1902) and
Rowntree (1901) in the early 20th century, were also important to the development of the academic study of welfare. However, the intention of early
researchers such as Booth and Rowntree was that the data they produced
should not simply be available for study but also be a means of stimulating
government action to address social problems. This conceptual linkage in
social policy between academic work and action by the state was very influential in the development of welfare state policies in the Fabian society and
the Labour party in the early 20th century.

However, the idea of the welfare state had an increasingly broad appeal so that by the time the Beveridge Report was published in 1944, all the political parties were interested in developing welfare along broadly similar lines. By the 1950s, the term 'Butskellism' was coined as a description of the consensus that existed between the Conservative and Labour parties over welfare (after Rab Butler, a Conservative who became Chancellor of the Exchequer in 1951 following Labour's Hugh Gaitskell).

Not surprisingly, the period of intense political activity as the welfare state was established after World War II was reflected in academic circles. During the post-war years, the discipline of social administration flourished in British universities as the public sector expanded and more professional education was required. The broad consensus over the role of the state in developing welfare services was evident in the style and content of the discipline. It was generally concerned with the design and development of services that would deliver state welfare most effectively, largely informed by professional ideas relating to the best ways of meeting human need. In 1950, Richard Titmuss became the first Professor of Social Administration at the London School of Economics. Although he was a passionate supporter of the welfare state, he was, however, also critical of its inability to deal adequately with continuing social problems.

Titmuss (1974) developed a model for classifying welfare systems according to their ideological basis. He distinguished between residual and institutional models of welfare. Residual systems offer welfare as a last resort, or safety net, to those who are in danger of falling into destitution. The principle of individual responsibility is encouraged, and welfare is targeted at those in greatest need. Recipients may have to prove themselves to be in poverty through some sort of means test and to show that their poverty is not their own fault. In residual systems, welfare is thus often experienced as stigmatising to recipients.

In contrast, institutional systems favour universal benefits, collectively financed through taxation. These are less likely to be experienced as stigmatising because they benefit a wide cross-section of society and are intended to reduce inequality.

 Institutional welfare has characterised Britain in the post-war years. How has it been challenged?

Questions began to be raised in the 1960s about the adequacy of the welfare state, given that it was apparently unable to respond effectively to social problems. Indeed, research in the 1960s became associated with the idea of the 'rediscovery' of poverty as researchers exposed problems that had been overlooked because of assumptions that the welfare state had the capacity to deal with them. In 1965, for example, Abel-Smith and Townsend published *The Poor and the Poorest*, which contained the results of their research into continuing poverty in London. Concern related to homelessness, depicted in the 1966 film *Cathy Come Home*, prompted the formation of the voluntary organisation Shelter.

During the 1960s, there was a growing realisation that the welfare state was not necessarily a benevolent institution and that it included some highly questionable practices. The concept of institutionalisation – that is, the loss of personal identity that occurs when people are subjected to institutional regimes – was developed (Goffman, 1961). In addition, evidence of the abuse of patients and residents in institutions was publicised. For example, Robb's book *Sans Everything*, published in 1967, showed how workers in psychogeriatric wards were capable of acts of cruelty and neglect. This raised more fundamental questions concerning the role of the welfare state as an instrument of social control, engaged in oppressive acts against vulnerable people.

It was at this time that the discipline became known as social policy rather than social administration, indicating a shift in perspective from a study of how to deliver welfare to a critical analysis of welfare policies and the role of the state. These critiques can be divided into:

● cultural
● materialist
● feminist
● postmodern
● comparative.

Cultural critiques of welfare

Culturalist critiques have challenged the way in which welfare services are designed and provided and the assumptions that are made about the needs and expectations of, for example, women, black and minority ethnic groups, and disabled and older people. There have been criticisms related to the uniformity of services and the lack of understanding of the differences between service users. For example, many people whose first language is not English require support with gaining access to health services. Since equality of access is a fundamental principle of the NHS, it could be argued that such support should be provided as a right, but there were few interpreting services available until the 1980s. More recently, some health authorities have supported the development of interpreting and advocacy services, although these are still not available throughout the UK (Benzeval, 1995).

Materialist critiques of welfare

Materialist critiques focused on the needs and demands of working-class people for more welfare in the context of the diminishing resources being made available for welfare, and commentators in the 1980s pointed to an emerging crisis of welfare as supply failed to meet demand (Hayek, 1983; Taylor-Gooby, 1985).

The critique of welfare presented by the 'new right' that informed Conservative government thinking in the 1980s shared the view of Marxist commentators that welfare was an unmanageable burden on the economic system. However, whereas the left argued that not enough welfare was being provided and that the state should do more to control capitalist enterprise, the right argued that there was too much welfare and that it needed to be privatised.

Theoretical and political perspectives have influenced the development of health policy. Health policy has shifted from a post-war consensual model to a more market-oriented model characterised by greater conflict and tension. Key debates in social policy concern how much difference social policies can make and whether egalitarian social policies can compensate for unequal societies.

Feminist critiques of welfare

From the outset, feminist critiques have questioned the assumptions that exist in welfare about women's caring roles and the relationship between these and their opportunities for paid work. Feminist critiques are also directed at mainstream social policy theories for failing to take gender roles into account when analysing welfare. Caring for family members when they are sick, educating children on healthy eating and hygiene, and ensuring the safety of family members and friends constitute the daily routine of health work in most families. This work is, however, not regarded as productive activity in the same way as paid health care is.

There is a considerable amount of evidence to show that formal health care systems have always depended on informal family care to enable them to function. When the NHS was established, for example, assumptions were made about mothers being available to provide care as and when professionals required them to. The schedules of child health clinics made no concession for mothers who were in paid employment. Indeed, in the 1950s assumptions about women's dependency on their husbands was so strong that women in teaching and nursing were expected to leave their jobs when they married. Women were classified according to their husbands' occupation in census returns and other social research.

Feminist theories provided a powerful critique of this value base, calling into question the assumptions of welfare providers about women as dependent wives and unpaid carers. The traditional division between caring work performed in the public and in the private spheres is artificial, and a 'reconception of caring' is required to take account of the caring work of women at home (Graham, 1983). Since the implementation of the NHS and Community Care Act in 1990, a great deal of research has been conducted into the effects of caring on carers' physical and mental health, finances, employment opportunities and participation in social life. Feminists have identified how assumptions relating to women's caring roles continue to be made in both policy and practice (see, for example, Pascall, 1997).

Critiques of feminist perspectives have also emerged that take inequality between women into account in their analysis of women's position in the welfare systems. Disabled women have pointed out that the depiction of women carers as exploited victims is not only deeply offensive to disabled people, but also presents a distorted picture of the relationships between disabled and non-disabled people. The contribution of disabled people to family life also needs to be recognised (Morris, 1992). Black women have argued that feminists have neglected to take account of their experiences. Racist and discriminatory values have meant that black women have been expected to take on low-grade, menial work. In the NHS, for example, black nurses have been routinely offered jobs below their level of qualifications and skills. Thus, the relationship of black women to paid employment cannot be understood in the same way as that of white women (Douglas, 1992).

> *Thinking about...*
>
> Think about how a health policy (for example concerning benefits, reproduction and childbirth, transport or housing) affects women

> **CONNECTIONS**
>
> Chapter 4 (Sociology) discusses feminist sociology and postmodernism in relation to health inequalities

Postmodernist critiques of welfare

Postmodernist thinking has in recent years called into question a whole range of assumptions underpinning the provision of welfare services, for example whether all groups in society attach the same meaning and value to welfare services. Postmodernism also contributes to the theoretical and methodological analyses in social policy. For example, postmodern analyses challenge the traditional divisions of welfare into categories of service users. Within mental health, the needs and demands of patients from different ethnic groups vary significantly, yet these variations are often neglected as services are organised along rigid lines. Watters (1996) argues that GPs often make assumptions that Asians 'somatize' their psychological problems. In other words, it is assumed that if they visit their GP with back or chest pains, they are 'masking' their true mental health problems. However, Watters argues these assumptions overlook the willingness of Asian people to explain the cause of their physical problem as psychological or social. The consequences of such stereotyping and poor communication on the part of GPs can be very serious, involving misdiagnosis and inappropriate treatment.

A challenge to traditional categorisation raises questions about how particular needs can be met within universalist models of welfare (see, for example, Thompson and Hoggett, 1996; Williams, 1992). Postmodernism has, however, itself been critiqued. Taylor-Gooby (1994) argues that postmodern analyses overemphasise the importance of changes to economic and social systems, and suggests that there are important elements of contemporary conditions that demonstrate continuity rather than change. The levels of insecurity, poverty and exploitation, for example, are reminiscent of pre-welfare state conditions.

Comparative critiques of welfare

As the discipline of social policy has developed, ideas about how welfare can be organised in order to gain maximum benefit from state, private, occupational, voluntary and informal sectors have benefited from comparative perspectives. Comparative models of welfare follow the trend set by Titmuss and others in categorising different models of social welfare based on the relationship between welfare and the economy. Residual welfare is, for example, associated with free enterprise and little state intervention, whereas institutional welfare is associated with a more interventionist role for the state and less freedom for private enterprise.

Analysing the relationship between state welfare and the market is important in tackling the questions posed at the beginning of this chapter:

- Who benefits from social policies?

Table 6.2   Comparative welfare regimes

1. Emphasis on the government's role in providing comprehensive welfare services funded through taxation, so a high level of employment is necessary. Social equality an important aim
   Examples: Sweden, Denmark

2. Government involvement in the organisation of welfare through both private and state insurance schemes and through the voluntary sector. Tend to be conservative in approach to family values
   Examples: Germany, France

3. State welfare provided at a minimal level, targeted at the poorest. The voluntary and informal sectors are expected to play a major role, and the private markets are relatively unregulated. Also known as 'residual' or 'laissez-faire' welfare states
   Examples: USA, Spain

Source: Esping-Anderson, 1990

- Whose values do they reflect?
- What is the relationship between social policies and broader social inequalities?

A simple comparison of the amount of money spent on welfare would not provide answers to these questions. In the USA in 1995, for example, health care absorbed 13.6% of gross domestic product (GDP) compared with 8.7% for Germany and 7.1% for the UK, yet about 15% of the population of the USA has no health insurance and only limited access to health care facilities.

Esping-Anderson (1990) has developed a classification of 'regimes' of welfare that attempts to take into account issues of citizen rights and inequality in welfare. According to Esping-Anderson, there are two dimensions of comparison that are of particular importance:

- the extent to which the state enables individuals to enjoy an acceptable standard of living independently of the labour market (what he calls 'decommodification')

- the extent to which a state promotes equality and social integration through welfare.

He identifies three regimes of welfare (Table 6.2).

Classifications such as Esping-Anderson's are a useful starting point in helping us to identify similarities and differences between countries.

 What other factors would need to be taken into account if comparisons were to include developing countries?

The United Nations Human Development Project (UNDP, 1993) provides useful data for such comparisons. Their 'human development index' is calculated from data on the per capita GDP, life expectancy and adult literacy in any country. It is necessary to take account of a range of social as well as economic factors because there is a clear difference between countries in the way in which resources are used for welfare. For example, Costa Rica has a very high level of adult literacy (92.8 per cent in 1990) compared with Brazil (81.1 per cent) even though it has a lower per capita GDP (UNDP, 1993).

Deacon (1997) refers to the levels of global inequity that exist and the way in which the welfare of people in some developing countries is adversely affected by dependency on the West and mounting debts. In addition, as he points out, continued and widening economic inequity, food deprivation, enforced migration and exposure to organised crime need to be taken into account.

Comparative social policy contributes to our understanding of both how and why welfare is organised in a particular way. In Ireland, for example, there is a long tradition of church involvement in health care. In Sweden, women's participation in paid employment has been higher than that in many other European countries, and this affects how the informal sphere operates. Comparative approaches demonstrate how concepts such as needs, rights, equity, autonomy and responsibility are expressed through policies in different ways in different contexts.

Classificatory systems have, however, been criticised by feminists for their tendency to concentrate on formal welfare provision and to neglect the contribution of the informal sector. Daly (1994), for example, argues that although Esping-Anderson's work is an advance on previous classifications, it still does not place an equal importance on the family as on the state or the market in producing welfare. As she points out, in all welfare states, even the most developed social democratic type, the family is the most significant provider of welfare.

METHODOLOGIES OF SOCIAL POLICY IN UNDERSTANDING HEALTH

A range of methodologies, empirical and non-empirical, qualitative and quantitative, can be identified in social policy. For example, the works of social researchers, such as Townsend's (1979) surveys of poverty, have contributed significantly to theory development. Townsend's research led to the development of the concept of 'relative deprivation', which describes the standard of living of any individual or group in comparison with the vast majority of the population. He argued that policies to tackle poverty needed to take into account social and cultural factors as well as individual human needs.

Data from qualitative research have been crucial in, for example, encouraging the voices of service users to be included in social policy theorising. Williams et al. (1999) argue that there is a need to understand the relationship between the personal history and the experiences of people who use welfare services and the material and social world. The idea of welfare users as passive recipients or

---

EXAMPLE 6.3

Using social survey data to analyse health service utilisation

The secondary analysis of data from social surveys is an important method that provides evidence of social trends that are significant to people's health. The General Household Survey can be used to examine the relationship between ethnicity and the use of health services by children and young people. The association between health need and health service use for children aged 0–19 can be tested.

After adjusting for differences in socio-economic position and health need, minority ethnic, particularly South Asian, children use GP services more than white children, and, in any given illness episode, there are likely to be more consultations. The utilisation of hospital outpatient and inpatient services, is, on the other hand, much lower for children in minority ethnic groups. In addition, there are differences between children of the same ethnic grouping. Those with parents born in the UK are more likely to utilise GP and outpatient services at the same rate as white children with UK-born parents, while minority ethnic children whose parents were born outside the UK are more likely to diverge from this pattern.

A number of explanatory factors may be involved in utilisation of health services, including the behaviour of both migrant parents and health staff. Their findings raise questions to be addressed in future research about the quality and nature of care received by minority groups and patterns of referral by GPs to hospitals and specialist services.

Source: Cooper et al., 1999

victims of the system has been profoundly challenged by a range of organisations, such as disabled people's and women's groups. Research that enables the voice of the service user to emerge presents a particular problem to policy-makers and service providers as the demand to be more sensitive to service users' own constructions of their needs sits uncomfortably with demands to provide more efficient and cost-effective services.

POLICY ANALYSIS

It is important to recognise that social policy is concerned not only with analysing welfare systems at the broad level: the analysis of *policy* also entails looking at how individual policies develop. Policy analysis is a core activity of research and theory-building. Policies may be analysed on the basis of whether they achieve their objectives, an evaluation of policies in practice being a major area of research. For example, the 1977 Working Group on Inequalities in Health (see Townsend and Davidson, 1982) was established to assess how successful the NHS had been in reducing inequality. More recently, there have been a number of analyses of the effect of the internal market on health care in the 1990s. Le Grand et al. (1998), for example, examined the evidence on whether the internal market achieved what it was intended to. They concluded that although the ideas behind the internal market were radical, financial and organisational constraints meant that there were fewer changes to the functioning of the NHS than might have been expected.

> **policy** – goals, decisions and purposeful actions generally associated with governments but also with a range of other organisations

However, policy analysis goes deeper than simple evaluations of policies against their stated aims and objectives. Policy analysis can be divided into the analysis for policy and the analysis of policy (Ham and Hill, 1993):

- analysis *for* policy is engaged with making a contribution to the solution of social problems
- analysis *of* policy is an academic activity concerned primarily with advancing understanding and knowledge.

Although this distinction is useful, there is a relationship between the two types as each influences the other: the development of knowledge has implications for policy-making, and policy-making is the subject of academic analysis.

THE POLICY PROCESS

Social policies can be understood as dynamic processes influenced by a range of groups and individuals that have a stake in the process. The policy process is not always visible, analysing what happens below the surface revealing the relationship between social policies and broader social divisions and inequalities. In particular, understanding the policy process enables us to understand relationships of power between the people involved. Ham and Hill (1993) maintain that a policy is a 'web of decisions rather than one decision', also arguing that it is important to recognise that non-decision-making is as important as decision-making to the policy analyst.

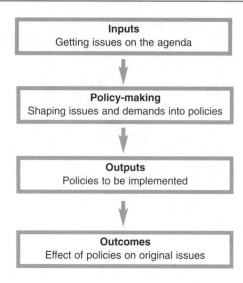

Figure 6.2   The policy process

Figure 6.2 shows the different elements of this process and how they affect each other. The relationship between policy-making and output, for example, may be examined to assess the efficiency of implementation systems. On the other hand, understanding the way in which issues get on the policy agenda in the first place can shed light on outcomes. There are several elements to the process.

Inputs

The way in which issues emerge as problems requiring government action reflects particular social and cultural values. Human needs and suffering do not always attract attention, and even where there is an awareness of a problem, this does not always translate into political action. Social phenomena may be perceived as problems by some but not others. Lone parenthood, for example, has been fairly consistently characterised as a social problem in recent years, but this characterisation is open to dispute.

Policy inputs may come from within governments themselves as well as from interest groups outside the political system. For example, in 1988, following a funding crisis in the NHS, the Prime Minister's review was established. Unusually for a review of the health service, this group did not include any medical professionals but was limited to a small group of cabinet ministers, chaired by the Prime Minister herself. This review thus needs to be understood in the light of the political importance of the NHS and the need for the government to take decisive action.

Getting an issue on to the agenda requires effective organisation and access to sources of power and influence. The ability of any group to lobby effectively is crucially important. Some groups are more privileged than others in having access to formal or informal networks of power. Professional and commercial groups, for example, have enjoyed greater influence over health policy than health service users (Allsop, 1995). However, where groups have organised effectively around particular issues, such as the need for better services for people with HIV, they have been successful.

Thinking about...

Can you think of an example of policy that 'has not happened' (Ham and Hill, 1993)?

Policy-making

The process of formulating issues or demands into policy proposals comes next in the policy process. Policy-makers have to consider how any issue fits in with their overall agenda, what the political implications of adopting an issue as policy might be and how likely it is that proposals will gain wider support and pass through the legislative process. Consultation enables policy-makers to test opinion. At a national level, this may be in the form of a Green Paper, such as *Our Healthier Nation*, (DoH, 1998), which was specifically designed to invite comment from interested parties.

A White Paper, such as *The New NHS: Modern, Dependable* (DoH, 1997) is a firm proposal from government for legislation. From this, a government bill is introduced to Parliament, to be followed by a long process of reading, debate and amendment within the House of Commons, the House of Lords and parliamentary committees.

The process of policy-making in the UK is long and complex. The establishment of the NHS in 1946, for example, was fraught with difficulties and obstacles. Aneurin Bevan, the Minister of Health at the time, negotiated with doctors' representatives, many of whom were opposed to the idea of the NHS. His approach was to offer financial incentives to win them over to his side. It was said at the time that Bevan 'stuffed their mouths with gold'.

EXAMPLE 6.4

Policy-making: the example of tobacco advertising and sponsorship

In July 1997, the Minister for Public Health in the newly elected Labour government announced that there was to be legislation to control tobacco advertising. The government had pledged to ban tobacco advertising in its election manifesto and had public opinion on its side. The Smee Report (DoH, 1992) drew attention to a link between advertising and sports sponsorship and young people's smoking habits. In addition, the European Union (EU) was proposing a ban on sponsorship.

By November 1997, however, the government had decided that Formula One racing would be made a special case as the Formula One organisers had threatened to withdraw from European venues and move the Grand Prix races to venues outside the EU countries. The government accepted their position, much to the dismay of organisations such as Action on Smoking and Health and the Health Education Authority (ASH, 1997). The tobacco companies argued that an existing voluntary agreement to restrict advertising, monitored by the Committee for the Monitoring of Agreements on Tobacco Advertising and Sponsorship was adequate. It was also argued that alternative sponsorship would be impossible to find and that prestigious sporting events would be lost to Britain.

In May 1998, members of the European Parliament voted to ban tobacco advertising throughout the EU (Tobacco Advertising Directive 98/43/EU), leaving Formula One organisers until 2006 to find alternative sponsorship. The tobacco industry appealed against the ban through the British courts. However, this was not successful, and in December 1999 the Secretary of State for Health announced that the European directive would be incorporated into British law. Advertising is to be banned, and the sponsorship of sporting events by tobacco companies will be phased out (DoH, 1999b).

Sources: ASH, 1997; DoH, 1992, 1996; Tobacco Advertising Directive 98/43/EU

Outputs

If a bill goes through all the stages mentioned above, it will become an Act of Parliament that requires implementation through central or local government or other agencies. At this stage, there is scope for yet further modification. Local conditions and priorities differ, and this will influence the implementation process. For example, the relationship between the overall strategic aims of the DoH and the health authorities is not straightforward. Government guidance may be issued on putting policies into operation, but how this is interpreted at the local level varies. The relationship between central government and local authorities is an important focus for analysis in social policy.

Pressure to change implementation procedures also often emerges. The Carers' National Association, for example, conducted research on the implementation of the 1995 Carers (Recognition and Services) Act, their findings revealing a gap between policy and practice in general and variations between local authorities in how they implemented the policy. In addition, legislation may meet some but not all the demands of interest groups: the Disability Discrimination Act 1995 met some of the demands of disabled people's groups for action to promote equality of opportunity but stopped short of establishing a commission for disability equality along the lines of the Commission for Racial Equality.

Outcomes

The question to be addressed at this stage is what difference does a policy make to people's lives? Given the scope for modification and change at earlier stages of the process, it is not surprising that the outcomes of the legislative process can be quite different from what was envisaged by the interest groups at the beginning. This often means that the process of campaigning and lobbying begins again as further reforms and changes are demanded. Policies also often have unforeseen consequences that may stimulate pressure for further policy action.

At this stage, the experiences of patients and service users also need to be taken into account. Policies to improve efficiency in the NHS have, for example, led to problems over the discharge from hospital of frail and chronically sick people, who may be regarded as 'bed-blockers'. How do individual patients experience problems over hospital discharge? How does it feel to be a bed-blocker? In what way can such feelings and experiences be articulated and heard by policy-makers and service providers?

The policy process is therefore not neat and linear but continuous and complex, influenced by the context in which it occurs. This involves social policy analysts in identifying the links between policy processes and broader economic, political and social systems, as well as taking into account the experiences of service users.

CASE STUDY – AGEING AND HEALTH CARE

The issue of health care for older people has been chosen as a case study because it encapsulates many of the themes and problems identified in this chapter. Key questions that are explored in this case study include:

- how to define a health (as opposed to a social) issue
- how a particular group's entitlement to health care services may be problematised
- how service users' views are, or are not, reflected in policy decisions.

HEALTH ISSUES IN OLD AGE

The provision of health care for older people clearly demonstrates the difficulty of determining what is a health issue. The relationship between social factors, such as social inequalities, levels of wealth and poverty and power on the one hand and health on the other, is shown particularly clearly in old age. Medical advances and an improvement in the standard of living have led to increased longevity in general, but social inequality tends to become more pronounced in old age.

In addition, the type of health care that has been dominant in the NHS can be seen to have been particularly problematic for older people. The dominance of the acute model and the emphasis on restoring people to full function has not taken account of the higher level of chronic illness in old age, chronic disorders having received less attention in health policy and fewer resources. 'Geriatric medicine' has attempted to take account of the wider range of factors that affect older people's health, but even here there is still an emphasis on restoring people to full independence. This becomes a problem for older people who have more complex needs and may lose their capacity for full independence.

The high social value placed on independence places older people in a position of relative powerlessness and low social status. In particular, older people become characterised as a burden.

AGEING AND THE DEMOGRAPHIC TIME BOMB

The White Paper *Saving Lives: Our Healthier Nation* (DoH, 1999a) has, as one of its two main goals, the improvement of the health of the nation as a whole by increasing the length of people's lives and the number of years people spend free from illness. Longevity therefore continues to be a policy goal and may be regarded as a success story, but, paradoxically, the consequences are seen as a problem.

Nearly half of all NHS expenditure goes on people aged 65 and over, and this has led to a long-standing discourse about the 'burden' of the increasing number of older people. Higher levels of need and demand for health care in old age have been presented as an economic problem. In an article in the *British Medical Journal* (Williams, 1997), Professor Alan Williams argued that age should be a criterion for rationing decisions. Having had a 'good innings', older people should not assume a right to health care equal to that of younger people. There has been vociferous opposition to this view from, among others, the charity Age Concern, who argue that to identify a class of people with less entitlement to services would be grossly inequitable.

It is important to remember also that old age is not synonymous with ill health as there are important differences between people in terms of their ageing process. Chronological age does not correspond neatly with biological age or social age, so people's demands for health care vary greatly. The majority of people over retirement age do not make great demands on the health services. However, the need for health care does change over the life span. At the stage of decline and ill health in late old age, demands are likely to be made. Looked at in this way, it is not old age itself that creates a burden but the relationship between old age and death in contemporary society.

SOCIAL POLICIES AND OLDER PEOPLE'S HEALTH

Historically, ageing and the needs of older people have featured prominently in the development of British social policies. A high number of older people in Victorian times were, for example, obliged to seek help from the workhouse because of poverty and ill health. The 'burying' of the Poor Law in 1948 was of particular relevance to older people, many of whom had first-hand experience of its punitive approach. The provision of retirement pensions was a significant development in British welfare. However, many health and social care services developed for older people were highly institutionalised.

When policies for community care were developed in the late 1980s, older people were regarded as a priority for attention. There was widespread agreement that an alternative to institutionalised regimes in geriatric hospital wards and residential care homes was needed (Means and Smith, 1998). The idea that older people would be enabled to live in their own homes through a reorganisation of services had, and still has, widespread appeal.

Community care is organised through a system of professional practice that has become known as 'care management'. This reflects the separation of purchaser and provider roles so that the assessment of people's needs is separated from the provision of services to meet those needs. The care manager (from the purchasing local authority), having established what individuals' needs are, should then develop a 'package of care' that suits them, purchasing this from a range of providers. The case of Alice James described earlier in this chapter shows the involvement of the state, informal, private, voluntary and occupational sectors in providing for her needs. A care manager would need to take account of Alice's needs and resources in designing her particular package of care.

The practice of care management should in theory ensure that the older person's needs are met in an integrated way, the individual having some say in how services are delivered, and the mixed economy of care offering a degree of choice over the preferred type of care. The reality has, however, been somewhat more problematic. The 1990 NHS and Community Care Act maintained the separation between health and social care services, both organisationally and in terms of funding. This has meant that the health needs of older people have continued to be categorised into separate areas of responsibility instead of being met in an integrated way.

Moreover, there are important differences in older people's entitlement to services in the different categories, health care being free and social care being means tested. This has had serious implications for older people's access to services. Some have experienced being 'shunted' from one service to the other as each service attempts to avoid the cost of care. An example of this is that one old person may be bathed for free by a district nurse whereas another may have to pay social services for a care assistant to bathe them.

In addition, the quality of care services provided in people's own homes has shown how institutionalised regimes continue to be applied outside the physical buildings of the institutions. Older people have found that they are obliged to comply with the rules and practices of the care provider organisations. Meal-times, bedtimes and bathing routines continue to be determined by others, and older people are in a weak position in terms of asserting their wishes if they rely on state services. Those who are able to purchase their own care have a much improved chance of determining their own lifestyle.

THE LONG-TERM CARE DEBATE

A Royal Commission on the Long-term Care of the Elderly, chaired by Professor Stewart Sutherland, presented its findings in March 1999 in a report entitled *With Respect to Old Age: Long-term Care – Rights and Responsibilities*. The majority group of the commission argued for a collectivist approach in which the cost of care in old age should be spread across the generations. They also argued that personal care (including bathing, hygiene and toileting) should be included as health care and provided free, whereas housing and ordinary food costs should be means tested. A minority group argued against the universalist approach of the majority, stressing individual responsibility and self-reliance. They maintained that targeted services were more appropriate, given the limitations of resources, and that people should be encouraged to use their own resources for help in old age. All the members agreed that there was a need for a more positive view of old age and that it should not be seen as a problem or a burden. They also stressed that services should be improved to ensure a better standard of care than currently exists in residential and nursing homes. The disagreement is over how the costs of care should be met and by whom.

This case study has shown that the issue of how long-term care for older people should be provided and funded remains a problem for policy-makers and professionals alike. It encapsulates the issues raised at the outset of this chapter concerning social values and principles and how these are put into practice through a welfare system. A fundamental problem for policy-makers is how to balance the rights of people for security and comfort in old age against the responsibilities of people to take care of themselves over the course of their lifetime.

SUMMARY

- The discipline of social policy enables us to understand how ideas about people's health and well-being are put into practice through welfare systems. Social policy also enables us to recognise that interventions are not always beneficial and that policies may not in practice enhance health and well-being. Critical approaches in social policy probe deeper to analyse the complex nature of welfare systems

- An analysis of the policy process provides further illumination of the relationship between policies and the economic, political and social contexts in which they are developed.

- Social policy includes fundamental philosophical questions about the way in which a society secures the health and well-being of its most vulnerable members, such as older people

- Social policy continues to experience a tension between the need to analyse and critique welfare policies and the need to provide information that can be used to develop policies. Social policy is, simultaneously, about values, principles and pragmatism

- The importance of social policy to Health Studies is that it enables us to see how ideas about people's health and well-being are shaped into policies and practices, and how this is a dynamic process that is continually being analysed and changed.

QUESTIONS FOR FURTHER DISCUSSION

1. Over the next two or three days, study reports or articles on health issues in one of the broadsheet newspapers. Think about the following:

   a. Who is raising the issue and whom do they represent?

   b. Is the issue on the policy agenda locally, nationally or internationally?

   c. Where is pressure being directed?

   d. What values are being expressed through this issue?

2. 'On the principle of the equal moral worth of all people, health care should not be rationed.' Discuss this proposition, with particular reference to old age.

3. Visit the *Our Healthier Nation* Internet site at: www.ohn.gov.uk.

   Search this to identify how this policy is to be implemented, and consider what is likely to be the impact of the policy in practice on the lives of school-age children, people of working age and retired people.

FURTHER READING

There are several very useful introductory texts on social policy. These will enable you to follow up general points related to the discipline.

Abel-Smith, B. (1994) *An Introduction to Health: Policy, Planning and Financing.* London: Longman.
   This text is unusual in that it takes a broader view of health than many texts, which tend to concentrate on health services.

Blakemore, K. (1998) *Social Policy: An Introduction.* Buckingham: Open University Press.
   This is a very readable text looking at the general themes of welfare and at particular areas. Chapter 7, on health policy and health professions, will enable you to explore this issue in greater depth.

Hallett, C. (ed.) (1996) *Women and Social Policy: An Introduction.* London: Prentice Hall/Harvester Wheatsheaf.
   This is a collection of readings on a range of welfare issues, with a discussion on the discipline and feminism.

Hill, M. (1996) *Social Policy: A Comparative Analysis.* London: Prentice Hall/Harvester Wheatsheaf.
   Provides an international perspective and a discussion of comparative social policy.

Langan, M. (ed.) (1998) *Welfare: Needs, Rights and Risks.* London: Routledge.
   This is a collection of readings on the three core issues of needs, rights and risks in social policy.

The following two books provide a comprehensive overview of health policy:

Allsop, J. (1995) *Health Policy and the NHS: Towards 2000*. London: Longman.

Ranade, W. (1997) *A Future for the NHS? Health Care for the Millennium*. London: Longman.

A good source of information is the King's Fund annual review of health policy *Health Care UK*. It is published every autumn.

You should also visit the DoH web site at http://www.doh.gov.uk to explore current and recent activities by central government in health. Some publications can be downloaded at no cost.

REFERENCES

Abel-Smith, B. and Townsend, P. (1965) *The Poor and the Poorest*. London: G. Bell.

Acheson, D. (1998) *Independent Inquiry into Inequalities in Health: A Report*. London: Stationery Office.

Allsop, J. (1995) *Health Policy and the NHS: Towards 2000*. London: Longman.

ASH (Action on Smoking and Health) (1997) *Tobacco and Formula One – Holes in the Government's Case*. Press release, ASH UK, 21 November 1997.

Benzeval, M. (1995) 'Health care for all? How to take equity seriously', in Harrison, A. and Bruscini, S. (eds) *Health Care UK 1994/5: An Annual Review of Health Care Policy*. London, King's Fund, pp. 66–71.

Beveridge, W. (1942) *Social Insurance and Allied Services* (The Beveridge Report). London: HMSO.

Booth, C. (1902) *Life and Labour of the People of London*. London: Macmillan – now Palgrave.

Cooper, H. Smaje, C. and Arber, S. (1999) Equity in health service use by children: examining the ethnic paradox. *Journal of Social Policy*, **28**(3): 457–78.

Daly, M. (1994) 'Comparing welfare states: towards a gender friendly approach', in Sainsbury, D. (ed.) *Gendering Welfare States*. London: Sage, pp. 101–17.

Deacon, B., with Hulse, M. and Stubbs, P. (1997) *Global Social Policy: International Organisations and the Future of Welfare*. London: Sage.

DHSS (Department of Health and Social Security) (1981) *Growing Older*. London: HMSO.

DHSS (Department of Health and Social Security) (1983) *NHS Management Inquiry*. London: HMSO.

DoH (Department of Health) (1992) *Effect of Tobacco Advertising on Tobacco Consumption: A Discussion Document Reviewing the Evidence*. London: DoH.

DoH (Department of Health) (1997) *The New NHS: Modern, Dependable*. London: Stationery Office.

DoH (Department of Health) (1998) *Our Healthier Nation*. London: Stationery Office.

DoH (Department of Health) (1999a) *Saving Lives: Our Healthier Nation*. London: Stationery Office

DoH (Department of Health) (1999b) Tobacco advertising to end by December. Press release 1999/0358. London: DoH.

Douglas, J. (1992) 'Black women's health matters: putting black women on the research agenda', in Roberts, H. (ed.) *Women's Health Matters*. London: Routledge, pp. 33–46.

Doyal, L. and Gough, I. (1991) *A Theory of Human Needs*. Basingstoke: Macmillan – now Palgrave.

Esping-Anderson, G. (1990) *The Three Worlds of Welfare Capitalism*. Cambridge: Polity Press.

Goffman, E. (1961) *Asylums: Essays on the Social Situation of Mental Patients and other Inmates*. Harmondsworth: Penguin.

Graham, H. (1983) 'Caring: a labour of love', in Finch, J. and Groves, D. (eds) *A Labour of Love: Women, Work and Caring*. London: Routledge & Kegan Paul, pp. 13–30.

Ham, C. and Hill, M. (1993) *The Policy Process in the Modern Capitalist State*. Hemel Hempstead: Harvester Wheatsheaf.

Hayek, F.A. (1983) *Knowledge, Evolution and Society*. London: Adam Smith Institute.

King's Fund (1997) *Management of the Introduction of Betaferon*. London: King's Fund.

Le Grand, J. and Bartlett, W. (1993) *Quasi-markets and Social Policy*. London: Macmillan – now Palgrave.

Le Grand, J., Mays, N. and Mulligan, J. (1998) *Learning from the NHS Internal Market: A Review of the Evidence*. London: King's Fund.

Marshall, T.H. (1950) *Citizenship and Social Class and other Essays*. Cambridge: Cambridge University Press.

Means, R. and Smith, R. (1998) *From Poor Law to Community Care: The Development of Welfare Services for Elderly People 1939–1971*. Bristol: Policy Press.

Morris, J. (1992) 'Us' and 'them'? Feminist research, community care and disability. *Critical Social Policy*, **33** (Winter): 22–39.

New, B. and Mays, N. (1997) 'Age, renal replacement therapy and rationing', in *Health Care UK 1996/7: The King's Fund Annual Review of Health Policy*. London: King's Fund, pp. 205–23.

Pascall, G. (1997) *Social Policy: A New Feminist Analysis*. London: Routledge.

Robb, B. (1967) *Sans Everything: A Case to Answer*. London: Nelson.

Rowntree, B.S. (1901) *Poverty: A Study of Town Life*. London: Macmillan – now Palgrave.

Royal Commission on Long-term Care of the Elderly (1999) *With Respect to Old Age: Long-term Care – Rights and Responsibilities*.

Secretaries of State for Health (1989) *Working for Patients*. London: HMSO.

Secretaries of State for Health, Social Security, Wales and Scotland (1989) *Caring for People: Community Care in the Next Decade and Beyond*. London: HSMO.

Taylor-Gooby, P. (1985) *Public Opinion, Ideology and State Welfare*. London: Routledge & Keegan Paul.

Taylor-Gooby, P. (1994) Post-modernism: a great leap backwards? *Journal of Social Policy*, **23**(3): 385–404.

Thompson, S. and Hoggett, P. (1996) Universalism, selectivism and particularism: towards a postmodern social policy. *Critical Social Policy*, **16**(1): 21–43.

Titmuss, R.M. (1974) *Social Policy: An Introduction*. London: Allen & Unwin.

Titmuss, R.M. (1987) 'The irresponsible society', in Abel-Smith, B. and Titmuss, K. (eds) *The Philosophy of Welfare – Selected Writings of R.M. Titmuss*. London: Allen & Unwin, pp. 60–86.

Townsend, P. (1979) *Poverty in the United Kingdom*. Harmondsworth: Penguin.

Townsend, P. and Davidson, N. (eds) (1982) *Inequalities in Health*. The Black Report. Harmondsworth: Penguin.

UNDP (United Nations Human Development Project) (1993) *Human Development Report, 1993*. New York: Oxford University Press.

Watters, C. (1996) 'Representations and realities: black people, community care and mental illness', in Ahmad, W.I.U. and Atkin, K. (eds) *'Race' and Community Care*. Buckingham: Open University Press, pp. 105–23.

Williams, A. (1997) Rationing health care by age: the case for. *British Medical Journal*, **314**: 820–2.

Williams, F. (1992) Somewhere over the rainbow: universality and diversity in social policy. *Social Policy Review*, **4**: 200–19.

Williams, F., Popay, J. and Oakley, A. (1999) *Welfare Research: A Critical Review*. London: UCL Press.

Organisation and Management

chapter

7

MARTIN WALTER

Learning outcomes •

This chapter will enable readers to:

- Gain a sound understanding of modern management theories and be able to relate them to examples of practical situations and issues, particularly in health care
- Be aware of the major theories on the motivation to work and their relationship to organisational structure and culture
- Appreciate the role of leadership and the effective management of organisations and of change, particularly in the health services
- Apply theories and models to solve problems of organisational change
- Better understand the nature and operation of health services organisations and how they may be managed.

OVERVIEW

Management, the professional administration of business concerns, public undertakings and organisations in general – as well as its many shortcomings – is seemingly always in the news, particularly in relation to the health services. This chapter will address the question of why this hard to define topic should be studied by students of health studies, regardless of their professional discipline or personal inclination to be involved in managerial work. This chapter outlines some of the major theoretical concepts relating to organisational and management studies, and applies these to the NHS. The NHS is a unique organisation with a huge and diverse remit. Its workforce and scale of operations make it a major British organisation, and, within its area of operations, many different organisational and management styles have been tried and tested. The first part of this chapter outlines the major features of the NHS as an organisation. The second part discusses different management models and their relevance to the NHS, outlining theories relating to the task of management, in particular motivation and team-building. The chapter concludes with an extended case study that examines these theories in relation to England's newly established Primary Care Groups.

INTRODUCTION

We all relate to organisations of various kinds – our local authority, the GP practice, local retailers, mail order companies, various educational establishments – no one can be entirely immune from 'management'. Indeed, the more we are aware of how these various organisations operate, the more successful we are likely to be in dealing with them.

Organisations vary enormously in their size, complexity and function. Most health care provision in the UK is provided by the NHS, which was introduced as a flagship of the post-war Labour government. Many factors, not least its size, complexity and visionary, idealistic aims, make the NHS unique. Applying those theories which examine and explain organisational culture, team-building, motivation to work and job design, leadership and change to the NHS is a good test of their adequacy and usefulness.

Management is the act or art of managing – the conducting or supervising of something such as a business or organisation. It is concerned with the arrangements for carrying out organisational processes and the execution of work (Mullins, 1999). It is unequivocally the responsibility of designated people rather than fate (Drucker, 1968) and depends on the skill, competence, knowledge, dedication, vision and integrity of those who carry out this function, that is, the managers. Management skills are therefore closely connected to the success or otherwise of the organisation.

About one hundred years ago the central tasks of management were defined by Henri Fayol as being concerned with (Pugh and Hickson, 1989):

- planning
- organising the structure
- organising human resources (people)
- co-ordinating or harmonising the various functions
- controlling the operation and outcome of the organisation.

Most health care systems have a great deal of difficulty in these aspects. The UK NHS, for example, has frequently changed its structure since it was first reorganised in 1974 and has always appeared to have a succession of staffing crises. It has always had problems in harmonising its various functions. One has only to think of operations cancelled on the morning of admission, or 'blocked beds' caused by failed discharge procedures, to establish this point.

THE CONTRIBUTION OF MANAGEMENT TO HEALTH STUDIES

Both organisational and managerial issues affect how an organisation is run – how effective, efficient or accountable it is. The key features of the UK NHS, and indeed of other large public sector-based health services throughout the world, are:

- size
- complexity
- culture.

The environment in which an organisation operates influences many of its aspects. The 'culture' stems from the first two features, which are influenced by the unique presence of so many different groups of staff attempting to work together and being mutually dependent on each other in order to perform their work.

SIZE

One of the most striking features of the UK health service is its size. About one million people work in or for the NHS, many more being employed within the private health sector. There are health care facilities of some kind in virtually every city, town and village in the country. Modern technology is ensuring that no one is now more than a telephone call away from assistance or advice, be it accident or emergency information or simply reassurance or practical, informed advice through the new telemedicine facility NHS Direct. Moreover, although they are now divided into quasi-independent Trusts, secondary health care providers are still very large undertakings, often employing well over 2,000 people. Other indicators of the size of the NHS are its capital value or annual expenditure (currently some £34 billion per annum): the NHS is the second most costly area of government expenditure, behind only social security (Prowle and Jones, 1997).

Handy (1993) believes that the 'size of an organisation has often proved to be the single most important variable in influencing a choice of structure (complexity) or of culture'. The sheer size of the new NHS compared with the disaggregated service that preceded it inevitably means that it has become highly bureaucratic, written rules and procedures governing its employment policies and organisational procedures.

COMPLEXITY

 What important factors contribute to the complexity of an organisation?

The UK endeavours to provide a truly comprehensive health service. The origin of this stems from the 1944 White Paper, a precursor to the 1946 National Health Service Act. The intention stated was to 'provide a comprehensive health service for the improvement of the physical and mental health of the people of England and Wales for the prevention, diagnosis and treatment of illness' (Ministry of Health, 1944). In fact, the NHS was founded on five principles:

● the collective principle – health care to be freely available to all regardless of means

● the comprehensive principle – to meet all conditions of health care need

● the universal principle – to meet all need in all locations regardless of cost

● the principle of equality – to provide the same level of provision across the country irrespective of location

● the principle of professional autonomy – essentially meaning clinical freedom for doctors, whether hospital consultants or GPs. Expenditure was placed in their hands: it was not the responsibility of the administration, the official term for management until the 1980s.

By endeavouring to uphold these principles the UK has developed a most complex health care organisation. Indeed, it would be very difficult to identify an organisation of greater complexity whatever the criteria employed. Complexity might be measured by:

- the number of different functions the organisation seeks to perform – preventive, curative and caring
- the growing specialisation of health services involving many different professional groups, each with its own professional body, qualifications, career pathways and unique contribution to care.

CONNECTIONS

Chapter 6 (Social Policy) discusses the development of welfare and emerging views on the role of the state

It is traditional to regard health services as being delivered by doctors and nurses, but this is far too simplistic a view. Complex teams of professionals provide modern health services. As well as 430,000 nurses and 16,000 consultants, the NHS has 118,000 technical staff, without whom modern health care could not be delivered. The professions allied to medicine consist of radiographers, both diagnostic and therapeutic; physiotherapists; occupational therapists; speech therapists; podiatrists (chiropodists); biomedical scientists and clinical scientists (laboratory-based professionals); a host of other technical staff to support the work of dialysis and cardiology units; and many other specialities. The NHS also has some 200,000 clerks and administrators, essential if the organisation is to function at all. The idea that such a large, complex organisation can be run by doctors and nurses alone is an obvious fallacy.

Then there are the clinical specialities themselves. Doctors' and nurses' careers differentiate into specialities soon after their basic qualifications are obtained. The area of expertise or clinical condition in which they specialise further complicates the traditional distinction between physicians and surgeons. Moreover, there is evidence to show that post-treatment survival improves with such specialisation (Gillis and Hole, 1996; RCSE, 2000; RCSE and BOA, 2000). Even general practice is regarded as a speciality, with its own Royal College, postgraduate membership examinations and Fellowship award.

Many branches of medicine are now subdivided, few practitioners being able to perform at the highest level in more than one discipline. Pathology, for example, now has many branches and specialities within those branches. Chemical pathology may include clinical chemistry, immunology and

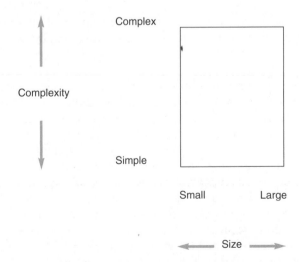

Figure 7.1   Template for assessing the size and complexity of organisations

endocrinology; haematology may well embrace blood serology as well as laboratory-based and clinical haematology; microbiology usually encompasses virology and parasitology; while morbid anatomy will cover cytology, clinical microscopy and post-mortem examination. The doctors who are employed in these many divisions usually request that their views be considered in most if not all decision-making processes. Thus there are a plethora of personal, professional and political views for management to consider in any and every area of organisational life.

 Look at Figure 7.1. Where would you place the NHS in the diagram? What other organisations can you place above or below it either in terms of size or complexity? Why are these organisations more or less complex?

CULTURE

The NHS is a very large, complex organisation with a strong, well-established culture. Schein (1992) defines 'culture' as:

> a pattern of shared basic assumptions that the group has learned as it solved its problems of external adaptation and internal integration, that has worked well enough to be considered valid, and, therefore, to be taught to new members as the correct way to perceive, think, and feel in relation to those problems.

organisational culture – a set of collectively held, relevant, distinctive and shared meanings, values and assumptions, which operate unconsciously and define an organisation's (unchallenged) view of itself, its environment and its mission. It also defines and governs the expected behaviour of its members

Indeed, Schein goes on to define 'basic assumptions' as 'unconscious taken-for-granted beliefs, perceptions, thoughts and feelings which are ultimately the source of values and actions (Schein, 1992). Basic assumptions, which underpin ***organisational culture***, are, by definition, very difficult to change.

 What are the features that characterise the 'culture' of the NHS and other large public sector health providers throughout the world?

The concept of organisational culture sets the 'tone' of an organisation. It includes everything from the visible organisational structures and processes, termed 'artifacts' by Schein and consisting of everything about an organisation that can be observed, including its special language, technology, patterns of deference and so forth, to more deeply held values that underpin observed behaviour. The basic underlying assumptions are values so strongly held that organisational members 'find behaviour based on any other premise inconceivable' (Schein, 1992). Thus, one might argue that the role of culture is to provide a sense of stability and predictability within an organisation, a safe and comfortable place in which to work provided that one's individual values are similar to, or congruent with, collectively held ones. It also means that, when a change in values is required, resistance to that change is very likely unless all stakeholders also share the proposed direction of the change.

Health service workers 'encultured' with the value that they should endeavour to meet all health need whenever and wherever it occurs may become resentful at having to live within a restrictive budget. After all, need, or the capacity of a patient to benefit from treatment, is defined by professionals, and budgetary control can circumscribe the perceived professional function in defining need. Thus, the underpinning values that have been absorbed and have worked well over many years, usually understood as clinical freedom, are being challenged by the new 'espoused values' of those who are seeking to instigate change. Notice at this point that we are not seeking to judge whether budgetary control in health care is right or wrong, a good thing or a bad thing: we are simply saying that to introduce a change of this nature invariably means that basic underlying assumptions are challenged, so resistance to the change is to be expected. In a way, we have a psychological contract with work. We have a set of expectations of our organisation, both of the inputs we are required to make and the achievements we can reasonably expect to flow from our work.

Problems may well occur, says Handy (1993), if the contract is not perceived identically by both parties. This frequently occurs when trying to introduce change. Expectations of how hard we need to work, the decisions we are expected to make and the results required of us are all challenged. Unilateral alterations to a normal contract of employment are subject to legal restraint, and disaffected employees may settle their grievances in an industrial relations tribunal or court. Changes to the psychological contract are, however, less easy to defend by legal means. The extent to which they are resisted may well depend as much on the strength and nature of the culture opposing them as on the legality, or otherwise, of the proposed change.

Handy offers a typology of organisational cultures, which are easily identifiable within health care organisations. To each culture he links both the name of the Greek God whose characteristics most resemble those of the culture, and an appropriate symbol. Handy's four cultures are:

1. role culture

2. club or power culture

3. task culture

4. person culture.

Role culture: *God – Apollo; symbol – a Greek temple*

The role culture is characterised by its highly **bureaucratic** structure. Staff and job functions are prescribed by rules, for example job descriptions, formal appraisals and standing instructions, all deliberately designed to limit the freedom and initiative of workers according to their position. Role culture workers are rewarded for their adherence to their delegated job functions rather than for innovation. Progression is often based upon the time served and a satisfactory performance at lower grades. This type of organisation sets out to bring

CONNECTIONS

Chapter 8 (Health Economics) discusses how economic principles are applied to rationing decisions and whether priority-setting can be considered ethical

Thinking about...

Think of your past place of employment or study. What were the main ingredients of your psychological contract? Did you feel, on balance, that you were a winner or a loser? Did you stay or leave, and what were your reasons for doing so?

bureaucracy – a term describing particular features of organisation in which structure, role relationships and procedures are specified in writing and are followed impartially and without deviation over long time periods, irrespective of the individual's personality or the personal preferences of the role occupants

stability and order to an uncertain world, its function being to guard against speculation and change; therefore altering its written rules or constitution is the only way to change it. All organisations of any size require some written rules, but for large ones they are essential. The need to ensure control and the type of work undertaken often mean that this culture is appropriate and/or inevitable.

Because of its size, the NHS has this as its underlying culture. Although the creation of clinical care groups and independent Trusts has sought to reduce bureaucracy by reducing the size of the operational units, this has been only partially successful. The size of the units is still substantial, and the need for central bureaucratic control continues, reinforced by the reforms of the late 1990s (DoH, 1997; Klein and Maynard, 1998).

To many people bureaucracy implies red tape, an inflexible adherence to rules and inefficiency. To others, however, notably the German sociologist Max Weber (1864–1920), bureaucracy is technically the most efficient organisational form – rational, legal, impersonal in operation and highly specialised. Weber identified his model of bureaucracy as an 'ideal type' incorporating the features of many organisations.

Enterprise discretion is generally greater at the top of the organisation, so decisions that are deemed to be beyond the competence of a worker are referred upwards. This tends to slow the process of decision-making and create frustration within the organisation, not least for its clients, who generally deal face to face with the most junior workers and/or clinical professionals (see Scholes, 1994).

Mullins (1999) discusses many of the identified dysfunctions of bureaucracy. The most significant is perhaps that the impersonal nature of bureaucracy and the limitations imposed on those who work at various levels within the hierarchy tend to create what Handy refers to as role occupants (Handy, 1993). These are people who are able to subordinate their individuality to the requirements of the role they occupy. Their commitment tends to be to the role rather than to the goals of organisation. This in turn produces the 'job's worth' mentality in which, on occasions, an adherence to the rules takes precedence even over common sense. The institutionalised lack of discretion implied by this situation has led Argyris (1964) to claim that bureaucracies can restrict individual psychological growth and development. Hay (1993) believes that hierarchies tend to create a 'controlling' ethos in which each layer tends to control the one below it while obeying the one above. In these situations, it is difficult for new ideas to emerge from below or bad practice to be challenged.

Thinking about...

What does the term 'bureaucracy' mean to you? What experiences have you had of a bureaucratic organisation?

EXAMPLE 7.1

'Whistleblowing'

Most NHS Trusts operate a risk management procedure (a bureaucratic process) that facilitates the reporting of the occurrence of clinical errors, usually by the completion of an 'adverse incident' form. Such errors could be administering the wrong drug to a patient, giving an incorrect dose of the right drug, or some other serious mistake. The primary purpose of the procedure is to gather information that will help in the design of better systems of operation, in order to reduce the incidence of such occurrences.

CONNECTIONS

Chapter 9 (Ethics and Law) discusses examples of medical negligence and its definition in law, as well as issues relating to the regulation of a profession

There is, however, undoubtedly a tendency for some professionals to discount the need for such reporting, the professional distaste for bureaucracy perhaps playing a part. They may ritualise or underplay the incident or 'cover' for their colleagues by simply keeping quiet. This may be done on the basis of an expectation of a return of the favour should the circumstances ever be reversed. There may, however, also be strong social pressures to conform to group norms and severe sanctions for 'whistleblowers' – those who do not do so. Because 'blowing the whistle' abrogates the bureaucratic order by the role occupant acting out of role and approaching a higher level within the organisation or even outside it than is permitted by the rules, the individual concerned incurs the wrath of management as well as of the conspirators. In some cases, whistleblowers have lost their jobs. In others (for example the case of the Bristol heart babies referred to in Chapter 9) they have chosen to work abroad knowing that they face little chance of future employment in the UK, given the power of the professions concerned to block their career. Indeed, the government has had to pass the Public Interest Disclosure Act (1998) to protect those who are able to break through the barriers of excessive employer control to raise serious issues of concern.

Club culture: *God – Zeus; symbol – a spider's web*

This is the culture of the entrepreneur; the person who started the organisation and who personally controls it. Not for him or her written rules and bureaucratic constraints, but freedom to get things done. This is the culture of the quick decision and the instant reward. Power and authority is vested in the Zeus person alone, and a satisfactory job performance on the part of subordinates means compliance with the wishes, and often the whims, of the central figure, who makes the rules and sets the tone for the whole unit. Harrison (1972) referred to this as the power culture.

Strong and determined 'Zeus' figures can find the confines of the health services role culture very constraining and may seek ways to carve out various areas of freedom for themselves. Making links with the private sector (private practice) has been a favourite route, while research projects offer an alternative as they require a rather different culture, albeit one that is often compatible with the 'club' way of doing things.

Task culture: *God – Athena; symbol – a net*

The task culture is one of teamwork. There are many teams within most health care organisations. Where this culture is well differentiated from the surrounding role culture, there will be autonomy and freedom for members to do their thing. Targets may be imposed from above, but methods of achievement remain a team decision. This culture is characterised by low status differences between members. Expertise is recognised more readily than grade or position. Research departments tend to be predominately club cultures or task cultures.

Thinking about...

Can you think of another example from within health services of a task culture?

Person culture: *God – Dionysus; symbol – a group of stars*

This is the culture of the person, Dionysus being the god who puts the person rather than the organisation first. He is the symbol of existentialism, the philosophical theory emphasising the existence of the individual person as a free and responsible agent determining his or her own development. Dionysians exist in organisations as architects in practices and as lawyers in chambers. In universities, they are the academics, while in health care, they are the clinical professionals who attend to patients or who interpret clinical data and provide expert opinion.

While most organisations require the expertise of a few of these people, health organisations have an enormous number of them. The NHS has 60,000 doctors, of whom 16,000 are consultants and 26,000 GPs. Loyalty to their profession, to their independence of clinical judgement and to themselves makes them immune to the normal organisational hierarchy. Dionysians are, accordingly, very difficult people to manage. Since the organisation is unable to function without them, they have great power, borne not of hierarchical position but of expertise and political clout. As we have seen, the autonomy of doctors was enshrined in the 1946 National Health Service Act. This fact alone makes health services management unique.

Doctors are, of course, not the only ones in health care with professional expertise. No doubt you can think of many others: the community nurse, practice nurse, health visitor, midwife, community psychiatric nurse, senior nurse specialist and practitioner – all within the nursing profession. But are there others who are neither doctors nor nurses? What about pharmacists, dentists, opticians, health promotion specialists, public health researchers and members of the professions allied to medicine mentioned earlier. All these fall, in varying degrees, into this category. We might call them quasi-Dionysians since they tend to work effectively in multicultural contexts and their degree of independence varies. Dionysians in health care represent the front-line troops who interface with the patients or who support those who do – the 'grinders' of the organisation, as Scholes (1994) has described them. These are the people whom Apollo is required to manage.

Of course, organisations and even departments and groups rarely exhibit pure cultural forms. A research department may have many task culture personnel, employ several Dionysians and be managed by a Zeus. However, they all need to relate to the underlying role culture if they are to work effectively.

EXAMPLE 7.2

Organisational cultures

Consider the following account of a meeting in a research department:

'Did you have your regular delivery of liquid nitrogen this morning?', enquired the manager of the research scientist.

'Yes', replied the researcher.

'May I have the delivery note, please', said the manager.

'What note?', replied the researcher, 'Oh, that rubbish. I cannot be troubled with that; I threw that in the bin, it's just another piece of paper cluttering up the lab. It means nothing to me. Why do you need it?'

'Because', said the manager, 'unless you sign the note to indicate that you have received it, today's delivery may be your last for some time.'

'Why on earth should that be', said the researcher, 'They come every week, regular as clockwork.'

The manager took a deep breath. 'The company have complained that they have not been paid for some time.'

'Why not?'

'Finance will not pay them because they have not received any delivery notes from you to say that the goods have been received. They will not pay for what we have not received.'

'But we have received the goods', exclaimed the researcher, growing more agitated as the thought occurred to him that this might have something to do with the 20 or so such notes he had discarded over the past few weeks since he had taken over the responsibility for requisitioning supplies.

'How are finance to know this?', asked the manager.

'Oh'

'The signed delivery notes come to me from you. I then send these to the supplies department, who placed the original standing order for the regular delivery. They note the fact and amount of the delivery, which varies slightly from week to week depending on the amount of liquid nitrogen delivered. This entry is made on a goods received sheet, on which are recorded all the goods received for all the departments. When each sheet is complete, it is signed and sent to the invoice section of the finance department, who match it with the invoice from the supplier. Those invoices which match with the goods received sheet entries are paid; the remainder are not.'

'Oh'

'Regular deliveries of goods that are not paid for are soon stopped. Now, do you want to look into that bin?'

- What cultures do the manager and the research scientist belong to?
- Are such cultural conflicts inevitable?
- How can an organisation manage and co-ordinate different cultures?

ENVIRONMENT

Organisations exist in an environment, not in a vacuum. What occurs in that environment will affect organisational growth and development. When management writers refer to the 'environment', they usually mean the many political, economic, sociological and technological (PEST) factors (Johnson and Scholes, 1999) that operate on organisations.

For many years, the NHS existed in a largely stable environment, one in which the rate of change was relatively slow. From 1948 until the early 1960s, the rate of medical development was relatively modest and confined mainly to the introduction of new antibiotics. Tranquillisers were introduced in 1969 and the contraceptive pill a year later. Automation in a variety of forms (for example laboratory analysers) and complex surgical equipment (such as heart–lung machines) began to appear in health care in the mid-1960s. The first liver transplant was performed in 1963 and the first heart transplant in 1967 (Durham and Stanley, 1999). Thus the internal environment of the NHS was deemed to be stable.

Inflation remained low, that is, between 2.5 and 3.0 per cent for most of that period. Although the population of the country expanded following World War II, the system was able to cope with the number of dependent elderly. Politically, there was 'no incentive to challenge the prevailing consensus' regarding the NHS, which had emerged as 'a national monument' from its first decade (Klein, 2000). Socially, there was great disparity in the distribution of resources within the service, but this did not begin to emerge as significant, that is, as a political issue, until the third decade of the NHS, the 1970s. The external environment therefore also appeared to be calm.

There was thus a long period, uninterrupted by the need for radical change, in which the five founding principles of the NHS were allowed to gestate, to develop and to be absorbed into the collective consciousness of both the NHS employees and the population in general. Moreover, the service provided by the NHS was perceived to fill a long-neglected need in society and was also cost free at the point of use. In this way, the cultural values of the service were thoroughly established.

The winds of change began to blow in the late 1960s and early 1970s as inflation rose and UK manufacturing performance continued to fall. In 1976, these and other factors led to the UK requiring an International Monetary Fund (IMF) loan, which, among other measures, led to the imposition of cash limits in the NHS financial accounting system. These changes in the general or 'external' environment were compounded by developments in the specific health care or 'internal' environment.

 How does the increasing trend towards globalisation affect the balance between internal and external environments?

Senior (1997) suggests that PEST factors influence organisations, including their strategies, structures and means of operating. The mnemonic has also appeared as STEP (Goodman, 1995), whereas Senior (1997) herself prefers PETS, and you are likely to encounter all three of these acronyms in the literature. The three most often cited PEST factors specific for health care are:

1. technical developments and innovation, including drugs and their associated cost

2. the rising number of dependent elderly in society

3. increasing public expectation of the developing NHS.

These have led to rising costs, and the consequent need for tight financial control has inevitably led to profound change at every level of the NHS.

Environmental winds of change (PEST factors) are felt in various degrees of turbulence. Ansoff and McDonnell (1990) provide a model for assessing environmental turbulence (Table 7.1). They suggest that the organisation's response should match the degree of environmental turbulence if performance is to be optimised. Turbulence at level 1 (change occurs more slowly than the organisa-

Table 7.1   Environmental turbulence model

Level	Label	Definition
1	Predictable	A repetitive environment characterised by stability in which challenges repeat themselves; change is slower than the organisation's ability to respond; the future is expected to be the same as the past
2	Forecastable by extrapolation	Complexity increases, but managers can still extrapolate from the past and forecast the future with confidence
3	Predictable threats and opportunities	Complexity increases further when the organisation's ability to respond becomes more problematic; the future can, however, still be predicted with some degree of confidence
4	Partially predictable opportunities	Turbulence increases with the addition of global and socio-political changes. The future is only partially predictable
5	Unpredictable surprises	Turbulence increases further, unexpected events and situations occurring more quickly than the organisation can respond

Source: Adapted from Ansoff and McDonnell, 1990

tion's ability to respond) is contrasted with that at the maximum level, 5 (at which change is unexpected and unpredictable, and occurs more quickly than the organisation can cope with). If we examine the response to the increasing turbulence from the late 1960s to the end of the millennium, we can see that increasingly radical change has been imposed on the NHS in response to ever more severe environmental conditions (Table 7.2).

For example, the first reorganisation of the NHS in 1974 merely changed the structure by creating an additional administrative layer between the district and the region, which was coterminous with local authority boundaries and absorbed most of the health care services previously supplied and managed by them. This was an exercise in bureaucracy that was readily accepted as many additional administrative posts were needed to create the 190 new area health authorities in England and Wales. The cultural values of the NHS were, however, left unscathed, and the behaviour of the large complex organisation continued largely as before. The second reorganisation in 1982, introduced by the Conservative government under Margaret Thatcher, merely removed the area tier but left the culture untouched. ***Consensus management***, the principle that all management decisions should be implemented only after an agreement between all the principal stakeholders, was to remain.

consensus management – a process of decision-making whereby action is only taken if all the participants in the process are unanimous

Although this change went smoothly, it amounted to little more than a rearrangement of deckchairs, and the government realised that this was not enough. The Griffiths inquiry into NHS management was set up, reporting in October 1983. The proposals were implemented in 1984. Traditional consensus management was too slow for most decision-making. There needed to be

Table 7.2 Environmental turbulence and change

Period	Perceived turbulence	Pest factors	Events
1948–1961	1	Low inflation; modest medical technological progress and implementation; containable demographic change; political satisfaction with the NHS	Finance system allows for revised estimates of expenditure to be submitted halfway through the financial year. Cost of the NHS rises above government expectations but is contained. Direct personal taxation rises
1962–1973	2	Rising inflation and worsening trade position in manuactured goods; industrial unrest; increasing technological advances in health care; first liver transplant (1963); measles vaccine introduced (1966); increase in number of clinical support staff (professions allied to medicine); introduction of computers to health care; rising cost of the NHS	Enoch Powell's Hospital Plan (an early reform) attempted to rationalise hospital number and location, bed number and occupancy. Concept of the district general hospital introduced. Introduction of the concept of planning to the NHS. Early attempts to plan jointly with the newly created social services departments of local authorities
1974–1982	3	Inflation high; IMF loan (1976); continual technological advance; CT scans introduced; rising public expectation of health services; first reported case of AIDS; health care costs, particularly of drugs, continue to rise	Bureaucratic reorganisation of the NHS (1976). Direct health services moved from local authorities to the NHS. Cash limits introduced (1976). Attempt to reallocate resources for health care more equitably throughout the country. Emphasis on cost containment. Second reorganisation (1982).
1983–1984	4	Inflation still a problem; continual technological advance; cost of health care continues to rise; political determination to reform the NHS	Griffiths' first report (DHSS, 1983). Introduction of general management to the NHS. Strong emphasis on cost control and cost reduction. Competitive tendering. First redundancies in the NHS
1985–1990	4	Inflation high towards the end of this period; awareness of the demographic time bomb of a growing number of elderly requiring care; announcement of further radical reforms for the NHS	Griffiths' second report Community Care: An Agenda for Action (Griffiths, 1988) and many others. NHS and Community Care Act 1990. Clinical care groups begin to appear in secondary and tertiary care. Local authority representation removed from local NHS boards. Downsizing of regional health authorities
1991–1997	5	High inflation at the start of the period, falling later; political decision to remove elderly requiring only social care from the NHS; political determination to introduce market ethos into the NHS; emphasis on consumerism in public services, targets for health introduced; NHS funding crisis (1996); record waiting lists (1997); government commitment to low personal direct taxation	Creation of NHS Trusts and GP fundholders. Creation of 'purchasers' and 'providers' to form the quasi-health care 'market'. Introduction of non-executive directors with business skills. Removal of regional health authorities; replaced by eight regional offices. Private Finance Initiative. Introduction of the Patient's Charter (DoH, 1991). Tacit encouragement of the public to complain about poor services. Requirement for all health facilities to have and publish a complaints procedure
1997–2000	5	Inflation relatively low; introduction of the minimum wage; European Union directive on working hours; government announces further reform of the NHS to abolish the health care market and remove GP fundholders; continued government commitment to low personal direct taxation	White Paper The New NHS: Modern, Dependable (DoH, 1997). Clinical governance promulgated. A First Class Service (DoH, 1998) published. Primary Care Groups introduced (1999). White Paper on public health (DoH, 1999)

someone 'in charge' because the consensus model allowed a great deal of internal 'political' influence to bear on organisational affairs. The Griffiths Report (DHSS, 1983) recommended the removal of consensus management and the introduction of the concept of general management and general managers in all health care facilities. The opposition to this move by the medical profession, and to some extent the nursing profession, illustrated the very nature of the proposed change. It attacked the long-established culture of the NHS, the unconsciously held assumptions about how the service should be run and the values that had worked well in an earlier environment.

The NHS had moved from being an **administered** service to a managed service. As the move from administration to management was contemplated, the term 'leadership' began to be used. The writer Rosemary Stewart quotes the words of a regional general manager, interviewed in a post-Griffiths study: 'A few years ago, I could not have used the word "leadership" without wincing and blushing, now I do use it' (Stewart, 1989). Although the government denied at the time that the implementation of the Griffiths recommendations was a 'reorganisation', its introduction was more fraught and its effects on the NHS more profound than anything that had gone before. There had been the beginnings of cultural change.

There is a link between a well-established organisational culture and resistance to change. We can note that an adherence to values is reinforced by the particular type of organisational culture we are seeking to change. Bureaucratic organisations, having a role culture, are slow to perceive the need for change and slow to change even if the need is recognised since their main function is to preserve stability (Handy, 1993). It follows that the required 'frame-breaking' change (Tushman et al., 1988) necessitated by the increasingly turbulent PEST factors in the 1980s and 90s could only be achieved by dismantling, as much as possible, the stranglehold of bureaucracy that had characterised the NHS from 1948.

In 1990, the NHS and Community Care Act introduced far-reaching reforms (DoH, 1990). These introduced a quasi-market in health care provision and included:

- a split between the purchasers and the providers of health services
- the creation of NHS Trusts
- GP fundholding.

These were changes at gale force 5 on the Ansoff and McDonnell scale. The speed and magnitude of their introduction (the suggestion of pilot studies being swept aside) left many in the NHS reeling. Managerial skills became more necessary as decisions were made at the operational level. Responsibility for staff and materials through budgetary control was placed firmly with departmental or sectional budget-holders. The traditional 'role occupants' of the NHS typically had had no such responsibilities since decisions were normally taken at a higher level in large public sector organisations.

The introduction of the quasi-market in the provision of health services introduced elements of competition into the NHS. NHS Trusts had to bid for their work in competition with each other and, in some instances, with the private sector. Although the criteria related mainly to cost, volume and quality, the main factor in contract negotiation was usually that of cost, money being cash limited by government policy and by forecasts of inflation.

administration – the practice of being accountable for carrying out the decisions of others. Involves initiating action within defined limits of authority, monitoring and recording progress, outcomes and events. It is an essential component of, particularly, a bureaucratic organisation

CONNECTIONS

Chapter 6 (Social Policy) discusses the policy context behind the introduction of the internal market in the NHS

EXAMPLE 7.3

International health care

A recent World Health Organization (WHO) report on the efficiency of health systems found that it is not the level of spending but its distribution that affects health care. The USA spends more of its gross domestic product (13.7 per cent) on health than any other country but ranks only 37th out of 191 WHO member states. In contrast, Oman has reduced child mortality from 230 per 1,000 to 15 per 1,000 in 20 years as a result of focused investment.

All countries face problems in funding health care. One of the key recommendations of the WHO report is to fund health services through pre-payment schemes such as taxes, insurance or social security rather than through payment when people need care, which can force people into debt should they suffer a major illness or emergency. In the USA, there has been a rapid expansion in private health insurance. At first, this made modern health care more accessible to the general public, but it also established medical autonomy and the freedom to diagnose, treat and charge fees commensurate with market forces. Rising prices led the government to introduce schemes such as Medicare and Medicaid to support the elderly and poor, who were being excluded by medical inflation.

The failings of many health systems can be attributed to many factors but include:

- unregulated 'free' markets in health care

- 'moonlighting' by doctors who work in both the private and public sectors

- the regulation of treatments by third parties such as insurance companies.

The management of health care systems is thus not necessarily based on sound evidence. There may be, as in the USA, intense lobbying by vested interests against regulation and any attempt to curb costs.

Source: WHO, 2000

The NHS remains, however, a public service organisation, and the need to provide services to meet public expectation conflicts with the private company ethos of increasing profits. Although the Labour government in 1997 removed references to the health care 'market', the need to contain costs and to increase quality – spending public resources only on the most effective interventions – remains a priority.

Fordism – a belief that there is one best way of structuring organisations for efficient production or operation. The client/customer is therefore limited in choice by the particular method(s) adopted, resulting in an organisational provider orientation rather than consumer orientation, the opposite of consumerism

THEORETICAL AND METHODOLOGICAL PERSPECTIVES

The search for effective approaches to the business of management has been a long one. **Henry Ford**, for example, believed that the organisation of car production would be best served by limiting the product range. The focus of other models of management is motivation – how to structure organisations and organise work so that employees work happily, productively and with a sense of responsibility for what they do.

SCIENTIFIC MANAGEMENT

F. W. Taylor proposed the 'scientific' approach to work in 1895. He believed that workers, left to themselves, were naturally inefficient and lazy; managers were ignorant of the most effective ways in which to organise work processes and left work organisation to the workers. Taylor, however, believed that there was one right way to tackle every task and set about a comprehensive series of measurements of all work undertaken in the steel works where he was employed as an engineer. Workers were required to follow Taylor's methods precisely, and to persuade them to do so, he arranged for additional payments to be made, these being directly linked to the amount of work accomplished. Since Taylor's methods enabled far more work to be completed each day than previously, he expected workers to adopt his methods enthusiastically. They were, he thought, the means to economic prosperity and would be welcomed by all.

Thinking about...

Would you like to be paid according to the amount of work you accomplished? What might be the disadvantage of this?

Taylor's model, however, was of economic man: the person who works primarily for money. In a nutshell, Taylor's assumptions were proved incorrect. The consequences of Taylor's methods destroyed the social structure of the worker's groups, militated against teamwork and created considerable hostility in spite of the higher level of earnings. The strict prescription of working practice, which included the length of work periods and rest breaks, was largely to blame. Although introduced in a number of industries in the USA in the first two decades of the 20th century, scientific management was eventually abandoned.

The disciplines of work study, method study and organisational ergonomics are used by today's managers to increase efficiency (and profitability) in a wide range of enterprises. Such techniques are often used in management services departments, which provide internal or external consultancy to their organisations, along with a host of other approaches, such as computer modelling and simulation techniques, that are usually grouped under the heading of operations research. Such departments are sometimes found in (or bought in by) large health providers, particularly those who are undertaking fundamental reorganisation (often referred to as business process re-engineering (BPR).

 How could the flow of patients attending an outpatient department be improved so that the *Patient's Charter* standards might be met without lowering the number of patients booked into each clinic?

Operations research staff would list and study all the elements of outpatient attendance, such as blood tests, collecting prescribed drugs from pharmacy and undergoing X-rays and/or other tests before seeing the doctor. The order in which these functions were carried out would need to be optimised and the resultant queuing phenomena modelled. Computer modelling enables decisions to be made about the adequacy of resources in all the departments concerned. How many blood-takers, radiographers and pharmacists are needed for each particular clinic? How can the work of each of these people be optimised? Unlike what happened in Taylor's approach, the results of such investigations would be made available to clients rather than imposed, and would flow from agreement between the researchers and the operational staff.

HUMAN RELATIONS MODEL

In the late 1920s, there began a series of social experiments set in the Western Electric Company's Hawthorne Works in Chicago. The experiments initially consisted of altering the lighting and ventilation of a section of the works in order to find the optimum conditions for maximum productivity. What was observed was that productivity rose whatever change was made, even when conditions were deliberately made worse. This was eventually attributed to the fact the workers saw themselves to be the centre of attention of management – sufficiently important to be chosen to take part in 'an experiment' – and responded accordingly. These experiments were deeply flawed and poorly conducted, but the interpretation of the findings was congruent with the emerging ideas of the human relations school of industrial management under the influence of Elton Mayo. The term 'the Hawthorne effect' is still used in some quarters to explain 'spontaneous' improvements in worker motivation or productivity.

human resource – the members/employees of the organisation and those who contribute to its function; the human component in any enterprise

In essence, the theory stated that the ***human resource*** is an important factor of production and should not be ignored in the job design and work organisation. This was a more acceptable model than scientific management, which had been rejected by workers and management alike. It has, however, singularly failed to provide a solution to the problem of effective organisation.

SOCIO-TECHNICAL SYSTEMS APPROACH

This approach was developed in the UK by Emery, Rice and Trist in the 1940s and 50s at the Tavistock Institute in London (Trist, 1973; Trist and Bamforth, 1951). It specifically considered the interrelationship between the technical aspects of work and the effect that this has on the cohesion and productivity of working groups. The introduction into work of ever more complex technology tends to increase the degree to which work processes are prescribed and individual freedom becomes limited. Computer screens, for example, now force us to enter data precisely: there are no degrees of freedom permitted.

Thinking about...

Think about an example of new technology and its effect on the work process. Is the technology easy to manage? Do you regard it as limiting or liberating?

The introduction of technology has not always been successful and the past century saw a number of examples in which workers, because of its inappropriate design, capability or implementation, rejected new technology. An attempt in the early 1990s to introduce an adequate computerised dispatch to the London Ambulance Service was rejected by staff as wholly unworkable. However, the later computer systems that were introduced, following greater staff consultation, were more successful.

The socio-technical systems approach seeks to design systems that are congruent with the way in which work is actually carried out, rather than to assume that workers will automatically comply with the constraints imposed by a new system. As Mumford pointed out in 1973, 'Work systems are usually designed in technical terms to meet technical and business objectives, with little thought given to the needs of people operating the system' (Mumford, 1973). Trist (1973), however, defined the socio-technical systems approach as one that should empower workers and raise their status from that of possible victims of technology and change to that of 'managers' of technology and of work systems.

The introduction of new technology into work processes has been a major factor in creating change. It has instigated environmental turbulence in the past and is set to create even more in the future as product life cycles fall and new products appear with ever-increasing rapidity.

SYSTEMS THEORY

Systems theory has contributed to the development of concepts in the management of organisations as well as many other disciplines. A 'system', such as an organisation, may be regarded as a set of interrelated and interdependent entities or functions that combine for a specific purpose or purposes. These entities or functions are designated as subsystems when they lie within the organisational boundary, and environmental factors when they lie outside it. It follows that a change in one or more of the subsystems will tend to create a varying degree of change in all other subsystems – the ripple effect. For example, a chief executive officer who sets new goals, attainment targets or tasks for an organisation may require new or retrained staff, leading to far-reaching alterations.

A further refinement of socio-technical system theory is Nadler and Tushman's (1979) diagnostic congruence model of organisational behaviour, which illustrates the relationship between organisational elements. According to this model, organisational efficiency and effectiveness are closely linked to the degree of congruence between the elements that make up every organisation – individuals, tasks, the organisational structure and the informal culture – and between the organisation as a whole and its environment (Figure 7.2). When change occurs, it threatens the congruence between these elements, and efficiency and/or effectiveness may be compromised.

For example, if a community Trust introduces a hospital at home service (*new task*), staff may need to be recruited or trained (*individuals*), and new lines of accountability and consultation will be agreed, with a corresponding change in

systems theory – a system may be regarded as any group of interrelated and independent entities or functions that combine for a specific purpose. The theory views organisations as systems that are susceptible, in their structure and operation, to environmental influence and dependent upon that environment for sustenance (input) and meaning (output). Organisational systems consist of different subsystems, which, when responding to change, tend to create 'ripple' effects throughout the entire superordinate system

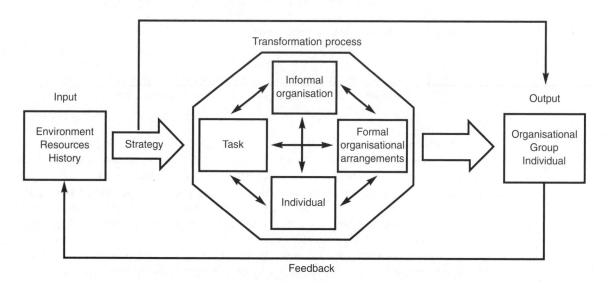

Figure 7.2   A congruence model of organisational behaviour
(Nadler and Tushman, 1979)

discharge policy (*new structure*). There will also need to be an attitudinal change within the organisation towards this quite different way of caring for acutely ill patients (*culture*). Moreover, there will need to be agreement across the organisational boundary so that GPs, relatives, social services and other agencies are willing and able to co-operate (*the environment*). Until all these adjustments have been made, neither the new service nor the Trust itself is likely to be capable of working effectively or efficiently.

The systems approach may help us to appreciate the problems of introducing rapid, successive changes to an organisation, particularly a highly bureaucratic one such as the NHS, without adequate time or effective management of the transition process (see Nadler, 1993).

LEADERSHIP STYLE

It became clear in the 1940s and 50s that the style of industrial leadership was highly significant. Even given all the appropriate organisational ingredients discussed above, the model of leadership employed was seen to be crucial to organisational effectiveness, particularly in industry. The NHS survived without a great deal of 'management' for many years, even discounting the concept of management until the 1970s. What has changed that makes this concept relevant?

The answer lies once more in the turbulence of the environment and the quickening pace of change in today's world. Stewart suggests that, in past times, administration was only thought to be necessary in the public service and involved carrying out policies (rather than making decisions) and being publicly accountable for doing so, whereas, on the other hand, managers *directed* (Stewart, 1996). Management has been observed to consist of three functions, with various roles within them. These functions are (Mintzberg, 1973):

- *interpersonal function:* managing interpersonal relationships of all kinds
- *managing information:* gathering data, analysing them and disseminating information
- *decision-making:* proactive and reactive, operational and strategic.

 What is the difference between administration, management and leadership? Is it possible to be a manager without being a leader?

Managerial authority is usually based on position, whereas leadership is based on personal qualities and the exercise of influence. A head nurse in a health facility is the designated manager of the staff nurses, suggest Callahan et al. (1986), yet the behaviour of the staff nurses is frequently influenced to a greater extent by the directives of the doctors. This may well of course occur in reverse, particularly where doctors are newly qualified and their nurse colleagues have greater expertise and experience. Leadership, or the ability to influence others and attract followers, can and does arise from any part of the organisation. Charismatic subordinates who have greater influence on their colleagues' views and behaviour could exercise more influence than a manager without leadership skills.

Leadership is one of the most important influences on organisational performance. It is the means by which the organisation achieves its objectives and may significantly affect the attitudes, behaviour and ultimate performance of individual workers. It is therefore a main focus of organisational behaviour theories.

There is no evidence to support the popularly held view that leadership qualities are inherited. This may simply be down to our inadequate understanding of human genetics, but there are certain characteristics found in most successful leaders that may be either inherited or acquired or both. While physical characteristics – age, appearance, height and weight – provide no correlation with leader ability, and intelligence only weakly so, personality findings are much stronger. Alertness, self-confidence, personal integrity and the need to dominate are frequently identified as traits found in leaders (Stogdill, 1974). Most of all, leaders have a high need for achievement, and most have strong interpersonal skills. Leaders communicate well. That is to say, not only do they speak and write clearly and often, keeping others informed, but they also communicate information accurately in order to establish shared meaning between themselves and workers of all designations and levels within the organisation. This is particularly challenging within the health service because of its sheer size and the range and cultural diversity of personnel employed.

Stewart (1989) has described leaders as possessing a number of attributes:

- *vision:* without which no one will follow
- *valour:* the courage to stand up for one's principles
- *virtue:* honourable principles
- *vigour:* the energy to pursue goals.

To these we might add:

- *visibility:* being regularly seen by everyone rather than being an organisational recluse
- *vigilance:* keeping watch over the organisation by regular environmental scanning.

> **Thinking about...**
>
> Think of people you know whom you perceive to be leaders. What personal qualities do they possess? Are they able to command respect from a wide range of different people? Why do you trust them? Why do you, or would you, follow them?

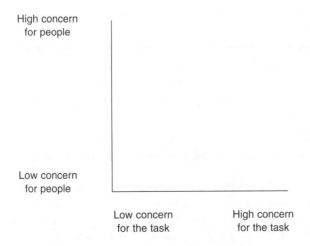

Figure 7.3   The leadership grid

Because of the number and complexity of their professional groups, it follows that leadership is very difficult to establish in health care organisations. The temptation is to favour the views of one professional group, or to vest leadership in that group, just because it is particularly powerful.

Another, simpler way of classifying leaders is to rate their commitment to people and to task accomplishment, and plot these ratings in a diagram. This approach was first identified in the Ohio studies in the 1950s when it became clear that these two variables – concern for people and concern for the task – were independent variables. Leadership might rate highly, or poorly, on one or both dimensions or consistently favour one style at the expense of the other. These ideas were later developed by Blake and Mouton (1964) and then further expanded by Blake and McCanse (1991) in what is now known as the leadership grid (Figure 7.3).

 Which 'style' of management/leadership do you believe characterised the NHS in its first three decades? Where would you place it on the graph in 1948? Are things different now? What, if anything, has brought about the change?

In the 1950s and 60s, leadership style tended to be regarded as constant for the individual leader, regardless of circumstances. Blake and Mounton (1964) designated a high concern for people and a low concern for the job as 'country club management'. By this, they meant that the need to maintain a comfortable, friendly work atmosphere always took precedence over the need to attain management objectives. A high concern for the task and a low concern for people was designated the authority compliance style of management, in which the human element, autonomy and freedom of choice were minimised. This is also not a style likely to be effective with skilled professionals.

Tannenbaum and Schmidt (1973) identify three sets of factors that determine leadership style:

● factors relating to the *manager*: leadership ability, personal value system, confidence in subordinates and tolerance of ambiguity

● factors relating to *subordinates*: need for independence, readiness to assume responsibility for decision-making, tolerance of ambiguity, interest in the problem, understanding of and identification with organisational goals, knowledge and experience pertinent to the problem, expectations about power-sharing

● factors relating to the *situation*: type of organisation, the group's effectiveness, the nature of the problem itself, time constraints.

Tannenbaum and Schmidt suggest that leadership style needs to change to meet the requirements of complex situations that may themselves vary. As we have seen, the health services are extremely complex. However, not all subordinates are the same, each one requiring an approach that will motivate rather than alienate that individual.

MOTIVATION

Ever since the failure of Taylor's regime of 'scientific management', management researchers have striven to understand the secrets of motivation. The NHS is a large, complex organisation: encouraging and enabling the workforce to fulfil its tasks is a major function of management.

? **How can we motivate health care workers?**

Mullins (1996) describes motivation as 'the direction and persistence of action'. This means that people will act in response to a motive providing that motive is appropriate for both the individual and the situation. Management's role in motivation is likely to be one of creating the conditions that provide the necessary incentives to enable staff to judge that their goals are important and can be attained.

The needs satisfactionists

The group of theorists known as the needs satisfactionists (see, for example, Alderfer, 1972; Herzberg, 1968; McClelland, 1988; Maslow, 1943) believe that human beings are driven to fulfil inherent unmet needs. We apparently all have them but not all in the same proportions and strength as each other. Table 7.3 illustrates the relationship between these needs as defined by the four writers.

These theorists believe that if one can fulfil some of the needs (shown in Table 7.3) at work, positive motivation to work can be achieved. However, Herzberg (1968) in particular found that a fulfilment of lower order needs, such as the need for an acceptable work environment, an appropriate supervision style, a reasonable company policy, good relationships at work and, surprisingly, pay, might reduce dissatisfaction but did not improve motivation. He called these *hygiene factors*. Higher order needs fulfilment, that is, related to achievement, a

Table 7.3 Classification of human need

	Maslow	Alderfer	McClelland	Herzberg
Top of hierarchy	Self-actualisation	Growth	Achievement	Challenging job
	Self-esteem (recognition)			Advancement Responsibility Recognition
	Affiliation (love, social)	Relatedness	Affiliation	Work relationships Supervision style
	Safety		Power	Company policy
Base of hierarchy	Physiological needs	Existence		Salary and benefits Working conditions

Source: Modified from Schein, 1988

recognition of achievement, challenging work, real responsibility and opportunities for personal growth and advancement were, however, motivating. He therefore called these the *motivators*. Such factors are clearly inextricably linked to job design, that is, what people do and are permitted/encouraged to do at work, hygiene factors being concerned with the context in which the work is performed. Both are important. According to Herzberg, if working conditions are improved, worker dissatisfaction is reduced, but when job content and design are improved, motivation is increased.

Although Herzberg's research methodology and also the interpretation of his findings have been challenged (see Jones and Page, 1987; Mullins, 1996) there appears to be empirical evidence to support the link between motivation and job design. Work by Hackman and Oldham (1975, 1979) suggests that to be motivating jobs should:

- be perceived as meaningful and challenging, providing individuals with an awareness of the significance of their work against the bigger picture of organisational aims
- provide an element of autonomy and control; in this way, individuals are aware of the part they play in the organisation's success
- enable individual workers to know the results they achieve, that is, what is their contribution to the organisation's success.

 Are all workers likely to respond in the same way to motivational factors?

The fact is that we are all different. Mitchell (1982) found that motivation is very much an individual matter. What may motivate me today in my particular set of circumstances may not motivate someone else, or me tomorrow, should those circumstances (my psychological contract) change. Although there is strong support among some writers (Berne, 1975; Clements, 1980; Hay, 1993) for recognition (positive stroking) as a motivator, the effect of this may be merely to make me feel better, satisfying my affiliation needs rather than challenging me to work more effectively.

The process theorists

The other major group of motivation theorists concentrate on the process undertaken to produce motivation in workers. Handy suggests that we tend to calculate the amount of effort that we believe is needed to achieve the required work performance and match this with the probability of receiving the reward, intrinsic or extrinsic, should we perform as required. This calculation is balanced by the perceived value of the reward to us at the time. Handy calls this his motivation calculus (Handy, 1993).

There is evidence to suggest that we select the work environment to suit our particular orientation, skills and needs (Holland, 1973; Schein, 1978). Schein describes a career anchor as a self-perception of an individual's needs, motives, talents and values, based on actual occupational experience. It is the set of needs, values and talents that the person is least willing to give up if forced to make a choice. These theories state that there are identifiable factors differentiating individuals in their choice of career, aiming for a career that is compatible with the individual's personal orientations and preferred environments.

It is assumed that people with similar orientations and needs subconsciously migrate towards work in which those needs may more readily be satisfied. The health service expects to recruit to its ranks those who want to work in the caring professions, with or without face-to-face contact with patients. The service can therefore suffer when there is a shortage of such people at times of scarce resources when employment conditions – for example salary – do not satisfy the minimum needs of even these people and when alternative employment opportunities are available.

WORKING IN TEAMS

Organisations are social devices to enable goals that cannot be attained by individuals working alone to be accomplished collectively. This is particularly true in the health services. Therefore teamwork, which was discounted by Taylor, is a most significant factor in health care delivery and **team-building** an essential aspect of organisational development. Teams need leaders, and teams require motivation.

The words 'group' and 'team' are often used interchangeably. A group can be described as any collection of people defined by a common purpose: located together, classified together or sharing beliefs. In an organisational context, however, a team may be defined as a group of workers selected by the organisation for a defined purpose. As a *group*, they may be expected to exhibit group characteristics. As a *team*, the organisation will expect them to perform their allotted functions without the intrusion of the any of the dysfunctional aspects of group behaviour such as *groupthink* or the *risky shift* (see the case study below). The approach to achieving this is often referred to as team-building and/or organisational development. Teams exist in many different forms, as can be seen in Table 7.4.

team-building – an essential component of organisational development whereby the needs and roles of individual group members, and team objectives, are identified and clarified, and responsibilities are negotiated and assigned. Team-building can take place both 'off the job' through facilitated training exercises and also through work-related activity, innovation and feedback on work performance

Table 7.4   A team classification

Types of team	Examples
Groups reporting to the same supervisor	Departmental teams, management teams
Groups of people with common aims	Research teams
Temporary groups for specific tasks	Project teams introducing new buildings, new services or the reconfiguration of services
Groups of people with interdependencies	Community nursing teams, hospital at home schemes; such teams may cross organisational boundaries
Groups of people with no formal links but who cannot accomplish tasks as individuals	Some project teams and some teams of experts involved in problem-solving

What other teams can you identify within the NHS?

When groups (and teams) are formed, they are observed to go through certain stages of development before they settle down to perform the function for which they came into being. Tuckman (1965) identified these stages as forming, storming, norming and performing.

- The *forming* phase – interactions are polite and guarded.

- The *storming* phase – interactions are made to test fundamental differences between group members. Different members may be professionally committed to their own ways of doing things. Various conflicts are likely to emerge, and even the leadership may be challenged.

- The *norming* phase – norming involves getting organised, confronting and resolving issues, focusing on the task ahead instead of the group and generally establishing systems and procedures. Kakabadse et al. (1988) believe that the duration of this phase depends on the skills and abilities of the leader.

- The *performing* phase – this is dependent upon the group members' willingness to resolve their differences, and again the leader can facilitate this. When this occurs, group members become more supportive and communicative, rely on each other more readily and combine in joint problem-solving rather than mutual blaming when problems are encountered. These stages are, however, by no means progressive. External and internal changes can cause the team to revert to earlier phases, particularly if team membership or the leader is changed.

In health services, individuals seldom work in isolation from others, the effectiveness of health care requiring the co-ordination and collaboration of various specialists. The NHS has, however, been subjected to many changes. Because change usually involves changes in team composition and function, team-building and team maintenance are particularly important.

EXAMPLE 7.4

Team-building on a ward

A hospital instituted new arrangements for managing the surgery wards, but some members of staff were unclear about their role in the new structure. Increased sickness absence and the heavy use of agency and bank staff had hindered establishing consistent patterns of work, including the new nursing regimes. After the first week, the manager arranged for some additional cover for the two wards. This enabled for there, once a week, to be a much longer hand-over period between shifts, during which time the permanent staff were able to meet. The ward manager used this time to make clear her requirements and to endorse the management structure by supporting her new deputy. However, she ensured that each qualified member of the nursing team had special responsibilities and that each week they would take turns to lead a brief discussion on their own area of work. The team would be encouraged to discuss ways in which problems could be overcome and standards improved.

Team-building may be regarded as a collection of strategies aimed at helping the team to move smoothly through the Tuckman stages described above. Activities can be organised on or away from the job. Group discussion can take place during 'away days', or various forms of sensitivity training can be arranged to enable the group to confront task-related problems or difficulties with intragroup relationships. On the job training may involve experimenting with individual roles and responsibilities, coupled with as much participation as possible to allow the group to resolve its own difficulties. The group, as a team, is, however, required to achieve organisational objectives and thus needs to focus on its task. The leader is also the manager and needs a flexible approach between these two aspects of the leadership role.

The most effective teams appear to consist of groups of people who undertake different but complementary functions. They are not similar in personality or function but play a different group role – sometimes more than one. Belbin (1981) originally identified several separate roles that characterise how group members interact with one another. To be fully effective, teams require all the roles to be performed. The roles are as follows:

Chairperson	Setting and managing the team's agenda, articulating its goals and summarising its decisions
Shaper	Introducing ideas, shaping discussion and pushing for particular decisions
Plant	Introducing new and sometimes novel ideas; lateral thinking
Monitor evaluator	Analysing group discussion and assessing group options
Company worker	Looking at the practical aspects of implementation, the feasibility of suggestions and their compatibility with existing systems
Teamworker	Taking responsibility for team interactions, smoothing difficulties in discussion and supporting team members generally
Resource investigator	Engaging in background activity to find ways and means of implementing decisions, providing facts and figures to support arguments
Completer/finisher	Emphasising the need to carry through decisions to completion and therefore also being concerned about feasibility and detail; motivates the team to action.

 Which roles support the team and help it to function?
Which are more 'task' oriented?

It is essential to have someone to supply ideas as well as someone else to challenge them and play devil's advocate. It is also necessary to have team members who are well organised and like to get things completed. A team is also helped by the presence of those who are sensitive and who have the ability to respond to situations and to promote team spirit as well as providing leadership. It is quite possible that the roles we play differ in different teams. We may play multiple roles in certain teams and perhaps tend to compensate for any deficiency in the composition of a particular team. Team-building may also encourage team members, as part of their growth and personal development, to take on different team roles and to become aware of the importance of diversity in contributing to better teamwork.

CASE STUDY – THE EMERGING PRIMARY CARE GROUP

The following case study about a newly formed Primary Care Group (PCG) set up after the NHS reforms of 1997 illustrates the ways in which organisations respond to change. This chapter has described the different cultures that exist within the NHS, this PCG illustrating different cultural values at different stages of its development. Management theory helps us to understand the role that leadership and motivation play in effective groups and teams. In this case study, you will be able to identify different stages of development, different roles being played and how the group might be enabled to reach a more productive stage of development.

PCGs are responsible for commissioning the health care for their catchment populations of around 120,000. Their membership consists of a Chief Officer, a non-executive director appointed by the health authority, one lay member, one social services nominee and about 10 'professional' members, of whom the majority are to be GPs.

In this example, the numerically dominant group was the GPs, seven of whom were proposed by their colleagues and appointed without dissent by the health authority. This election took place very quickly, so the GP members were able to meet as a group before the non-GP members were appointed. The remaining 'professional' members – two nurses and two social services workers – and the one lay member were required to apply for their positions and underwent a rigorous selection procedure. Some applicants were rejected simply because of a lack of knowledge.

All GPs are currently self-employed independent contractors who are paid by the health services in relation to the number of patients on their lists and the amount of work they perform. They are therefore business oriented and have considerable knowledge and expertise not possessed by some of the non-medical members. The GPs had previously been fundholders and had as such enjoyed considerable freedom in providing special treatments for their own patients and arranging 'deals' with local Trusts to 'fast track' their patients needing hospital or community care. Moreover, they had all been members of the health authority's GP commissioning group so already constituted a 'performing' team. Not all the GPs were, however, equally enthusiastic about their involvement with the PCG, and it became obvious that there were some 'sleeping partners' in the group. GPs receive an additional allowance of £7,000 per annum for PCG membership, whereas nurses receive £4,000 per annum. This is paid simply for membership and is not performance related.

The GP members at first sought to exclude the non-medical members by saying that the agenda of the PCG would be of interest only to GPs. (This exemplifies the phenomenon known as 'risky shift' in which well-established and cohesive groups are observed to make risky decisions because group norms take precedence over clarity of thought. In these cases, it is observed that individual group members are unlikely to reach the same decision as the group collectively.) Other members felt excluded, and the Chief Officer needed to remind the group of its function and statutory obligations.

The group elected as its chair a GP who appeared also to have leadership qualities, had a vision of the group's potential to improve health in the local area and accepted the role for the group envisioned in the government White Paper *The New NHS: Modern, Dependable* (DoH, 1997). The nurses resolved that, in order to ensure that they had a voice, they would need to take their roles very seriously and develop competence, reading and studying all the papers and statistics from the health authority and developing a view on what should or should not be decided. Consequently, the chair approached one of the nurses and suggested she should become vice-chair. This proposal was met with less than enthusiasm by the other GP members but was, when formally proposed, accepted by the whole group without dissent. It was later discovered that the putative terms of reference that had been adopted by the group stipulated that a quorum for the meeting be four GPs and the chair (himself a GP). Following guidance from the Chief Officer, the group readily amended that to four GPs and three non-GPs to reflect the balance in the group membership generally.

The vice-chair drew up a business plan that gave each member key responsibilities. This was a new experience for most members for whereas GPs are experienced medical business persons, they act independently and have usually had little experience of formal business planning, whereas the vice-chair held a postgraduate management qualification. The recognition of their expertise now being given to the nurse members by the entire group helped them to feel equal members of the team. They felt that they were beginning to influence health policy in their area. The group could now begin to tackle some difficult problems.

The group was informed by the health authority that it should not allow open questions from members of the public or Community Health Council members at its meetings. The reason given was that, because of inexperience, another PCG had relayed misleading or inaccurate information to the public. The emerging PCG was able to resist this recommendation and continued to hold its meetings as before.

Yet other issues remain unresolved. The thorny issue of complaints handling has yet to be addressed, as has the related matter of public consultation. In both these cases, individual group members' perceptions of the relative importance and relevance of these issues to health care is effectively preventing the group making rapid progress. The group as a whole has accepted that these matters are relatively unimportant, yet an examination of the wider issues of clinical governance and the government's policy towards consumer involvement would challenge this view. Where none of the group members can think outside the prevailing group paradigm, the term 'groupthink' is often applied. Those playing strong shaper roles are sometimes able to impose a group paradigm over a long period of time.

The group has applied for Trust status from April 2001. Primary Care Trusts commission secondary health services and employ community staff who provide community services. This is an important step, and it is likely that the team membership will change. Management expertise will be needed and the sources of this identified. The role of members will change, and the status of GPs may well change fundamentally – from that of independent contractor to that of employee.

SUMMARY

- Understanding the complexity and culture of the organisation of the NHS requires an understanding of management theories

- The various models of management – scientific management, the human relations school, the socio-technical systems approach and systems theory (as well as many others) – all shed a degree of light on the complexity of management. Each is, however, inadequate on its own to provide a satisfactory guide for the health services manager

- Leadership remains a crucial aspect of management since it is a means of staff motivation, particularly in a time of change and environmental turbulence. Leadership needs to offer protection, permission and empowerment to staff to change their behaviour and reach new goals

- Motivation is the self-generation of personal energy, commitment and resolve to achieve acceptable organisational goals

- Organisational culture is the most elusive and resistant factor in the management of change and in the harmonisation of teamwork in health care

- Team-building and team effectiveness are the keys to health care organisational effectiveness.

QUESTIONS FOR FURTHER DISCUSSION

1. Can the NHS ever rid itself of its dominant bureaucratic culture? What would a non-bureaucratic health service be like?

2. To what extent is money a motivator for professional health care staff?

3. How can different professions be welded together into an effective team? Could a professionally cross-trained (or generic) health worker replace many of the current well-differentiated professions? Would this help or hinder the development of a teamwork ethos in health care?

FURTHER READING

Allsop, J. (1995) *Health Policy and the NHS: Towards 2000*, 2nd edn. London: Longman.
Covers ground similar to that of Klein (see below) but from a social policy perspective.

Clegg, C., Legge, K. and Walsh, S. (1999) *The Experience of Managing: A Skills Guide*. Basingstoke: Macmillan – now Palgrave.
Deals with the processes and skills of managing. From appraisal and assertion to problem-solving and time management, the book concentrates on the skills required to do the job effectively. It is not specifically about health services management.

Klein, R. (2000) *The New Politics of the NHS*, 4th edn. London: Longman.
An excellent political analysis of the development of the NHS and the issues that have dogged its development since its inception.

Schein, E.H. (1988) *Organisational Psychology*, 3rd edn. Englewood Cliffs, NJ: Prentice Hall.
A clear, concise, authoritative exposition of the themes covered in this chapter and many more that are relevant for all managers.

Stewart, R. (1996) *Leading in the NHS: A Practical Guide*, 2nd edn. Basingstoke: Macmillan – now Palgrave.

For those in positions of leadership in the NHS, this is a useful, practical book based upon observation and research.

Vroom, V.H. and Deci, E.L. (1992) *Management and Motivation*, 2nd edn. London: Penguin. Edited original papers by 42 authors on motivation, from Taylor (1911) and Maslow (1943) to MacGregor (1957) and Kanter (1987).

REFERENCES

Alderfer, C.P. (1972) *Existence, Relatedness and Growth: Human Needs in Organisation Settings*. New York: Free Press.

Ansoff, I.H. and McDonnell, E.J. (1990) *Implanting Strategic Management*. Englewood Cliffs, NJ: Prentice Hall.

Argyris, C. (1964) *Integrating the Individual and the Organisation*. Chichester: John Wiley & Sons.

Belbin, R.M. (1981) *Management Teams: Why They Succeed or Fail*. London: Heinemann.

Berne, E. (1975) *What Do You Say after You Say Hello?* London: Corgi Books.

Blake, R.R. and McCanse, A.A. (1991) *Leadership Dilemmas: Grid Solutions*. Houston: Gulf Publishing.

Blake, R.R. and Mouton, J.S. (1964) *The Managerial Grid*. Houston: Gulf Publishing.

Callahan, R.E., Fleenor, C.P. and Knudson, H.R. (1986) *Understanding Organisational Behaviour: A Managerial Viewpoint*. Columbus, OH: Charles E. Merrill.

Clements, R. (1980) *A Guide to Transactional Analysis: A Handbook for Manager and Trainers*. Woking: Insight Training.

DHSS (Department of Health and Social Security) (1983) *NHS Management Inquiry: Letter to the Secretary of State for Health and Social Security and Recommendations for Action*. London: DHSS.

DoH (Department of Health) (1988) *A First Class Service: Quality in the NHS*. London: DoH.

DoH (Department of Health) (1990) *NHS and Community Care Act*. London: Stationery Office.

DoH (Department of Health) (1991) *The Patient's Charter*. London: DoH.

DoH (Department of Health) (1997) *The New NHS: Modern, Dependable*. London: Stationery Office.

DoH (Department of Health) (1999) *Saving Lives: Our Healthier Nation*. London: Stationery Office.

Drucker, P. (1968) *The Practice of Management*. London: Pan.

Gillis, C.R. and Hole, D.J. (1996) Survival outcomes of care by specialist surgeons in breast cancer: a study of 3786 patients in the West of Scotland. *British Medical Journal*, **312**: 145–8.

Goodman, M. (1995) *Creative Management*. Hemel Hempstead: Prentice Hall.

Griffiths, R. (1988) *Community Care: Agenda for Action*. London: HMSO.

Hackman, J.R. and Oldham, G.R. (1975) Development of the job diagnostic survey. *Journal of Applied Psychology*, **60**: 159–70.

Hackman, J.R. and Oldham, G.R. (1979) *Work Redesign*. Reading, MA: Addison Wesley.

Handy, C.B. (1993) *Understanding Organisations*, 4th edn. London: Penguin.

Harrison, R. (1972) How to describe your organisation. *Harvard Business Review*, Sept–Oct.

Hay, J. (1993) *Working it Out at Work – Understanding Attitudes and Building Relationships*. Watford: Sherwood Publishing.

Herzberg, F. (1968) 'One more time: how do you motivate employees?', in Vroom, V.H. and Deci, E.L. (eds) (1992) *Management and Motivation*, 2nd edn. London: Penguin.

Holland, J.L. (1973) *Making Vocational Choices: A Theory of Careers*. Englewood Cliffs, NJ: Prentice Hall.

Johnson, G. and Scholes, K. (1999) *Exploring Corporate Strategy: Text and Cases*, 5th edn. Hemel Hempstead: Prentice Hall Europe.

Jones, L. and Page, D. (1987) Theories of motivation. *Education and Training*, May/June: 12–16.

Kakabadse, A., Ludlow, R. and Vinnicombe, S. (1988) *Working in Organisations*. London: Penguin.

Klein, R. (2000) *The New Politics of the NHS*, 4th edn. London: Longman.

Klein, R. and Maynard, A. (1998) On the way to Calvary. *British Medical Journal*, **317**: 5.

McClelland, D.C. (1988) *Human Motivation*. Cambridge: Cambridge University Press.

Maslow, A.H. (1943) A theory of human motivation. *Psychological Review*, **50**: 370–96.

Ministry of Health (1944) *A National Health Service*. Coalition Government White Paper. London: MoH.

Mintzberg, H. (1973) *The Nature of Managerial Work*. New York: Harper & Row.

Mitchell, T.R. (1982) Motivation: new directions for theory, research and practice. *Academy of Management Review*, **7**(1): 80–8.

Mullins, L.J. (1999) *Management and Organisational Behaviour*, 4th edn. London: Pitman.

Mumford, E. (1973) Designing systems for job satisfaction. *Omega*, **1**(4): 493–8.

Nadler, D.A. (1993) 'Concepts for the management of organisational change', in Mabey, C. and Mayon-White, B. (eds) *Managing Change*, 2nd edn. Buckingham: Open University Press/Paul Chapman, pp. 85–98.

Nadler, D.A and Tushman, M.L. (1979) 'A congruence model for diagnosing organisational behaviour', in Kolb, D., Rubin, I. and McIntyre, J. (eds) *Organisational Psychology: A Book of Readings*, 3rd edn. Englewood Cliffs, NJ: Prentice Hall.

Prowle, M. and Jones, T. (1997) *Health Service Finance: An Introduction*, 4th edn. London: CAET.

Pugh, D.S. and Hickson, D.J. (1989) *Writers on Organisations*, 4th edn. London: Penguin.

RCSE (Royal College of Surgeons of England) (2000) *Children's Surgery – a First Class Service*. London: RSCE.

RCSE (Royal College of Surgeons of England) and BOA (British Orthopaedic Association) (2000) *Better Care for the Severely Injured*. London: RSCE/BOA.

Schein, E.H. (1978) *Career Dynamics*. Reading, MA: Addison-Wesley.

Schein, E.H. (1988) *Organisational Psychology*, 3rd edn. Englewood Cliffs, NJ: Prentice Hall.

Schein, E.H. (1992) *Organisational Culture and Leadership*, 2nd edn. San Francisco: Jossey-Bass.

Scholes, K. (1994) *Strategic Management in Professional Service Organisations (PSOs) – the Finders, Minders and Grinders*. Sheffield: Sheffield Business School.

Senior, B. (1997) *Organisational Change*. London: Pitman.

Stewart, R. (1989) *Leading in the NHS: A Practical Guide*. Basingstoke: Macmillan – now Palgrave.

Stewart, R. (1996) *Leading in the NHS: A Practical Guide*, 2nd edn. Basingstoke: Macmillan – now Palgrave.

Stogdill, R.M. (1974) *Handbook of Leadership: A Survey of Theory and Research*. New York: Free Press.

Tannenbaum, R. and Schmidt, W.H. (1973) How to choose a leadership pattern. *Harvard Business Review* May/June: 162–80.

Trist, E.A. (1973) 'Critique of scientific management in terms of socio-technical theory', in Weir, M. (ed.) *Job Satisfaction*. London: Fontana, pp. 81–90.

Trist, E.A. and Bamforth, K.W. (1951) Some social and psychological consequences of the longwall method of coal-getting. *Human Relations*, **4**(1): 6–24, 37–8.

Tuckman, B.W. (1965) Developmental sequences in small groups. *Psychological Bulletin*, **63**(6): 384–99.

Tushman, M.L., Newman, W.H. and Romanelli, E. (1988) 'Convergence and upheaval: managing the unsteady pace of organisational evolution', in Tushman, M.L. and Moore, W.L. (eds) *Readings in the Management of Innovation*. New York: Ballinger.

WHO (World Health Organization) (2000) *The World Health Report 2000 – Health Systems – Improving Performance*. Geneva: WHO.

Health Economics

DAVID COHEN

CONTENTS

Learning outcomes •••••••••••••••••••••••••••

This chapter will enable readers to:

- Appreciate why economics exists
- Understand the basic principles of economics
- Understand how these principles can be applied to health
- Be familiar with and describe the different types of economic appraisal
- Understand how the economic approach can help in understanding the nature of health.

OVERVIEW

There is a growing awareness worldwide that the resources available to maintain and improve health are finite whereas the demands made on these resources appear to be virtually infinite. Consequently, many are looking to economics – the science of making choices in situations of scarcity – for assistance. This chapter explains what economics is and, equally importantly, what it is not. The emphasis throughout is on how economics does not deal with problems that are uniquely economic but instead addresses common issues through different eyes. Economics is about the allocation of resources to production and the distribution of those outputs to society. The way in which this is done in unregulated markets is explained in the first part of the chapter, being followed by a discussion of what might make health care differ from other market goods. Problems in the allocation and distribution of services in non-market situations, such as with the UK National Health Service, are examined with particular emphasis on the difficulties that arise when health care is given according to people's 'needs' rather than their ability to pay. The second part explains the cost–benefit approach, this being defended through a return to the basic economic principle of scarcity, the fact that choice always involves sacrifice and the importance of being explicit about the criteria on which inescapable choices are made. Efficiency is defended as a criterion for choice on the basis that it seeks to maximise the health that can be achieved from whatever level of resources are available. There is an explanation of the four key techniques of economic appraisal: cost–benefit, cost-effectiveness, cost–utility and cost-minimisation analyses. It is emphasised that these tools ought to be employed only with a firm understanding of the principles upon which they are based. The chapter ends with a case study exploring how an economic framework helps in health programme planning.

INTRODUCTION

The past few decades have witnessed an unprecedented growth in health care expenditure worldwide. An example of the magnitude of this rise can be seen in the case of the UK, where, in 1973, £3,364 million was spent on health care, both public and private. This was equivalent to £60 per person, representing 4.6 per cent of the gross domestic product (GDP). By 1998, this had increased to £55,977 million, equivalent to £946 per person and 6.7 per cent of the GDP. When inflation is taken into account, £239 was spent in 1998 for every £100 in 1973 (OHE,

1999). This increase has occurred under both Labour and Conservative governments. Figure 8.1 shows that all countries belonging to the Organization for
Economic Cooperation and Development (OECD) also had a major increase in
the relative share of total available resources being spent on health care.

With overall economic growth during this period, some increase in health
care spending was to be expected and indeed ought to be regarded as a good
thing. After all, more spending on health care should mean more health for
the population. Yet the increased spending on health care does not appear to
have been accompanied by a corresponding fall in the demand being made on
the health care systems. In the UK, for example, 545,000 people were on
waiting lists for non-urgent surgery in 1998 compared with 594,000 in 1981
(OHE, 1999).

Given these trends, it is not surprising that there is a growing recognition that
resources for health care are unlikely ever to be sufficient to meet all health

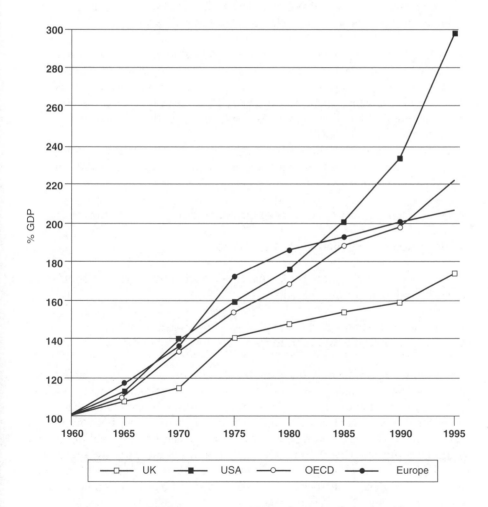

Figure 8.1   Relative increase in total health expenditure as a
percentage of gross domestic product (GDP) at
market prices (1960 = 100) (from OHE, 1997)

needs. This, in turn, means an increasing acceptance that not everything that can be done will be done and that choices are inescapable. Economics is the science of making choices.

 What do you understand by 'economics'? What insights might its study offer into health and health care provision?

Economics has been defined as:

> the study of how men [this was 1976!] and society end up choosing, with or without the use of money, to employ scarce productive resources to produce various commodities over time and distribute them for consumption, now and in the future, among various groups and people in society. It analyses the costs and benefits of improving patterns of resource allocation. (Samuelson, 1976)

inputs – all the resources used in a production process

outputs – the end result of a production process. The principal output of all health care activity is 'health' (represented as an absolute improvement in health, the prevention or slowing of a reduction in health, or a reduction in the risk of future ill health)

resources – those things which contribute to the production of outputs. Within economics, money is not considered to be a resource because it does not directly contribute to production. Instead, money provides a command over resources since it is (normally) needed to pay for them

The discipline exists because the resources (***inputs***) available to produce goods and services (***outputs***) are finite whereas humankind's desire to consume these goods and services appears to be virtually infinite. Economics concerns how society makes a choice about how much of its scarce ***resources*** are allocated to the production of what, and how these outputs of production are then distributed to members of society.

Economics is a discipline – a recognised body of thought – and health economics the application of this body of thought to the topic 'health'. It thus deals with questions such as:

● How much of society's scarce resources should be devoted to the production of health?
● How should health outputs be distributed?

These are couched in words that make them recognisable as 'economic' questions, but what about the following?

● What is the best way of treating people with disease x?
● Should we introduce a programme to screen for disease y?

These may appear to be clinical and policy issues respectively rather than economic ones. Indeed, decisions of this sort are regularly made without seeking the assistance of economists. Yet from the perspective of economics, both can also be viewed as legitimate economic questions since both involve the use of scarce resources (inputs) and both are concerned with making people healthier (outputs). Health economics is first and foremost a 'way of thinking' based on a defined set of principles. It does not address a unique set of problems but puts a different perspective on issues and problems that others would address from their own perspectives.

The two questions above could be rephrased by asking 'What is the most cost effective way of treating people with disease x?' and 'Do the benefits of introducing a programme to screen for disease y outweigh the costs?'

What knowledge would a health economist need to answer these questions?

Health economics can be viewed as a 'toolkit' containing a number of different appraisal techniques. All are concerned with examining policies and interventions by comparing the resources needed (**cost**) with the effects produced (**benefit**). The broad umbrella of the cost–benefit approach also includes cost-effectiveness analysis, cost–utility analysis and cost-minimisation analysis, which are discussed later in this chapter.

If health economics is concerned with the production of health, it must clearly be concerned with more than just interventions provided by health professionals. Road safety and environmental measures also affect people's health. Macroeconomic issues, such as the effect of unemployment on health, and policy issues such as increasing taxes to reduce the demand for unhealthy goods, are also within the remit of health economics.

THE CONTRIBUTION OF ECONOMICS TO HEALTH STUDIES

Economics deals with two basic problems:

- the allocation of resources to production
- the distribution of the outputs of that production.

One way of dealing with these is for government to eschew any role at all, leaving everything to 'market forces' – essentially the interaction of **supply** and **demand**. How much of a country's resources to allocate to the production of shoes, for example, and what mechanism to employ to distribute shoes are rarely issues to which governments pay much heed. If left alone, market forces do the job perfectly well. If any government feels that it is somehow wrong when poor people cannot afford the shoes they need, the response is normally one of income redistribution.

MARKET FORCES AND HEALTH CARE

The principle of market forces and the relationship between supply and demand are key concepts in economics. Demand is defined as that quantity of a good for which consumers are willing and able to pay at any given price. Economic theory says that consumers will demand more at a lower price than they will at a higher price, as shown by the line dd in Figure 8.2. Similarly, supply is defined as that quantity which producers are willing to offer for sale at a given price. The theory states that they will wish to supply smaller quantities when prices are low than when prices are high, as shown by the line ss in Figure 8.2. There are textbooks full of theories to explain why this is the case, but

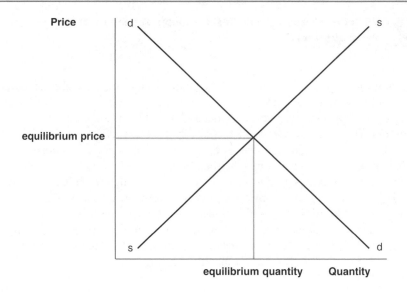

Figure 8.2   Supply, demand and market equilibrium

for present purposes we will simply assume that such supply and demand behaviour makes intuitive sense.

A market is where the exchange takes place, the price determining how much money changes hands for every unit of the good bought and sold. If at any price the quantity that producers supply exceeds the quantity that consumers demand, there will be a pressure on prices to fall. The opposite occurs when demand exceeds supply – there will be a pressure on prices to rise.

There is one price, the 'equilibrium price', at which supply and demand are equal and there is no pressure from within the market for the price to change. The quantity that is both supplied and demanded at the equilibrium price is called, not surprisingly, the 'equilibrium quantity'.

This simple analysis shows how market forces have solved the allocation problem. Some level of resources is required to produce the equilibrium quantity, but no one has told producers how many resources to allocate to the production of this good: it just happened. The market has also dealt with the distribution problem since – by definition – only those consumers willing and able to pay the equilibrium price can consume the good. Price can therefore be seen as a rationing mechanism limiting the distribution of the good only to those who demand it at the equilibrium price.

Markets do not settle down at an equilibrium and stay there for all time. Changes are occurring outside the market that cause supply and demand to change. On the demand side, people's incomes, tastes and preferences, as well as the prices of other goods, are constantly changing. On the supply side, production techniques and the cost of materials are also constantly altering. Equilibrium is thus rarely reached, but that hardly matters. What does matter is that if demand and supply are not in equilibrium at any moment, economic theory can explain what will happen to the price, which will in turn trigger a whole set of other predictable economic forces to come into effect. Consumer demand for a good may initially cause prices to rise and also production and supply to increase. Concerns about food safety have, for example, led to a demand for organic produce, but the intensive and rigorous farming methods mean short supply and a high price. However, many more farmers now use organic methods, resulting in a higher equilibrium price that more consumers are prepared to pay.

 Is health care different from other market goods? Why do so few countries leave the allocation and distribution of health care entirely to market forces?

Although not stated explicitly, a number of assumptions have to hold for the free market to work in the way described. Donaldson and Gerard (1993) outline these as:

- consumers making their own choices (consumer sovereignty)
- consumers being well informed
- consumers' choices affecting only themselves
- competition between suppliers.

In a free market, no elite with some 'preferred' set of values is telling consumers what they should or should not demand. Individuals are assumed to be the best judges of their own welfare, and economic theory shows how, subject to certain assumptions, perfectly competitive and unregulated markets produce socially optimum results. In the case of health care, however, the appropriateness of consumer sovereignty can be challenged. Is the patient necessarily the best judge of his or her own welfare? Does the patient necessarily want to *be* the judge? Many may prefer to be left out of the decision process altogether and leave it to the doctor, who 'knows best what's good for me'.

Market theory assumes that consumers are well informed and can judge how much **utility** (satisfaction) they get from consuming a good. In the case of health care, however, individuals will rarely be able to diagnose themselves, are unlikely to be aware of the range of available treatments and cannot judge how much utility they will get from treatment even after consuming it since they do not know what would have happened in the absence of any treatment. They have to rely on the doctor's superior knowledge so there is an 'asymmetry of information' between supplier and consumer, doctors both deciding the treatment that the patient will demand and supplying it.

A consumer thinking about buying a new car may of course be no more knowledgeable about cars than she is about health care, yet she is unlikely to leave the decision about which car to buy totally to the salesman. Why not? The difference between these two cases is simply that she trusts the doctor – at least more than she trusts the salesman. Doctors are expected to act according to a code of medical ethics; car salesmen are not. But it is debatable whether or not an ethical code means that doctors will end up making the same consumption decisions that fully informed consumers would make if they had the medical knowledge. Anyone arguing that they will not is calling for some form of government intervention in the free health care market.

> utility – the 'satisfaction' derived from consumption. Goods and services are demanded for the utility they provide. In the case of health care, utility is derived from the resulting health improvements rather than directly from the health services themselves

CONNECTIONS

Chapter 9 (Ethics and
Law) discusses how
codes of practice influ-
ence the work of health
care practitioners

Implicit in the theory showing how unregulated markets produce socially
optimal results is the assumption that individuals' consumption decisions affect
them and them alone. This may not, however, always be the case. Someone's
decision to buy a guard dog that barks all night may well provide their neigh-
bour with a great deal of negative utility. Where such 'externalities' (positive or
negative) exist, it can be easily shown that unregulated markets will not
produce a socially optimal solution. Health care arguably has externalities, both
positive and negative. The decision to seek treatment for a communicable
disease affects not only the treated individual, but also others in that their risk
of catching the disease is reduced. It has also been argued that a 'humanitarian
externality' may exist in health care if people derive positive utility from the
knowledge that others are receiving the health care that they need.

For the market to work as described, a number of assumptions are also
needed on the supply side, chief among these being assumptions concerning the
competitive behaviour of firms. In reality, private health care markets are rarely
if ever characterised by many small hospitals competing with each other on
grounds of price. Elements of monopoly powers normally exist together with
many other features, which suggests that the free market model does not
describe what happens in the market for health care.

Health care is thus arguably very different from other goods or services in the
market place. Various forms of regulation could be introduced, however, to
overcome specific problems without taking the step of removing health care
from the market place. In the end, the issue can only be settled by resorting to
philosophy and ideology. Most countries intervene in some measure in the
provision of health care because the majority of the population regard access to
health care, like access to the ballot box, as a 'fundamental human right' rather
than as part of society's reward system.

THE ALLOCATION AND DISTRIBUTION OF HEALTH CARE 'OFF THE MARKET'

If health care is taken off the market, some alternative means of allocation and
distribution have to be found. On the allocation side, this is normally done by a
committee deciding what proportion of total public expenditure will be spent
each year on health care. On the distribution side, health care is provided to
those who need it.

need – within economics,
this term refers to an
individual's capacity to
benefit from an intervention

In 1948, health care was taken 'off the market' in the UK by the creation of the
NHS. It was assumed that doctors would determine how much **need** there was
and government would simply allocate the appropriate volume of resources to
ensure that all needs would be met. This clearly has not happened. To explain
why requires a deeper examination of what is meant by need.

To an economist, need means 'capacity to benefit' from treatment. Economists use the terms 'wants' and 'demands' to refer to consumer-based judgements and 'need' to refer to judgements made by some third party. In a private
health care system, the consumer will be given a nose-straightening operation if
he or she is willing to pay the money price. In a zero-priced public health care
system, the doctor will judge whether or not the individual needs the operation – perhaps because of breathing difficulties. If there is no clinical need, the
operation will be denied.

Thinking about...

In your view, should a
person with a crooked
nose be able to have
NHS surgery to correct
it? What criteria would
you use to decide
whether that person
should have treatment?

Defined in terms of capacity to benefit from treatment, need is clearly a dynamic concept. Every new medical development that allows the previously untreatable to be treated is increasing need. Similarly, any development that allows the previously treatable to be better treated is also increasing need. It was not long ago, for example, that there was nothing that could be done to prevent very premature, low birthweight babies dying. Today, thanks to new technology, those same babies have a need for neonatal intensive care.

There can of course be developments that actually free up resources for other uses, but in most cases, new interventions involve an increase in resource use. Given the pace of new technological development, it is hardly surprising that year on year increases in expenditure on health care are not hitting the target of meeting total need. It is possible to argue, however, that whereas need may grow with time, it is still finite at any given point in time. This would be true but for the fact that need is also both relative and subjective.

Relativity can be shown by the fact that many of today's needs would not have been considered to be needs 50 years ago when diseases such as smallpox, diphtheria and polio were the pressing problems of the day. Similarly, the current pressure on resources is raising questions about whether some needs ought to be considered needs at all. In some parts of the UK, interventions such as tattoo removal, gender reorientation and fertility treatment are currently being withdrawn from the needs-based NHS.

Subjectivity of need can be demonstrated by the wide variation in treatments given to similar populations that cannot be explained by a difference in disease prevalence. Moreover, it is not only a judgement of whether or not a patient needs treatment, but also one of how much they need. All may agree on a patient's need for physiotherapy, but how often and for how long are subjective judgements.

> ## CONNECTIONS
>
> To an economist, need means 'capacity to benefit'. Chapter 9 (Ethics and Law) explores the example of Viagra and how its distribution is related to particular values that we hold about what matters in health

---

EXAMPLE 8.1

The relativity of need: the case of Viagra

Until the introduction of Viagra (sildenafil), erectile dysfunction in men had always been considered to represent a clinical need. Available treatments included:

- psychological management

- vacuum constriction devices

- intracavernosal injection therapy

- transurethral drug delivery (MUSE)

- a penile prosthesis

- surgery.

All were provided free on the UK NHS apart from vacuum pumps, which patients in some parts of the country had to purchase privately. The cost of meeting erectile dysfunction need was not an issue.

In 1997, Viagra was licensed by the US Federal Drug Administration. Prior to its launch, the sexual function disorder market in the US had total sales of $157 million, mainly on MUSE. Within 4 weeks of Viagra being launched, the market increased to over 10 times its previous size, Viagra capturing a staggering 97.5 per cent of the total market (IMS America, 1998). In the UK, with its publicly funded, zero-priced health care system, it was estimated that Viagra could add £1 billion per annum to the NHS drugs bill (*Mail*, 8 July, 1998). The government very quickly stepped in, setting specific criteria for who could and who could not be prescribed Viagra on the NHS. Those who did not meet the criteria obviously did not 'need' Viagra. Moreover, the decision of whether or not there was a need was no longer to be left to doctors.

In a world of infinite resources, all men who could benefit from treatment would be prescribed Viagra. In the real world of scarcity and choice, those at the less severe end of the sexual dysfunction continuum are judged not to need it.

? Why will resources for health care always be scarce?

Economists argue that, even if health need were finite, it would still not be in society's interest to allocate sufficient resources to meet all health need. This somewhat provocative statement can be justified by focusing on the fact that society clearly has needs other than those relating to health (education, defence, transport and law and order, for example). However, since the total amount available to spend on all of these is finite, spending in one area means having less to spend in another. Similarly, more public expenditure means higher taxes and thus less to spend on private consumption.

Both the balance between private and public expenditure and the distribution of the latter between the different public sector areas is driven by a fundamental principle known as 'diminishing marginal benefit'. This states that as any activity expands, the extra benefit produced by each extra unit of input gets progressively smaller. For example, a single nurse working in a community will be aware that she cannot, on her own, possibly meet all the health needs of the community. If she is at all rational, she will focus her efforts on where the need is greatest, that is, where she can produce the greatest benefit from her finite time.

Increased spending on health produces positive marginal health benefits, but at the cost of forgoing the benefits that the spending could have achieved elsewhere in the economy. Each incremental increase in health care spending, however, produces a smaller and smaller marginal benefit, which has to be weighed against the potential marginal benefit gain (that is, sacrifice) elsewhere. If the increased spending on health is funded by decreasing spending elsewhere, the marginal gain will be weighed against the marginal sacrifice, which, by the same principle, will be getting bigger and bigger with each incremental reduction. If the marginal gain exceeds the marginal sacrifice, the total benefit increases, but this can go on for only so long. Eventually, the continually decreasing marginal benefits in health will no longer exceed the marginal losses elsewhere.

If society has a multiplicity of need, the socially optimal balance of expenditure will be at that point at which any further shifts will begin to make total benefit fall, that is, society will begin to be made worse off, and this will not be at the point at which all health need is being met. Put another way, since the share of total societal resources devoted to health will always be less than the level at which all needs can be met, some form of *rationing* is inevitable.

rationing – a mechanism to reconcile an excess of demand over supply. In competitive markets, consumption is rationed by price; that is, only those willing and able to pay the market price can consume the goods. With public provision, consumption is rationed using more explicit methods such as waiting lists, limited prescribing lists and so on. Often euphemistically referred to as prioritisation

THEORETICAL AND METHODOLOGICAL APPROACHES

RESOURCES AND MONEY

Anything being considered – from the level of broad policies down to individual interventions – involves the use of resources. Given scarcity, choice is inescapable.

By definition, resources are things which contribute to the production of output. Producing corn requires resources such as land, seeds, workers and tractors. No amount of money will produce corn unless it is used to buy land, hire workers and so on. Resources in health care include doctors, nurses, hospital buildings, bandages and drugs. Again, money pays for these resources, but, by definition, volunteers and informal carers are also resources even though they do not receive monetary reward. The distinction between money and resources is thus important. More money normally means control over more resources, but this is not always the case. A shortage of nurses trained in intensive care will constrain activity in an intensive care unit regardless of the cash available.

For present purposes, money also has a second function in that it provides a common measure of value: £20 worth of doctor time and £10 worth of medicine make up £30 worth of resources. Expressing resources in terms of a common measure allows them to be added together and compared with other combinations of resources. The same is true for outputs. By definition, all the outputs of health care are of value, and expressing each in terms of its money value allows different outputs to be added and compared.

Thinking about...

Do you think a monetary value can be put on health? Can you compare the life of a premature baby (whose life depends on intensive care) with the pain relief of thousands of older people achieved through simple hip replacement?

The output of health care

Economists have long argued that, while not necessarily its only output, the principal output of the health care industry is 'health'. The inverted commas reflect the fact that many health services, for example palliative care of the terminally ill, are not intended to raise health status as such. However, if 'health' is perceived in the broad sense of well-being, all effective interventions will make people better off than they would otherwise have been.

The practical difficulties of viewing output in this way stem from the fact that health is notoriously difficult to define, measure and value. Broad definitions, such as that by the World Health Organization of health as a 'state of complete

CONNECTIONS

Chapter 10 (Health Promotion) looks at the problems of determining health outcomes

physical, mental and social well-being' (WHO, 1946), are unhelpful when trying to compare the output of alternative therapies.

In practice therefore, intermediate measures are often used as proxies for the final (health) outputs. This is acceptable as long as the link between the proxy measure and health is well established. Thus, evidence that a reduction in smoking prevalence will result in a reduction in smoking-related morbidity and mortality means that 'number of quitters' is an acceptable proxy for the output of a smoking cessation programme, even though smoking is not a disease and quitting is not in itself a health gain. The less well established the link between the proxy and health is, the less useful is the proxy.

The economic notion of cost

To an economist, cost means sacrifice: an accountant will measure cost as the amount of money spent; an economist will look at what has been forgone. The term 'opportunity cost' is used in economics to emphasise this notion of an opportunity forgone. Within economics, 'cost' is used as a shorthand for 'opportunity cost'.

A cost can thus be incurred without money changing hands. A new clinic that takes a nurse off a ward for one hour a week will not affect the nursing wages bill, but it will involve the sacrifice of the benefit that the nurse could have achieved in one hour on the ward. Similarly, freeing an hour of nurse time provides the opportunity to use that hour to produce benefits that could not otherwise be produced. The freed-up hour is valued regardless of the fact that no money will be saved.

? **On what basis should resource allocation choices be made?**

efficiency – making the best use of available resources. Allocative efficiency assesses whether, or to what extent, an objective should be pursued. Technical efficiency assesses the best way of achieving a given objective

The principal criterion used in economics is **efficiency**, which maximises the benefits from the available resources. It concerns the relationship between inputs and outputs, that is, most benefit being available at least cost. Being efficient means getting as much health as is possible from the available resources; being inefficient means getting less.

It is important to note, however, that whereas efficiency is a good rule to be guided by, it is never a substitute for decision-making (Drummond, 1981). Demonstrating that A is more efficient than B suggests that A should be pursued unless alternative criteria can be identified to argue otherwise. B may be justified on, for example, equity, public relations or political expediency grounds, and no economist would argue that these are not relevant alternative criteria. However, it becomes difficult to argue for the pursuit of inefficient B over efficient A on grounds such as the political power of the doctors involved, historical precedent or who can get most public support by waving a shroud in front of a television camera.

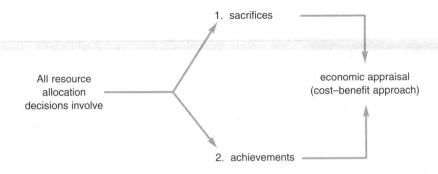

Figure 8.3   The cost–benefit framework

The cost–benefit approach

Figure 8.3 illustrates the cost–benefit way of thinking. The principle of weighing gains against sacrifices is the cost–benefit approach. In each situation, there are costs, which mean that an alternative must be forgone. There may also be particular benefits that result.

Notice that something will fail the cost–benefit test if the benefits achieved are judged to be of lower value than the benefits forgone by not using the resources in other ways. In this case, the gains and sacrifices are both couched in terms of health. Failing the cost–benefit test does not mean that these health gains are not worth some amount of money.

 Is it ethical to make health care decisions on the basis of their cost effectiveness?

It is important to stress that the cost–benefit approach is not being advocated at the level of decision-making relating to the individual patient; it is natural for doctors and other health professionals to want to do what is best for their patients. Doctors have always practised under a system of medical ethics that has conventionally focused on the two ethical theories of 'virtue' and 'duty' (Jonsen and Hellegers, 1987). These are individualistic ethics based on the doctor's responsibility for the individual patient, a guiding principle of which has long been that it is unethical to do anything that does more harm than good.

Given that a doctor's first duty will inevitably be to his or her patient, a doctor's preference for making clinical decisions on the basis of clinical effectiveness rather than cost effectiveness is understandable. It is still legitimate to take the costs that others will have to bear into account, but the patient in front of the doctor is a person with a name, a face, a family, a history. Efficiency is still relevant, but it is relatively unimportant.

> **CONNECTIONS**
>
> Chapter 9 (Ethics and Law) discusses the guiding principles of beneficence and non-maleficence, which, in medical ethics, means that health workers should not take any action that does more harm than good

More recently, and due to an increasing awareness of the scarcity of resources, ethicists have begun to focus on a third ethical theory, that of the 'common good' (Mooney, 1992). This is a social ethic based on responsibility for the health of populations. In this, the guiding principle of only doing those things which do more good than harm still applies, but the terms reflect a social perspective. On this basis, any intervention that yields only a small benefit to the patient but will mean a large sacrifice to other patients will, from a social perspective, be doing more harm than good. Those responsible for health policy-making and for broad resource allocation decisions have to see their duty as being to the whole population – including the potential future consumers of health care.

A decision to put additional resources into developing neonatal intensive care units will be made before any of the babies who will benefit from them have been conceived. Similarly, it is not possible to identify the individuals who will benefit from increasing the level of resources going into mass screening or immunisation campaigns. These are statistical lives without names, faces, families or histories. At this level of decision-making, efficiency is a very important factor since being inefficient means achieving less health than could have been achieved – and what is ethical about that?

Thinking about...

Think about some health policy decisions that benefit populations but may adversely affect individuals

CONNECTIONS

Chapter 9 (Ethics and Law) also discusses the case of Child B in relation to the role of law in clinical judgements and resource allocation

EXAMPLE 8.2

The case of Child B

In 1995, a 10-year-old girl referred to as Child B suffered a relapse of acute myeloid leukaemia. Having previously undergone two courses of chemotherapy and a bone marrow transplant, her doctors considered that further active treatment would not be in her best interests. The chances of remission following further chemotherapy were put at between 10 and 20 per cent, with a similar chance of survival following further bone marrow transplantation. The treatments would cost £15,000 and £60,000 respectively.

Child B was denied further active treatment by her local health authority on two grounds: first that, because of the suffering involved, further treatment would not be in her best interest, and second, that the resources available were finite and the needs of other patients had to be borne in mind. Her father took the case to court.

The judge ruled in the father's favour, claiming that the health authority had not adequately explained their funding priorities. This decision was, however, overturned by the Court of Appeal on the same day (*Times*, 15 March, 1995). The Master of the Rolls rejected the original judge's criticism of the health authority, claiming that it was common knowledge that health resources were scarce and therefore the health authority had not exceeded its powers or acted unreasonably. Child B was subsequently admitted to a private hospital after an anonymous donor provided £75,000 for her treatment. Sadly, she died soon afterwards.

It could perhaps be argued that, ethically speaking, the duty of the health authority was to endeavour to preserve life. However, in economic terms, the treatment of this individual would have incurred a high sacrifice elsewhere. In other words, the opportunity costs far outweighed the benefit to the individual patient.

Economics is often given a bad press when it comes to health care because of a mistaken belief that it is all about saving money, but that is not what economics is trying to do. The need to choose is a reality; the question is whether or not choices are made on the basis of rational and defensible criteria. Economic thinking and the techniques of economic appraisal are aids to decision-making that can lead to greater efficiency and hence a greater overall level of health.

TECHNIQUES OF ECONOMIC APPRAISAL

All the techniques of economic appraisal fall under the broad umbrella of the cost–benefit approach. All are concerned with examining one or more interventions by comparing the resources needed against the effects produced. How they differ depends essentially on how these effects (benefits) are perceived, which in turn depends on the objective of the appraisal.

Cost–benefit analysis

The most comprehensive technique of economic appraisal is ***cost–benefit analysis***. Its objective is to assess whether – or to what extent – something is worth doing. Cost–benefit analysis thus addresses allocative efficiency in that it tells us whether, or how many, resources should be allocated to this programme. This involves weighing all the benefits of a programme (or the extra benefit from an expansion of the programme) against the total (or extra) cost of achieving them. This can only be done if all the costs and benefits are expressed in common units. Money is normally used as this common measure, but in principle any other common measure will do. It is important to stress that cost–benefit analysis is concerned with expressing costs and benefits in terms of their monetary value. Although similar to a financial appraisal, cost–benefit analysis is not, however, concerned with money spent and money received.

In economics, costs are all the resources directly or indirectly used by the programme that have alternative uses, that is, which incur opportunity costs. Benefits are everything of value that results. Cost–benefit analysis normally adopts a 'social welfare' perspective in that all costs are considered regardless of who bears them, and all benefits are included regardless of to whom they accrue. Cost and benefit variables are first identified, then measured in appropriate physical or other relevant units and finally valued.

Where they exist, market prices are normally used to express the money value of costs and benefits. Where market prices do not exist, 'shadow prices' can be used. For example, the time of volunteers does not command a market price, but it is possible to impute a price to volunteers' time using the wages of paid workers who do roughly the same work as a proxy.

The valuation of health and other intangible benefits and costs is, however, clearly no easy task. A variety of methods are available to do this, which will not be detailed here (see, for example, Drummond et al., 1997). Nevertheless, many people find the very act of placing a monetary value on such things as pain relief or the extension of life to be at best distasteful and at worst immoral. According to the economic way of thinking, the values are always there – the only issue is

cost–benefit analysis – a technique of economic appraisal that assesses allocative efficiency by comparing the money value of all the costs of a policy, programme or intervention against the money value of all the benefits

Thinking about...

Do you think you can put a monetary value on health?

whether they are to be explicit or implicit. Economic analysis attempts to make valuations explicit in order to assist the pursuit of efficiency. The rejection of a programme with an implied value of a life of £1,000, for example, is difficult to defend when another programme is currently running with an implied value of a life of £100,000. Efficiency in terms of maximising the number of lives saved per pound spent will be improved by making a marginal reduction in the latter programme in order to support the former.

Many people feel an understandable distaste at the idea on putting a money value on intangible health benefits: such things ought somehow to be above considerations of cost. Yet if cost is perceived in terms of sacrifice, it is evident from both individual behaviour and collective decision-making that this is clearly not the case.

The example of a simple headache can illustrate this point. A person with a mild headache who readily accepts a free pain relief tablet may not be willing to pay a high money price. In the latter case, he will have to consider opportunity costs since paying for the tablet means having to forgo the benefits from spending the money on other things. His refusal to pay £1,000 for the tablet would demonstrate an explicit valuation of his own pain relief at less than £1,000. This is, of course, a personal judgement based on, among other things, how much money he has to spend and his own tolerance to pain, but the example shows that the value of his own pain relief is not infinite.

The same can be demonstrated through collective decision-making. The rejection of a proposal to build a flyover at a dangerous intersection on grounds of costs implies that the value of the anticipated lives saved and injuries avoided is less than the cost of building the flyover. The fact that preventable road deaths are tolerated shows that society does not put an infinite value on the lives that could be saved.

Cost-effectiveness analysis

cost-effectiveness analysis – a technique of economic appraisal that assesses technical efficiency by comparing the money value of the costs of a policy, programme or intervention against a single, non-monetary measure of its effectiveness (for example number of life years gained)

Often the issue is not whether or not to do something but more simply how to do it. For example, if the question is one of deciding how to treat people with raised blood pressure – given that a decision has already been taken to treat them – ***cost-effectiveness analysis*** can compare alternative blood pressure-reducing interventions in terms of their cost per unit reduction. Cost-effectiveness analysis addresses technical efficiency in the sense that it can tell us the best way to do something but not whether or not that something is worth doing. That is an allocative efficiency issue that can only be dealt with by cost–benefit analysis.

Cost-effectiveness analysis is a simpler technique than cost–benefit analysis. By perceiving benefits more narrowly and measuring them only in physical units, it avoids the difficult task of benefit valuation. At the same time, it provides information that is much more limited since it can only compare alternative ways of pursuing the given objective – in this case to reduce blood pressure. It says nothing about how efficient any blood pressure reduction programme is compared with other programmes of health care.

Cost-effectiveness analysis can, however, be broadened by using more general benefit measures which are not unique to the programme in question. For example, since reducing blood pressure is expected to reduce mortality, the objective of a blood pressure reduction programme can be expressed in broader life-saving terms. By comparing alternative ways of reducing blood pressure in terms of cost per life year saved, the most cost-effective way of reducing blood pressure can then be compared with the cost effectiveness of any other life-saving programme.

 Why might it be difficult to assess the effectiveness of blood pressure reduction measures?

This involves a more complex appraisal. Whereas blood pressure can be accurately measured, translating today's reduced blood pressure into tomorrow's lives saved involves a greater use of assumptions and estimations. This broader cost-effective analysis will still be limited, however, because it cannot indicate whether interventions to reduce blood pressure are more efficient than interventions that improve the quality of life without necessarily extending it. The technique also has the disadvantage of having to assume that each year of life is of equal value regardless of the quality of that life.

Cost–utility analysis

This problem can be overcome by broadening the object to take in both life extension and quality of life improvements, or, stated more generally, to produce 'health'. The advantage of so doing is that the cost effectiveness of all the interventions, whether preventive, curative or caring, can then be compared in terms of cost per unit of 'health' produced.

If 'health' is the output of health care, some means of measuring health is needed. Perfect measures of health will, however, never exist because health is both multidimensional and value laden. People in pain, suffering depression or who have impaired vision or restricted mobility all are in a state of health that is less than perfect. Although each of the dimensions of ill health can be measured independently (more versus less pain, greater versus lesser visual impairment and so on), a measure of 'health' will have to combine all of these into a unidimensional criterion. Who will have worse health, the person with depression or the person in pain? Such a decision obviously involves a value judgement, but who should be the judge? The depressed person will quite rightly feel that depression is the worse state and will value an improvement from depression to perfect health more highly than an improvement from a state of pain to perfect health. The person in pain may, not surprisingly, disagree. A 'perfect' health status measure therefore cannot exist until such problems are reconciled.

Nevertheless, economists have made considerable progress in measuring health by focusing on the idea that all interventions must either extend life, improve the quality of life or achieve some combination of the two. Therefore, in principle, all effective interventions produce quality adjusted life years (**QALYs**). If the effectiveness of any programme is measured in terms of QALYs, a comparison of cost per QALY can indicate the most technically efficient ways of producing health. Economic evaluations that use QALYs (or similar utility-based health measures) are known as cost–utility analyses.

cost–utility analysis – a form of cost-effectiveness analysis in which the single, non-monetary measure of effectiveness is the quality adjusted life year or a similar, utility-based, measure of health status

QALY – quality adjusted life year. A measure of health output that captures both length of life and quality of life

Cost-minimisation analysis

Cost-minimisation analysis is a technique that is embarked upon only when it is known with certainty that the outcomes of two or more different interventions cannot vary. In this case, it is solely a question of finding the cheapest alternative. There are few examples, however, of where a difference in outcome between alternatives cannot vary. More commonly, cost effectiveness and cost–utility analysis become cost-minimisation analysis following a demonstration of no differences in outcomes.

PRIORITY-SETTING IN HEALTH CARE

In a perfect world of infinite resources, priority-setting would not be necessary: everyone would receive whatever health care they needed fully and immediately. Sadly, we do not live in such a perfect world. In the real world of scarce resources, not everything that can be done will be done, so some means of prioritising is necessary if what does and what does not get done is to be at all rationally based.

Prioritising is needed at all levels of decision-making from broad policies to decisions about treating individual patients. An illustration of how economic thinking can help at both levels is provided in Example 8.3.

EXAMPLE 8.3

Priority-setting in health care

In the early 1970s, Grogono and Woodgate (1971) attempted to prioritise patients in need of non-urgent surgery using an index based on 10 dimensions of ill health. The thinking behind this was that while treating people purely on a first come, first served basis may have its attractions, surgeons are unlikely to ignore factors such as how much pain patients are in, or whether or not their condition is preventing them going out to work, when deciding priorities for treatment. If surgeons are therefore implicitly making judgements of need on the basis of undeclared criteria, would it not be possible, and more ethical, to make these criteria explicit? Grogono and Woodgate came up with the following list:

- ability to work
- hobbies and recreation
- malaise, pain or suffering
- worry or unhappiness
- ability to communicate
- ability to sleep
- independence of others
- ability to eat/enjoy food

- bladder and bowels

- sex life

The idea was that, in the course of a normal consultation, it ought to be possible to give patients a score of 0, 0.5 or 1 according to whether they were normal, impaired or incapacitated on each of the dimensions. These figures could be added together: the higher the Grogono–Woodgate index score, the higher the patient's priority.

The problem with the Grogono–Woodgate index is that the dimensions are not weighted to reflect their relative importance. The absence of weighting implies that all are valued equally, which is clearly unrealistic. Most people would probably agree that someone with a score of 1 as a result of double incontinence is worse off than someone with a score of 1 resulting from an inability to participate in hobbies and recreation. If so, and assuming that effective interventions exist for both, the former has a greater need. But this is a value judgement rather than a clinical judgement.

In this approach, prioritisation was not made between patients according to diagnosis, for example hernias versus ingrown toenails, but according to how the condition was affecting them in terms of pain or their ability to get out and about. The sought-after valuations occur between the dimensions of ill health rather than between diagnosed conditions.

In an early attempt to see whether there were such things as 'social values', Rosser and Kind (1978) used a matrix of eight rows representing different degrees of 'disability' and four columns representing different degrees of 'distress' in order to produce the grid shown in Figure 8.4. Everyone will agree that a cell

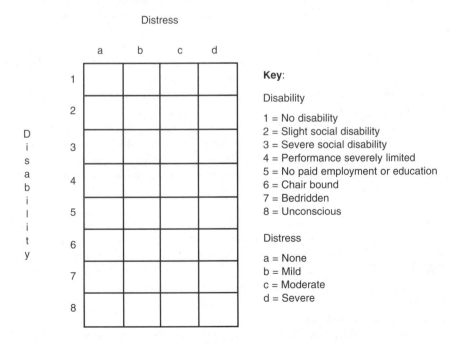

Figure 8.4   The Rosser grid

representing less pain and less disability is valued more highly that one representing more pain and more disability, but what about a cell representing less pain and more disability? Each of us can have our own view depending on our own values, but if 90 per cent of a representative sample of the population preferred one cell to the other, would such a consensus not allow us to say that 'society' puts a higher value on one state than the other?

Rosser and Kind (1978) took a sample of people representing doctors, nurses, patients and health individuals and asked them to rank each health state in the matrix and then give a score of 1 to the top-ranked state (which would inevitably be no disability and no distress) and a score of 0 to the state judged to be equivalent to death. All other states were to be scored cardinally (0.8, for example, being 'twice as good' as 0.4), negative scores being permitted for states judged to be worse than death.

Although this exercise can be criticised on a number of grounds, for example that the sample was small and possibly unrepresentative, the fact that reasonably consistent scores were produced suggests that there can be such a thing as 'social values'. Health gains could now be measured directly, the difference in score between the pre-treatment cell and the post-treatment cell representing the extent of the health gain. More recently, and using other means, social valuations of health states from much larger and more representative samples have been obtained (see, for example, EuroQol Group, 1990). These have allowed the development of cost–utility analysis.

CASE STUDY – APPLYING THE MARGINAL DECISION RULES

This case study illustrates how an economic framework can be of value in prioritising between broad programmes of health care, even without the formal use of economic appraisals or complete and accurate data. Note the emphasis on how openness and explicitness in the making of *value judgements* (as opposed to clinical judgements) are the key to rational planning.

The political and economic climate of the late 1980s focused on the issue of 'value for money' in the public sector. This involved a shift in emphasis away from measures of activity (what was being done) towards measures of output (what was being achieved). In the NHS, this meant moving away from a focus on the number of patients being treated and towards the effect that the treatments were actually having on their health.

In Wales, policy documents stressed that this meant thinking about health care interventions not in terms of their number but in terms of their ability to add 'years to life' and 'life to years'. (Note the similarity between this and the QALY approach discussed above.) Prioritising would thus mean concentrating effort and expenditure on those activities which added most years to life and life to years (in other words – although they did not use the jargon – which produced most QALYs).

The Welsh prioritisation documents, however, not only considered prioritising where additional funding should be directed, but also, and bravely, took account of the pattern of *current* expenditure to see whether resources might be redirected away from the less beneficial activities and towards more beneficial ones. This was done by identifying 10 'health gain areas' (for example cancer, respiratory disease, cardiovascular disease and injuries) and asking each of the Welsh health districts to set up a working group for each health gain area that represented a broad spectrum of professional, managerial, voluntary and other lay groups. Each group was to examine the current balance of expenditure on the different activities within the area and produce a 'Local Strategy for Health' document that would:

1. identify priority areas for new investment

2. identify other areas in which disinvestments could be made that would release resources to support the investments. How to spend new money was to be treated as a separate issue.

The first round of Local Strategy for Health documents was judged to have been a failure. Very few areas for disinvestment were identified – in many cases none at all. It was evident that the groups were not used to thinking in terms of disinvesting in beneficial activities, and whenever a potential candidate was proposed, there was always someone to champion its cause. Only activities that were agreed to be doing no good to anybody were selected for disinvestment, although why these activities were going on in the first place is another question. A failure to achieve the goal was apparently due to the absence of a framework in which the issues could be considered.

It was evident that several important principles of the economic way of thinking were missing. There was:

● a lack of awareness by each group of the principles of economics in general, such as scarcity, opportunity cost and the need for choice
● a lack of awareness that what were being sought were marginal changes in the scale of activity rather than the abandonment of effective interventions
● a lack of understanding of how marginal costs and benefits change with a change in the scale of activity
● a lack of appreciation that trade-offs are inescapable and that maximum health gain will not be achieved while the potential for small health losses to be exchanged for large health gains remains.

Mid Glamorgan Health Authority engaged economists to run a pilot marginal analysis exercise with the Maternal and Early Child Health group. The group met for a one-day seminar where the first two hours were devoted to an explanation of the principles of health economics upon which the marginal analysis exercise would be based. This appreciation of economic thinking was judged to have been an essential prerequisite to the running of the exercise.

Equipped with information on the current pattern of expenditure in the Maternal and Early Child Health gain area, the group was asked to identify potential candidates for expansion if extra funding became available and potential candidates for contraction if overall funding were reduced. Participants were understandably uncomfortable with the latter part of this process, but it was stressed that they were considering reducing, and not eliminating, services. Moreover, they were at this stage not recommending reductions but identifying where they might be considered if reductions were to be made. Ten potential areas for investment and 10 areas for disinvestment emerged.

The group was then asked to estimate the effect, in terms of both workload and health, of an increase of £100,000 to be spent on interventions on the investment list and a decrease in spending of £100,000 on interventions on the disinvestment list. A representative from the finance department provided crude estimates of what this meant in terms of number of staff and so on. As well as debating crude estimates of effects, the group held discussions to try to rank the potential gainers and losers. In particular, the group tried to match each gainer with a loser in a shift that would uncontentiously result in an overall benefit gain. The group's involvement in the exercise was now complete.

It was always recognised that the evidence available on the day would be crude. It was known that subsequent marginal costing or an examination of the literature on effectiveness might have produced evidence leading to different recommendations had it been available on the day. Accordingly, a second stage of the exercise was to set up by a second team to assess each investment and disinvestment candidate against a set of criteria including:

- the strength of evidence on effectiveness
- the distance from the current targets
- how much jurisdiction the authority had to effect the changes.

On this basis, five clear winners and four clear losers emerged from the original list of 20. Recommended reallocations were restricted to these nine, as shown in Table 8.1.

Although there were inevitably criticisms of certain aspects of the exercise, the overall view was that it had been successful. The exercise was then repeated with three other health gain groups (cancer, respiratory disease and cardio-vascular disease) before the results were presented to a joint meeting of the district and family health services authorities. The economists involved in the exercises attended and, as with each health gain group, used the first part of the meeting to explain the principles of health economics. There appeared again to be a consensus – felt especially strongly by the non-professional authority

Table 8.1.   Proposals for investment and disinvestment in maternal and early child health

Investment proposals	Disinvestment proposals
Targeted family planning	Antenatal care for women with low-risk pregnancies
Support for women with high-risk pregnancies	Admission of children to hospital for reasons not based on clinical need
Continuity of care	Ear, nose and throat operations of questionable benefit
Counselling (termination, stillbirth, genetic and so on)	Generic prescribing and the development of a joint formulary
Community and primary care for children	

members – that this was invaluable to understanding the process and interpreting the results. Although unanimity of opinion was neither expected nor achieved, the overall view was that the exercises had been worthwhile, and the recommendations were formally incorporated into the next strategy document (adapted from Cohen, 1994, 1995; Cohen and Davies, 1995).

ECONOMICS AS A BEHAVIOURAL SCIENCE

Economics is the study of trade-offs. It explicitly recognises that health improvements are achieved at a cost, that is, by forgoing (trading off) the benefits of something else in exchange. Although this has been discussed above in terms of choices regarding the distribution of health care, the same way of thinking can be applied to decisions made by individuals regarding their own behaviour. This may at first sight seem odd, and indeed one of the reasons why health issues were ignored by economists for so long was the belief that health was so important that no individual would be willing to trade it off for anything else (Fuchs, 1972). It is, however, easy to show that this is not in fact the case.

Thinking about...

Can you think of an example of where you trade your health for some other benefit?

Smokers who are aware of the associated health risks are trading off the risk of future illness or death against the present satisfaction and pleasure they get from smoking. Careful driving reduces risk but can mean longer journeys. 'Few people if any, seek to maximise their health and life expectancy per se. To do so, involves sacrificing opportunities to eat, drink, play games, drive and so on that at the margin may be a greater source of utility than any additional (expected) minute or so of life' (Cullis and West, 1979).

Of all disciplines that examine health, economics is perhaps unique by its focus on *optimum* health as opposed to *maximum* health. Optimum health is achieved when the marginal benefits of improved health (or the reduced risk of future ill health) are outweighed by the marginal opportunity cost. Note the similarity between this principle applied at the individual level and the same principle applied at the collective level in the case study. Optimum health is thus likely to be lower than maximum health. While maximum health is something that everyone wants, it is clearly not something that everyone demands (in the sense that demand equals willingness to pay for).

SUMMARY

● The focus of health economics is on finding rational ways to allocate scarce resources to health care services

● In a period of scarce resources, priority-setting is important. Economics provides a framework for this to take place at broad policy level and in individual treatment decisions. Various techniques have been used to assess what type of value can be put on aspects of health

● Health economics uses different types of economic appraisal technique to help to make more effective decisions: cost–benefit analysis is the process of weighing gains against sacrifices. Benefits need to be set against the cost, which means that an alternative is forgone. Economics is not concerned with optimum health. The health improvements need to outweigh the benefits from doing something else.

QUESTIONS FOR FURTHER DISCUSSION

1. Why is it important that health services operate efficiently?

2. Is it unethical to put a monetary value on human life and suffering?

3. Can there be any justification in disinvesting in programmes known to be effective?

RECOMMENDED FURTHER READING

Donaldson, G. and Gerard, K. (1993) *Economics of Health Care Financing*. London: Macmillan – now Palgrave.
    Covers the theoretical issues in an applied way, giving examples of how these economic issues are being addressed in different health care systems.

Drummond, M.F., O'Brien, B., Stoddart, G.L. and Torrance, G.W. (1997) *Methods for the Economic Evaluation of Health Care Programmes,* 2nd edn. Oxford: Oxford Medical Publications.

Jefferson, T., Demicheli, V. and Mugford, M. (1996) *Elementary Economic Evaluation in Health Care*. London: BMJ Publishing.
    These two books explain the 'how' of economics. Both offer guidance to those wishing to undertake economic evaluations.

Edgar, A., Salek, S., Shickle, D. and Cohen, D. (1998) *The Ethical QALY: Ethical Issues in Healthcare Resource Allocations*. Surrey: Euromed Publications.
    Assesses the role that quality of life measures can play in the allocation of health care resources, with an emphasis on the ethics of doing so.

Mooney, G. (1992) *Economics Medicine and Health Care*, 2nd edn. London: Harvester Wheatsheaf.

Mooney, G. (1994) *Key Issues in Health Economics*. London: Harvester Wheatsheaf.
    Companion volumes that together provide a good overview of the economic way of the thinking and the range of issues addressed by the discipline. They deal with conceptual issues such the nature of the commodity of health care and whose values ought to be used in deciding how to use scarce health care resources.

REFERENCES

Cohen, D. (1994) Marginal analysis in practice: an alternative to needs assessment for contracting health care. *British Medical Journal*, **309**: 781–5.

Cohen, D. (1995) Messages from Mid Glamorgan: a multi-programme experiment with marginal analysis. *Health Policy*, **33**: 147–55.

Cohen, D. and Davies, P. (1995) Priority setting in Mid Glamorgan: applying marginal analysis. *British Journal of Healthcare Management*, 1 September: 455–7.

Cullis, J.G. and West, P.A. (1979) *The Economics of Health: An Introduction*. London: Martin Robertson.

Donaldson, C. and Gerard, K. (1993) *Economics of Health Care Financing*. London: Macmillan – now Palgrave.

Drummond, M.F. (1981) *Principles of Economic Appraisal in Health Care*. Oxford: Oxford Medical Publications.

Drummond, M.F, O'Brien, B., Stoddart, G.L. and Torrance, G.W. (1997) *Methods for the Economic Evaluation of Health Care Programmes*, 2nd edn. Oxford: Oxford Medical Publications.

EuroQol Group (1990) EuroQol – a new facility for the measurement of health related quality of life. *Health Policy*, **16**: 199–208.

Fuchs, V.R. (1972) Health care and the US economic system. *Milbank Memorial Fund Quarterly*, **50**: 211–37.

Grogono, A.W. and Woodgate, D.J. (1971) Index for measuring health. *Lancet*, **2**(7732): 1024–6.

IMS America (1998) *Viagra Prescriptions Continue to Climb*. IMS America Health Facts Press Release, 4 May.

Jonsen, A.R. and Hellegers, A.E. (1987) 'Conceptual foundations for an ethics of medical care', in Tancredi, L.R. (ed.) *Ethics of Health Care*. Washington: National Academy of Sciences.

Mooney, G. (1992) *Economics Medicine and Health Care*, 2nd edn. London: Harvester Wheatsheaf.

OHE (Office of Health Economics) (1997) *Compendium of Health Statistics*. London: OHE.

OHE (Office of Health Economics) (1999) *Compendium of Health Statistics*. London: OHE.

Rosser, R. and Kind, P. (1978) A scale of valuations of states of illness: Is there a social consensus? *International Journal of Epidemiology*, **7**: 347–58.

Samuelson, P.A. (1976) *Economics*. Tokyo: McGraw-Hill.

WHO (World Health Organization) (1946) *Preamble of the Constitution of the World Health Organization*. Geneva: WHO.

Ethics and Law

PETER DUNCAN

CONTENTS

Learning outcomes ●●●●●●●●●●●●●●●●●●●●●●●●●●●●●

This chapter will enable readers to:

● Understand the key concerns and principles of ethics and law
● Understand and describe how the theory and methodology of ethics informs and illuminates policy and practice in health care
● Understand and describe how law and its methods inform and illuminate health care policy and practice
● Understand and describe how and why ethical judgements on the dilemmas posed by health care may differ substantially from legal judgements.

OVERVIEW

This chapter explores the central relevance of ethics and law to Health Studies. It begins with several examples of the kinds of dilemma facing those involved in health care provision in developed countries – issues surrounding the nature and value of life, the rationing of scarce resources and the accountability of health professionals to the public whom they are supposed to serve. There have in the UK recently been legal cases investigating whether a doctor is right to hasten a patient's death, whether economic priorities can determine treatment and whether a health authority was negligent in not investigating the standards of consultant cardiac surgeons. These are dilemmas that can only be fully understood by a consideration of the disciplines of ethics and law. Furthermore, 'dilemmas' are not confined simply to 'life and death' situations but cover the whole span of health care activity, from prevention and health promotion through treatment to rehabilitation. In the first part of the chapter ethical theory is discussed and related to practical health examples; then law, its nature and application to health are explored. The second part exposes difficulties in the relationship between ethics and law, and poses the essential question: is what we must do (our legal obligation) always the same, in health care, as what we ought to do (our ethical or moral duty)? The chapter closes with an extended example of the dilemma posed by termination of pregnancy, drawing out some of the themes and difficulties posed by the two disciplines for health care.

INTRODUCTION

Those involved in and planning health care are faced by major decisions concerning:

● life and death
● the power held by professions and the point at which the level of power becomes unacceptable
● priorities for the way in which we spend public money.

In addition, such decisions and issues are not only relevant when we are talking about 'acute' treatment and care: for those concerned with the prevention of disease and the promotion of health, they are of equal relevance. In the area of health care rationing, for example, to what extent should we devote resources to population health promotion when this might result in some individuals being deprived of the treatment and care they acutely need? To what extent should a health professional use his or her power to 'persuade' someone to give up what the professional believes to be an 'unhealthy' behaviour? Given medicine's increased ability to 'decide', in a technical sense, when life can end, does killing become acceptable in certain circumstances? As the expectations of the health services rise, and as more people are helped to live longer, the burden on the NHS is increased. Recent reforms have stressed the importance of both clinical excellence and limits to public expenditure. To what extent should economic priorities determine treatment (or the lack of it)?

Such dilemmas can of course be helpfully investigated by disciplines such as sociology (in relation to, say, the understanding of professional power) and economics (considering, for example, the financial cost of particular health care decisions). Doubtless pathology, genetics, pharmacology and other medical disciplines would also have a lot to say about aspects of 'life' and 'death' dilemmas, but these dilemmas cannot simply be thought about in these 'nuts and bolts' ways. They concern **values** (for example the value of 'health for its own sake' as against the value of economic efficiency).

Whereas we hold values as individuals, we also frequently expect others to hold the same kind of values as ourselves, for example that killing is wrong. Such values can be thought of as normative. We often believe that a certain value – such as 'killing is wrong' – is so important that we establish prescriptive rules to prevent action against the value taking place or to punish those who do act in such a way. Such issues become the subject of laws, which society as a whole upholds and enforces. This is the territory of ethics and of law, making a consideration of these two disciplines vital to the study and understanding of health.

values – things which are valuable. Value may be subjective (something is valued simply because it is wanted), instrumental (something is valued because it has a useful function) or intrinsic (something is valued because it has fundamental and irreducible importance). It is of course possible for something to be valuable in more than just one of these separate senses

THE CONTRIBUTION OF ETHICS TO HEALTH STUDIES

There are three main branches of philosophy:

● epistemology (enquiry into the nature and grounds of belief, experience and knowledge)
● metaphysics (the study of the nature of being)
● ethics (enquiry into how we ought to act and conduct ourselves).

Ethics is the branch of philosophy that has traditionally concerned itself with examining the worth or value of conduct, with developing and defending views on what might be meant by a 'worthwhile life' and with how such a life could be led. Different ethical traditions have developed separate – and conflicting – views on the purpose of ethics (metaethical views) and on the kind of conduct in which we should actually engage (normative views). In particular, Western philosophy has been profoundly shaped by three theories of ethics: *Aristotelianism*, *deontology* and *utilitarianism*. Each of these three theories can in turn be seen as essentially a product of the times in which it was originally born. These theories are based on trying to determine:

- what is meant by leading a good or virtuous life (the focus particularly of Aristotelianism)
- what kinds of duty or obligation we owe each other (the focus particularly of deontology)
- how we might take account of consequences when deciding a particular course of action (the focus especially of utilitarianism).

ARISTOTELIANISM

Aristotle was a Greek philosopher who lived from 384–322BC. His *Ethics* is representative of ethical theories that aim to work out what a good (moral) life might mean and how the development of such a life can be encouraged. Aristotle attempted to do this by looking at the nature of the world and the individuals within it in order to assess what being virtuous might mean. For this reason, Aristotle is frequently thought of as an empiricist. In viewing the world, he argued that we become virtuous by performing virtuous actions.

For Aristotle, it is the moderate action, leading him to the famous 'doctrine of the golden mean' (Russell, 1979). Every virtue is a mean between two extremes (or vices). For Aristotle, what is most important is not simply the identification of the mean (the virtuous) in all aspects of human action. It is the idea that, through reflection and contemplation, we should develop our lives so that we know how to act according to the mean – in other words, how to act virtuously (or morally). We thus become more morally expert, reflection and the consequent performance of virtuous action determining what it means to lead 'the worthwhile (good) life'.

> *Thinking about...*
>
> Can you think what a virtuous action might be?

EXAMPLE 9.1

The dilemma of life

In 1998, Dr David Moor, a Northumbrian GP, was charged with murder after allegedly giving his 85-year-old terminally ill patient George Liddell a huge dose of diamorphine, which must, according to the prosecution, have been intended to kill. In his own defence, Dr Moor claimed that, 'All I tried to do was relieve his agony, his distress and suffering' (Dyer, 1999), and in his summing up on the case the judge, Mr Justice Holland, suggested to the jury that:

> They might consider it ironic that Dr Moor found himself facing the charge because he was *caring* enough to come out on his day off to see Mr Liddell. (Dyer, 1999, italics added)

Whether Dr Moor did the right thing and acted morally may depend on our conception of caring. It could be argued that Dr Moor was acting virtuously and caring for Mr Liddell because the requirement in this situation was to relieve his pain, *even* if it meant that a possible outcome was the hastening of his death.

Question: In your view did Dr Moor carry out a virtuous act?

Much depends here on the intention of Dr Moor's action and the situation in which it took place. If the intention were to kill, Dr Moor would (in legal terms) have been culpable. If it was to care, then arguably, in Aristotelian terms, he was acting virtuously. It is necessary to emphasise the word 'arguably' because of the extremity of the situation and the related action. If the virtuous is the mean between two extremes, the virtue of caring lies somewhere in the middle between excessive 'caring' leading to dependency and loss of autonomy and not caring at all (or not caring in the 'right' way). Given that we do not usually understand caring as killing, Dr Moor's action could only be seen as a 'mean' within a situation of enormous and distorted extremes. The guidance offered by Aristotelianism in this particular situation might therefore be somewhat limited, although it does allow for an interpretation of the action. That interpretation is likely to become more substantial if we look beyond the particular situation involving Mr Liddell, consider a range of others in which Dr Moor had been involved and from that try to determine whether he demonstrated 'caring' according to more usual means. If this was possible (and it was in part what Dr Moor's defenders and supporters tried to do), it could be suggested that he was leading the 'worthwhile (good) life'.

IMMANUEL KANT AND DEONTOLOGY

duties – things that we morally or legally ought to do. Duty is usually distinguished from obligation. We incur obligations because of specific circumstances, but duty is something of longer standing and primarily connected with role. A nurse, for example, has a duty to care in a long-standing and general sense because he or she is a nurse. Nurses also incur obligations to care in a much more short-term sense and with regard to particular people (patients) by virtue of placing themselves in situations in which caring is required

Immanuel Kant (1724–1804) was a German philosopher who developed ideas representative of deontology – thinking based on the notion that we owe each other particular **duties** or obligations.

Kant claimed the existence of a reality independent of our experience. Part of his justification for this claim lay in his analysis of our experience as humans. We live in a world subject to scientific laws of causation, yet we retain freedom of will, having the capacity to act morally or otherwise. Our moral choices must therefore be framed within an independent reality. Kant argued that reason exists independently of experience and that the right use of reason is directed towards moral ends. Reason moves us to act out of duty for its own sake and independently of any thought about the consequences. This leads to Kant's famous statement of the categorical imperative: 'I ought never to act in such a way *that I can also will that my maxim should become a universal law*' (Paton, 1948, original emphasis).

How then, is the difficulty overcome? One way (which of course the strict deontologist could not accept) is to allow that consideration of consequences to play an important part in making moral decisions. This leads to the third ethical tradition to be considered – utilitarianism.

EXAMPLE 9.2

Kant and the dilemma of life

? **In your view, was Dr Moor carrying out his duty?**

At first glance, Kant's view that we hold certain moral obligations independent of ideas about consequences seems to hold the possibility of a definitive judgement in the case of

Dr Moor. Killing is always wrong; therefore we should judge the GP to have committed an act of which we morally disapprove even if he were to be found not guilty of criminal charges. There is, however, a major difficulty at this point. We seldom act with regard to only one moral imperative: we usually have multiple ethical considerations. Dr Moor would have known of course that killing is wrong, but he would also have known that allowing suffering is wrong (or, framed more positively, that he had a duty to care for his patient, Mr Liddell). If Dr Moor had not administered diamorphine, Mr Liddell would have suffered intolerable pain, yet administering the drug carried the risk of killing Mr Liddell. The deontologist faces a problem at this point. Either there is agreement that conflicting duties exist, in which case killing may not always be wrong, or there is a persistence in the belief that the overriding duty is not to kill. But not acting will result in continued suffering.

J.S. MILL AND UTILITARIANISM

John Stuart Mill (1806–1873) was a Scottish philosopher and probably the most famous advocate of the ethical theory known as **utilitarianism**. In this view, careful thought needs to be given to the consequences of any action, and if those consequences are likely to be adverse for some, the reason for the action must be robust.

If it is put simply, the theory of utilitarianism seems appealing:

> Utility, or the greatest happiness principle, holds that actions are right in proportion as they tend to promote happiness, wrong as they tend to produce the reverse of happiness. By happiness is intended pleasure, and the absence of pain; by unhappiness, pain, and the privation of pleasure. (Mill, 1962)

Utilitarianism – and consequentialist ethical theory in general – corresponds with a belief held by many that whereas there are important moral duties, action simply for the sake of duty, whatever the consequences, is problematic. In addition, a deliberation about consequences may well include thoughts about the level of 'happiness' or 'unhappiness' likely to accrue from a particular course of action.

utilitarianism – the moral theory asserting that we always ought to do what will produce the greatest good

---

EXAMPLE 9.3

J.S. Mill and the dilemma of life

? **In your view, were the consequences of Dr Moor's action beneficial?**

Dr Moor's view might have been that the hastening of death for Mr Liddell would have been a merciful release for the patient himself and the end of much anguish for his family. But there are at least two difficulties in relying too heavily on thought about consequences for moral decision-making:

1. How is it ever possible fully to know the consequences of any particular action? It is imaginable that Dr Moor's administration of diamorphine may have resulted in side-effects that caused Mr Liddell considerable distress before his death. The choice may not have been a clear-cut one between on the one hand intolerable pain, and on the other a peaceful death. Introducing a chance of the existence of a complex set of possible consequences may make some likely to see Dr Moor less as a practitioner acting in the patient's best interests and more as someone toying with a person's fate.

2. What if Dr Moor's actions had resulted in members of Mr Liddell's family actually being terribly distressed by his death, far more so than if his passing had been different?

Dr Moor may not have intended this to be the case, but if either or both of these had been the consequences of his actions, the end result could be argued to have been more misery than if he had not acted. Utilitarianism contains the paradoxical possibility that someone can intend an action to be ethical but for it to become unethical as it is mediated by circumstances (even more problematic of course being the notion that someone can intend an unethical action but circumstances render it unexpectedly ethical). These difficulties all contribute to the view that a reliance solely on consequences as the measure of moral judgement makes ethics a somewhat haphazard business.

THE CONTRIBUTION OF LAW TO HEALTH STUDIES

 How would you define 'law' and what is its contribution to the study of health?

A straightforward definition of 'law' might be 'the development and study of a society's prescriptive laws and rules'. Given this, it is likely that law will (either actually or potentially) have a view on many health care dilemmas. In the case of Dr Moor, he was actually being tried against the laws of the country in which his alleged crime – murder – took place. The law makes certain prescriptions related to the status and protection of foetuses and in what types of circumstance that protection could be legitimately neglected. There are laws relating to the provision of health services, which could inform or influence debates and dilemmas connected to health care rationing (although, as will be seen, there is a large degree of vagueness in this area).

In addition, the study of law helps us to recognise the value placed by society on health and the expectations we have about the ways in which health workers conduct themselves. In the 'Bristol heart babies' case for example, two surgeons were found guilty of professional misconduct by the General Medical Council (GMC) in 1998 (Hill, 1999). This highlights the matter of rules and the capacity for self-regulation that a particular professional cabal (medicine) has been allowed to develop. The high number of deaths in paediatric cardiac surgery at Bristol Royal Infirmary was known about by the hospital, the Royal College of Surgeons and the Department of Health for three years before action was finally taken. For some, the Bristol case demonstrates the fundamental weakness in allowing the self-governance of professions.

THE SOURCES OF LAW

The laws governing all those who live in England and Wales (general laws) have historically had two sources: legislation or statute; and law decided through the courts, that is, case law. (In Scotland, there are both different statutes and a different system of courts.)

Legislation (statute law)

This source of law has traditionally been developed and enacted by Parliament at Westminster. During this century, **statute law** has assumed great significance. Acts of Parliament (statutes) are primary legislation and become law after both Houses of Parliament have passed them and Royal Assent has been received. Recent examples of primary legislation directly affecting health care provision include the 1990 National Health Service and Community Care Act – which established the introduction of the so-called 'internal market' – and the legislative changes applied to the NHS by the Labour government in 1999, based on the White Paper *The New NHS: Modern, Dependable* (DoH, 1998).

statute law – a law made by a sovereign or legislative authority

As well as enacting primary legislation, Parliament has the ability to delegate the right to the relevant Secretary of State (in the case of the legislation above, for Health) to draw up regulations or orders dealing with details or future situations that cannot be included in the main act. This is known as 'delegated legislation'.

Case law

This is law emerging from decisions made in the courts of England and Wales. Court decisions may be the only authority with regard to a particular issue, or they may be the authority charged with interpreting a particular piece of legislation. If, however, there is a conflict between case and statute, the latter must always be followed. If the outcome of this is not acceptable, it is the responsibility of legislators to consider changing the statute accordingly. Case law's essential ingredient is legal precedent, judges referring back to similar cases in order to make decisions that are consistent. Not all decisions made by the courts are binding on later cases. The English court system is hierarchical, a decision made by a higher court becoming binding on lower ones. Cases creating precedent have generally been heard in the Court of Appeal or the House of Lords. (The House of Lords is the highest court in the land and can therefore overturn any decision made in lower courts and, in some circumstances, decide not to follow a decision that it might have made previously.)

case law – the part of law developed through decisions made in particular cases

A striking example of health care-related case law is that of Anthony Bland. Mr Bland was a young football supporter who fell into persistent vegetative state following massive injury at the Hillsborough football stadium disaster in April 1989. Mr Bland's parents petitioned the courts to declare that it would be lawful for doctors to remove life support and allow him to die. In a highly distinctive judgement (*Airedale NHS Trust (Respondents)* v. *Bland*, House of Lords Judgement, 4 February 1993), the Law Lords ruled that, on the basis of opinions given by Mr Bland's loved ones about his character before being injured, he

Thinking about...

In your view, is it acceptable for the law in this case to make a judgement about the nature of life? Can you think of other examples in which the law decides about life or death?

would, given his state at the time of judgement, have chosen to die rather than live. The principle of self-determination was allowed over that of the sanctity of life, although in their judgement the Lords emphasised continuing treatment as not being in the patient's best interests, rather than Anthony Bland's right to choose death (Dworkin, 1995).

While statute decided by Parliament, together with case law, has historically been the source of law for England and Wales, recent years have seen European law become a further crucial influence over its development.

European law

The European Communities Act 1972 allowed for the application of European Community law within the UK. The essential purpose of applying European law to member states of what is now the European Union is to effect harmonisation, frequently to support economic aims (for example the free movement of goods and labour). There is, however, a different kind of impact on our domestic law emerging from Europe. The Human Rights Act 1998 incorporates the European Convention on Human Rights into domestic law for the first time, meaning that the courts will have a new duty to take into account case law decided by the European Court of Human Rights in Strasbourg (Outhwaite, 1999). Key articles that are likely to affect the health service include:

● the right to life (Article 2)
● the right not to be subjected to inhuman or degrading treatment (Article 3)
● the right to liberty (Article 5)
● the right to marry and found a family (Article 12).

Criminal law and civil law

Most criminal law derives from statute (although murder is defined through common law). Such laws create offences, which can be prosecuted. Usually, the Crown Prosecution Service (CPS) undertakes the prosecution of offences against the criminal law. In the case of Dr Moor, for example, it was the CPS who decided to prosecute for murder. In some specific areas, however, other bodies have the power to engage in criminal prosecutions: local authorities can, for example, prosecute environmental health-related offences.

Civil law, on the other hand, enables individual citizens to make legal claims against others (either individuals or organisations) where a civil wrong has been committed. Such wrongs include negligence and breach of statutory duty (part of a group of wrongs sometimes being referred to as *torts*).

Although it is necessary to make the distinction between criminal and civil law, it should be noted that some actions can be pursued both as criminal offences and as civil wrongs.

THEORETICAL AND METHODOLOGICAL PERSPECTIVES

In 1998, the government proposed the setting up of the National Institute for Clinical Excellence (NICE) to advise on effective treatment. As expectations of the health services rise and more people are helped to live longer, the burden on the NHS is increased. Recent organisational reform has emphasised the importance of both clinical excellence and limits on public expenditure.

Resource decisions can, in part, be framed as being made on the basis of empirical evidence (cost–benefit, cost effectiveness, a knowledge of the total financial package available to the NHS and so on). There comes a point, however (and it is remarkable how relatively infrequently this process is exposed), at which the decision gets whittled down to being one that at its heart is about *values*. In this case, there is essentially competition between a course of action founded substantially on values related to economics, and one based on values connected to health and well-being.

> **CONNECTIONS**
>
> Chapter 8 (Health Economics) discusses the techniques used by economists to establish priorities in resource allocation

THEORETICAL AND METHODOLOGICAL PERSPECTIVES IN ETHICS

The territory of ethics – the examination and discussion of the values underpinning conduct – is largely *conceptual*, and in the case of many of the concepts discussed in ethics, there is a large degree of dispute, or *contestedness*.

Some philosophers have attempted to suggest that value ('ought') judgements have a status roughly equivalent to those concerning empirical fact, that in asserting, for example that 'killing is wrong', someone is suggesting an undeniable truth. Aristotle, Kant and Mill are very important representatives of philosophers attempting normative moral projects. In more recent times, contemporary thinkers viewing health care have tried to suggest that there are important principles that should underlie work in this field of activity. Among others, Beauchamp and Childress (1994) and Gillon (1994) have suggested that the following principles are particularly important for health care workers:

- respect for **autonomy**: the obligation to respect the autonomy of others – for example patients or clients – to the extent that this is compatible with the autonomy of all who are likely to be affected by the action being considered

- **beneficence**: the ethical commitment in health care to produce benefit for patients or clients

- **non-maleficence**: the obligation not to harm patients or clients, closely linked to the previous principle, because any given action has the potential to result in both benefit and harm. The obligation on health care professionals is to ensure that the balance is always in favour of benefit in any given situation

- **justice**: the obligation to act fairly when dealing with competing claims to do with, for example, resources or rights.

autonomy – the capacity to be in charge yourself of your actions and your destiny. The principle of respect for autonomy asserts that we have a moral obligation to allow this capacity to individuals to the extent that it does not infringe on the equal rights of others

beneficence – the production of good, or benefit. This is frequently regarded as a moral obligation that ought to be held by health care workers

non-maleficence – doing no harm. Again, this is frequently regarded as a moral obligation that ought to be held by health care workers and is closely connected with beneficence

justice – fairness in terms of one or other (or more) of: resource allocation (distributive justice), meeting natural rights (rights-based justice) and the law (legal justice)

Importantly, the four principles are prima facie, which means that each is binding unless it conflicts with another, in which case a choice must be made between the competing principles as to which one should be followed. Those who support the four principles argue that whereas they cannot yield a definitive ethical judgement in all health care situations, they do provide a framework for considering, and reasoning about, obligations.

The study of ethics cannot provide us with ready-made answers to difficult situations (as these simply do not exist), but it does give us the 'tools' to enable reflection on the dilemmas we confront and thus helps us to make greater sense of them. Arguably (because this is a relatively unfashionable view in moral philosophical circles), actively attempting to understand ethical dilemmas through reflection will help us to become more moral individuals, a return to the Aristotelian idea that the purpose of ethics is to help us to lead the good (worthwhile) life.

If we are to become 'better' at dealing with the ethical difficulties facing us in health care, we need at least three things:

- an awareness of moral theory
- an awareness of the kind of principles, duties and obligations to which we might want to agree as we work in this field
- a capacity to reflect on how theory and principles connect with our own intuition, thus developing the ability to think coherently, in a moral sense, by and for ourselves.

Thinking about...

Think of some situations in which a health worker may have a clash of principles – for example acting as an advocate for a client and putting forward his or her wishes, which may not be perceived as being in the client's best interest

---

EXAMPLE 9.4

Some techniques for the development of moral reflection and intuition

Sue Hunt is a health visitor who is concerned about the nature of smoking advice being given by her colleagues in the multipartner general practice where she is based. Her anxiety centres on whether she and her colleagues – including the GPs – are being too directive, possibly even coercive, in the advice they give. Sue has recently attended some study sessions and done some reading on ethical problems in health care. She has recognised again the ease with which health care workers may assume control in a given situation and may imagine that the advice they provide ought to be directive and readily accepted by their patients.

Sue decides to explore further whether the smoking cessation advice work she and her colleagues undertake might indeed pose ethical problems. She arranges to discuss the issue with her mentor, a more experienced health visitor based at another surgery. Together, they talk through her concerns and agree the following plan of action:

- Sue will undertake a short 'self-audit' of her own advice-giving on smoking cessation. She will make notes in a diary after each relevant session with patients for a period of a week. She will then describe the advice she gave, how she dealt with questions, the reaction of the patients and how she dealt with that reaction

- At the end of the week, she will use the notes actively to reflect on her advice-giving practice. To what extent did she feel she was respecting patients' autonomy and listening to what they said? If it was hard to do so, why was this? (For example, were listening difficulties related to pressure of time or a feeling that you 'had to do something'?)

- Following the audit and reflection, Sue will seek the views of her health visitor colleagues in the practice and see whether they have similar perceptions and experiences in this area

- She will use her experience, and hopefully that of her colleagues, to frame a presentation to other colleagues in the practice on difficulties and possibilities with giving advice that is patient centred

- Sue will review progress with her mentor in a month's time.

From this example, it is possible to identify processes such as understanding moral theory through reading, mentoring, reflective diary-keeping and discussion as all potentially contributing to the development of moral reflection and intuition.

THEORETICAL AND METHODOLOGICAL PERSPECTIVES IN LAW

In the previous discussion on the methodology of ethics, the view was expressed that it could be characterised as an analysis of the nature of particular (and particularly difficult) concepts. The methodology of law is, similarly, analytic, but whereas, generally speaking, moral philosophers struggle with disputed concepts, those studying law frequently engage with written statutes and recorded cases. Such engagement often occurs with the purpose of discovering whether legislation or existing precedent is sufficient to apply to a new case or whether a new precedent will have to be set. To this extent, there will always be – actually or potentially – a particular legal perspective (a judgement) on a situation. Analysis in law can yield rather more absolute conclusions than analysis in ethics, although, as will be discussed in the following section, this does not mean that we cannot be unhappy or doubtful about some of the conclusions that the law makes.

The provision of a health care service exposes some of the limitations of the law and its relative weakness. The UK is said to have committed itself – through the NHS – to the provision of a comprehensive health care service equally available to all according to need and free of charge at the point of delivery (McHale et al., 1997). This commitment has been expressed by all recent governments despite what could be regarded as different attitudes to the context within which health care services are delivered (in particular, the contrast between the so-called 'internal market' created by the Conservative government through the NHS and Community Care Act 1990, and the 'duties of partnership' between health-related agencies, which formed a central part of the Labour government's NHS reforms after 1997).

This political commitment can be seen as being representative of the value placed by our society on health and health care. A legal framework – expressed through the NHS Act 1977 and related legislation – seeks to ensure this commitment. The 1977 Act states that the Secretary of State has a general duty to:

CONNECTIONS

Chapter 6 (Social Policy) discusses the political context influencing the organisational changes in the NHS

Continue the promotion in England and Wales of a comprehensive health service designed to secure improvement:

a) in the physical and mental health of the people of those countries

b) in the prevention, diagnosis and treatment of illness, and for that purpose to provide or secure the effective provision of services in accordance with this act.

Section 3(1) of the Act requires the Secretary of State to provide health services to the extent he considers necessary to 'meet all reasonable requirements'. The Secretary of State's power is, with certain exceptions, discretionary. There is very frequently no legal right to insist that particular services are available, and the courts have a deep reluctance to scrutinise decisions made by health service organisations who have denied patients access to the services they want.

In this area, the law's position is difficult. It might be generally accepted that individuals have a *right* to health care, but, generally speaking, statute allows the nature of that right to be decided by those controlling health care. In addition, unless a right can be acted on, it is hardly a right at all. There are two main ways in which individuals can attempt to enforce their rights to health care, both with their roots in the civil law. These are:

● the public law action for judicial review, which allows a challenge to be made to the decisions of public bodies on the basis that they have been irrational, illegal or procedurally improper

● claims for compensation on the basis of the right to health care having been breached.

EXAMPLE 9.5

Child B

The case of Child B in 1995 provides an example of a judicial review *(R. v. Cambridge DHA, ex p. B)*. The father of a 10-year-old girl (referred to at the time as Child B) brought a review of the decision by Cambridge Health Authority not to fund further treatment of her leukaemia. Her doctors in Cambridge made the clinical judgement that she would not benefit from further chemotherapy or a second bone marrow transplant. A second opinion sought by the child's father disputed this, but the health authority declined to pay for the treatment proposed. The case was taken to the High Court, where Mr Justice Laws judged that the authority had not adequately explained the priorities that had led to its decision in this case. He required it to be re-examined, although he did not order the treatment to be funded. The health authority took the case to the Court of Appeal, where it was heard by Sir Thomas Bingham, Master of the Rolls. Sir Thomas began his judgement by suggesting the very high value placed by society on human life but concluded that the courts could neither make judgements on health care resource allocation nor require a health authority to be explicit about its decision-making. Child B died in May 1996.

The case of Child B underlines the reluctance of the law to interfere in both clinical judgements and decisions on resource allocation (rationing). Arguably, then, whereas as a society we place a high value on health and health care, we are as individuals extremely limited in our capacity to pursue that right. Interestingly, however, it has been suggested that the introduction of the Human Rights Act 1998 will greatly strengthen individual rights to particular forms of health care and treatment.

The law also expresses societal expectations of how health care professionals should conduct themselves and the obligations they have to clients or patients. Professionals, it is agreed, owe those whom they serve a general duty of care. If this is breached, the professional has acted not only unprofessionally, but also acted negligently. If patients' or clients' expectations of the duty of care are not met, they may wish to seek redress in civil law through a negligence action – from patients' perspectives, to achieve compensation in some way for the wrong believed to have been done. This reinforces the point that legal mechanisms serve both closely connected purposes of law applied to health care:

> **CONNECTIONS**
>
> Chapter 8 (Health Economics) also discusses the case of Child B and the economic considerations involved in individual treatment

- the expression of societal values
- the expectations we have of professionals.

It appears quite right, then, in terms of the law, to talk about individual *expectations* of health care professionals: there is an expectation that they hold a duty of care, and if there is a failure in this respect, there is an equal expectation that they should be subject to redress. (This is perhaps something of an optimistic view because the legal system is in practice so complex, and its use so costly, that individuals very often have little chance of fulfilling the complete 'expectation equation'.)

The basis of the duty of care was laid in a judgement in 1932 by Lord Atkin (*Donoghue* v. *Stevenson*). He judged that someone must take reasonable care to avoid actions or omissions in action that could be reasonably foreseen to cause injury to someone directly affected by those acts. (Note that this is quite different from an obligation to act for the benefit of another, which generally does not exist in English law.) Breaching this duty and causing harm is negligence; a civil liability has thus been created so compensation can be claimed. If a negligence action is to be successful, three things must, on the balance of probability, be established:

- The plaintiff (the person pursuing redress) must establish that the defendant (the person defending the action) owes her or him a duty of care
- This duty has been breached
- The result of the breach has been that the plaintiff suffered harm not so unforeseeable as to be regarded in law as too remote.

If health care professionals consider the duty of care, it is likely that they will want to ask a number of questions. First, to whom do they owe a duty? The law would usually deem that they have a duty to their patients and probably their patients' relatives, as well as to their colleagues.

Second, when would a duty be regarded to have been breached? The law would probably take the view that the duty has been breached if the required standard of care has not been met. The 'Bolam test' (based on the judgement resulting from *Bolam* v. *Friern Hospital Management Committee*, 1957) indicates that health care professionals would breach the standard of care if they failed to meet the standards of their peers. This, however, is not a simple test, at least in part because the law is less likely to take a judgement on 'acceptable care' provided by some professional groups in health care than others.

Third, what is the extent of proof required that the damage or harm done was actually caused by negligent professional behaviour? In the case described in *Barnett* v. *Chelsea and Kensington Hospital Management Committee* (1968), a night watchman was turned away from a hospital accident and emergency department, later to die of arsenic poisoning. While it was judged that there is an obligation to provide care to someone presenting at an accident and emergency department, it was also judged that the factors causing death in this case were not within the capacity of a medical practitioner to treat, and therefore the doctor who turned the patient away could not be held liable for his death.

<table>
<tr><td>

Thinking about...

When you consult health care practitioners, what are your expectations of them?

CONNECTIONS

Chapter 3 (Health Psychology) considers how the beliefs of the patient and the doctor may affect the nature of professional consultations

</td><td>

THE RELATIONSHIP BETWEEN ETHICS AND LAW: IS WHAT WE *MUST* DO THE SAME AS WHAT WE *OUGHT* TO DO?

When we approach health care professionals, we generally do so because we need help and have an expectation and confidence that those whom we approach can offer us such assistance. We believe – or hope we can believe – that they will take their duty of care towards us seriously, respect our confidentiality, inform us of what they intend to do on our behalf and why, and only go ahead and do it if we consent to their proposed actions.

Yet health care practice, and the relationships between professionals and patients, is frequently messy and difficult. We are right to expect the possibility of redress when things go wrong, and the law might to some extent be able to provide this as part of its role in 'formally' expressing societal expectations of both the health care systems operating on our behalf and the individual professionals working within them. But when we go to health care professionals, our expectations are not simply that they will operate within relatively narrow and legalistic conceptions such as those of 'negligence' and 'duty of care'. It has been argued, for example, that in law the duty of care centres on the requirement to avoid actions or omissions that are likely to result in injury or harm. Would we seek the help of a practitioner simply because we knew that he or she had an excellent reputation for avoiding harm (which is largely all the general law requires him or her to do)?

</td></tr>
</table>

This is moving towards the view that there is a difference between what we *must* do (that which the law requires us to do) and what we *ought* to do (that which – for want of better words – our personal and professional moral character obliges us to do). In addition, it may be that it is the health care professional who does what he or she ought to do (rather than simply what must be done) whom we would regard as a 'good' or 'moral' practitioner (Rumbold and Lesser, 1995).

In the case described above of Dr Moor, cleared of murdering his patient, it could be argued that he did what he felt he ought to do in relieving his patient Mr Liddell's pain even though it hastened his death. In this instance, the law 'agreed' that this was the right action. In other cases in which there is arguably a similar motivation, the conclusion of a jury might, however, be different. In 1992, Dr Nigel Cox was tried for the attempted murder of one of his patients, Mrs Lillian Boyes. She was dying from a crippling and agonisingly painful form of rheumatoid arthritis and begged Dr Cox to kill her, which he did with a lethal injection of potassium chloride (Dworkin, 1995). He was convicted and received a suspended jail sentence. Both Dr Moor and Dr Cox wanted to relieve their patients of terrible suffering. The roots of the different outcomes of the legal cases lie in the decision of the jurors and the direction of the judges, but the law itself remains the same: killing is wrong. Yet we might want to argue that both doctors *ought* to have performed the action they did. (Or, equally, we might want to argue that both actions by both men were wrong.)

The law was reluctant to intervene in a judgement made by Cambridge Health Authority about the extent to which the priority of treatment for Child B superseded the many other priorities it believed itself to have. Sir Thomas Bingham, in the Court of Appeal, effectively ruled that the authority had no legal obligation to fund treatment for Child B. Yet while there might not have been a legal obligation (as this treatment *must* be funded), at least some would argue that it *ought* to have been paid for; here was a young girl with a life-threatening condition whose prognosis was to some degree disputed by doctors who knew her case. The problem of rationing and priority-setting is made more acute by the undoubted fact that the health authority had to make choices about what to fund across a whole range of possible health promotion, prevention, treatment and care activities given the duties delegated to it by the Secretary of State. Would it have been better, for example, if the authority had funded treatment for Child B at the expense of a smoking prevention programme (which if effective might ultimately – in 20 or 30 years time – have saved or prolonged several hundred lives)?

The death of 29 babies and toddlers at Bristol Royal Infirmary following heart surgery performed by two cardiac surgeons raises a complex set of issues. Lying centrally is one of professional competence. One of the surgeons and the infirmary chief executive were eventually found guilty of serious professional misconduct by the GMC and banned from practising medicine. The other surgeon was banned from operating on children for three years and later sacked. A public inquiry into children's heart surgery at Bristol Royal Infirmary began in spring 1999 and is likely to be the longest and most wide-ranging investigation into medical standards in the UK. The role of the inquiry is not, however, to act as a professional disciplinary body.

> **CONNECTIONS**
>
> Chapter 8 (Health Economics) argues that there can be an ethical basis to priority-setting

Arguably in this case, *must* and *ought* should be indistinguishable from one another, in a way that is indisputable and unlike the other situations we have reviewed. We *must* have protection to ensure that those who are charged with our fundamental well-being are competent to undertake the task. And those who perform the task (and others who regulate them) *ought* to ensure that this is the case. Yet despite this indisputability, 29 children died before action was taken, and even when cases were proved against the professionals concerned, varying degrees of sanctions against them were applied (and were objected to). This state of affairs seems to suggest that what we might consider to be the *moral* duty to professional competence held by those working in health care might not be matched by equally rigorous laws.

At least part of the difficulty in this case is that the regulation of the doctors concerned was essentially undertaken by other doctors – ultimately through the GMC. This concept of self-regulation (which was until very recently commonly applied across a range of professions, including others in health care, such as nursing) might lead to the creation of a climate in which it actually becomes hard for professionals to do what they might feel they *ought*. In 1990, a young consultant anaesthetist working at Bristol Royal Infirmary wrote to the local health authority raising his concerns about what seemed to be a higher than average death rate among babies undergoing cardiac surgery. These allegations were dismissed, the anaesthetist later claiming that the main surgeon had threatened to ruin his career prospects if he pursued the matter (Hill, 1999).

That professionals should find it so threatening to 'blow the whistle' on others is another disturbing feature of the Bristol case. This – and other instances – have contributed to the GMC strengthening its mechanisms for self-regulation. It is, however, interesting to note, in the context of the 1999 legislative changes to the NHS, that the government gave assurances to the medical profession that the principle of self-regulation itself would be 'safeguarded' (*Health Service Journal*, 1999).

> **CONNECTIONS**
>
> Chapter 7 (Organisation and Management) discusses the structure of the NHS and how this militates against 'whistleblowing'

 What are the advantages and disadvantages of a professional group regulating itself?

It could be argued that it is indeed professionals themselves – by virtue of both their technical expertise and their moral commitment – who stand the best chance of closing the *must–ought* 'gap'. After all, cases such as Bristol are relatively rare, even though we may naturally be concerned that they exist at all. One of the ways in which professional groups have attempted to close the gap is through the development of codes of conduct.

CLOSING THE 'GAP' BETWEEN WHAT WE MUST DO AND WHAT WE OUGHT TO DO? CONSENT AND PROFESSIONAL CONDUCT

code of conduct – an attempt to prescribe the ways in which members of an occupational or professional group ought to behave. Such attempts are frequently made by representatives of that occupational or professional group itself

Nurses, midwives and health visitors are bound to practise according to the duties set out in a ***code of conduct***. At the time of writing, the United Kingdom Central Council for Nursing, Midwifery and Health Visiting (UKCC) was the body charged with maintaining both the code and the register of practitioners bound by it. A breach of the code was grounds for applying legally based sanctions (removal from the professional register) (Pyne, 1995). This state of affairs is set to continue, although the government has legislated for a change to the nature of the regulatory body (the UKCC) and the extent to which it possessed the capacity for self-regulation of the professions under its jurisdiction. It seems, however, to be clear that a commitment to the code of conduct by nurses binds them to certain things that are both what they ought to do (the code being an expression of moral commitments) and what they *must* do (the nurse being likely to be sanctioned if the commitments are neglected or breached).

Article 5 of the code declares that the registered nurse, midwife or health visitor must:

> Work in an open and co-operative manner with patients, clients and their families, foster their independence and recognise and respect their involvement in the planning and delivery of care. (UKCC, 1992)

One thing that this broad statement may imply is a commitment on the part of the nurse to ensuring that patients are fully informed about their care and consent as appropriate to all its aspects. The nurse, therefore, both *ought* to and *must* engage in processes aimed at achieving informed consent on the part of his or her patients.

 What difficulties do you think there might be with the concept of informed consent?

Informed consent is a very reasonable obligation and expectation. The difficulty comes when we start going beyond generality and thinking about what it might mean in practice. Informed consent involves two processes – informing and consenting (Gorovitz, 1985). The end result of informing should be understanding yet there are many possible barriers to understanding, particularly in the health care context:

● Patients or clients are frequently in a critical state in which their ability to understand is limited
● Individuals have different capacities with regard to understanding
● Informing has a cost in that it is time consuming and demanding of skills that health professionals have in different measures.

Moreover, some people do not *want* to be informed, this dread of 'bad news' being understandable. Consenting should also be regarded not simply as one instance of a patient or client acquiescing but an ongoing process, with a health care practitioner's duty perhaps being continually to nurture and confirm understanding and awareness.

Teasing out the complexities of informed consent as a duty for the health worker raises at least two problems for the code of conduct in its supposed role of closing the gap between what the practitioner *ought* to do and what he or she *must* do. First, it exposes the generality of the code, which perhaps makes it much more difficult – at least in some cases – to decide when it is being breached. There will be many circumstances in which nurses and health workers are 'pushed' to achieve informed consent; at what point is it possible to step in and suggest that duty has been breached? This problem relates particularly to the *'must'* side of the gap. Professionals generally know what they must do, but is it possible to blame them when they *cannot* do it? The second problem is that by pushing deeper into this article of the code, we are made aware of potentially how much commitment a health worker must have conscientiously to practise according to its general requirements. This problem relates especially to the *'ought'* side of the gap. The health worker must be involved in a continuous process of deliberation with him- or herself, and possibly of negotiation and agreement with clients or patients. We might think we expect this sort of commitment from nurses and other professionals, but is it a reasonable expectation?

It appears, then, that regarding codes of conduct as devices to close the gap between '*must*' and '*ought*' in the actions of health care professionals is simplistic. Codes by themselves are at once too general and too intimidating. We can probably expect health workers broadly to work according to their code, and it is right to demand sanctions to be applied to those who grossly offend against it. But these are by and large exceptional cases and do not help the many practitioners who are involved in the messy and complicated everyday context of health care. We outlined above a range of 'techniques' that might help people to develop their capacity to determine what they *ought* to do (as well as what they *must* do).

CASE STUDY – TERMINATION OF PREGNANCY

The disciplines of ethics and law are fundamentally preoccupied with the 'life and death' decisions often encountered in health care. Towards the start of this chapter, the example of Dr Moor was used to introduce the central concern of the disciplines with the ends of life. Both ethics and law are equally preoccupied with questions and conduct related to life's beginnings and it is on this area that the case study focuses. It will also tease out still further the tension that frequently exists in health care between what we *must* do and what we *ought* to do.

Consider the situation of a young woman, Liz, who is 10 weeks into an unintended pregnancy. She is not keen to have the baby. Her boyfriend Matt is more committed to the relationship and is delighted about the pregnancy. What might be the view of a thoughtful health care practitioner on whether Liz should have an abortion?

According to the law, Liz is likely to be able to have an abortion. The Infant Life Preservation Act 1929 makes it a criminal offence to destroy the life of a child who is likely to be capable of being born alive. However, the Abortion Act 1967, as amended by the Human Fertilisation and Embryology Act 1990, provides a statutory defence for abortion. According to the Act as amended, someone performing an abortion shall not be guilty of an offence if they are a registered medical practitioner, if an opinion in good faith has been formed by two such practitioners that the pregnancy has not exceeded its 24th week, and that continuing the pregnancy would involve a greater risk than termination of damage to the physical or mental health of the woman concerned or to any of her existing children.

Liz is just less than 10 weeks pregnant. It could be argued, given her gestation, that continuing with her pregnancy is likely to pose a greater risk to her health than termination (given that there are medical risks, however small in particular cases, associated with childbirth itself). Furthermore, it would be easy for the practitioners forming the opinion to argue that if Liz does not want the baby she is carrying, to force her to do so would be a great deal more damaging to her mental health than if she were allowed to have a termination. It would therefore be quite reasonable under the law for the practitioners to defend a decision to allow her access to an abortion. A doctor practising in England and Wales cannot, therefore, be shown to have undertaken a termination unlawfully provided that the conditions above are met (Mason and McCall Smith, 1999).

So Liz *can* legally have an abortion. If Liz's gestational period were greater than 24 weeks, certain much stronger conditions apply to the defence of abortion. If a termination is to be legally defended after this time, it must be necessary to prevent grave permanent injury to the physical or mental health of the woman, or continuing the pregnancy would involve risk to the life of the woman greater than if the pregnancy were to be terminated, or there is substantial risk that if the child were to be born, it would be likely to suffer from physical or mental abnormalities such that it would be seriously handicapped. The law is clear: abortion *must* not be allowed or take place on a foetus over 24 weeks unless one or other of these conditions applies.

In the case of abortion, then, the law is able to tell us what *can* or *must* (or *cannot* or *must not*) happen, but what *ought* to happen? As was argued earlier, '*ought*' questions move us to the territory of ethics, although it may be that, in this example, reference to legal opinion may connect with moral deliberation. One way of considering what *ought* to happen in Liz's case is to examine the nature and extent of moral claims that might be held by those it involves. Taken at face value, there are at least three sets of claims in the case: those of Liz, those of the unborn child and those of Matt.

The moral claims of Liz

Liz's fundamental claim might be that having a baby at this stage of her life would significantly harm her own well-being. Assessed against the four ethical principles identified earlier in the chapter as being important for those involved in health care, this claim might be further explored. If Liz were to be strongly encouraged or even coerced into continuing with her pregnancy when she did not want to do so, her autonomy would not be being respected. Equally, the principle of beneficence would be breached. How can we be producing benefit for Liz when the outcome of the care given to her will clearly be something she does not want and would not easily be able to come to terms with? Moreover, continuing with the pregnancy would be likely to harm Liz, almost certainly psychologically and possibly physically (because, as suggested above, a physical risk, however small, is always associated with pregnancy). Finally, if the pregnancy were to carry on, the principle of justice may be breached: Liz's natural right to have a child or otherwise would be contravened.

At this stage in thinking about what *ought* to happen or not, Liz's claims appear to be extremely strong. However, it is necessary to examine a further set of claims – those of the foetus.

The moral claims of Liz's unborn baby

Thinking about the moral claims of the unborn baby, or foetus, is problematic. We usually talk about the moral claims and rights of people. When, and under what conditions, does a foetus become a person? At what stage, if any, does that person have rights, most obviously the right to life?

As we have seen throughout this chapter, the question 'What is a person?' is essentially a moral one. In the cases of, for example, Anthony Bland and Dr Moor's patient George Liddell, we might be prepared to agree that the law allowed their deaths because they had lost important attributes of personhood. We might understand Mr Bland's persistent vegetative state as being not living at all in a moral sense, even though, in a scientific one, he was still alive.

It is similarly the case at the beginnings of life. Moral philosophers have attempted to construct accounts of personhood and what it is to value life (that is to say, to regard a life as worth preserving). It has been suggested, for example, that the valuable life is one in which the individual concerned has the capacity him- or herself to value that life (Harris, 1985). But what exactly does this mean? If it were to be taken as read, it could mean that we might not regard as valuable a large number of lives, for example those of people with severe mental handicap. Would we be happy about this?

The tendency of the law is to regard the foetus as having no rights until birth, although there is equally a concern to give it as positive an identity as possible (Mason and McCall Smith, 1999). This difficult position does not, however, help avoid the potential dichotomy of opinion over the idea of the foetus having moral claims or rights, of being in some sense an independent person. If it is believed that the foetus assumes this status, it could be argued that the mother might become simply a baby-carrying machine. If this is not thought to be the case, the foetus could be seen as becoming just another part of a woman's body, to do with as she wishes.

If we consider that Liz's unborn baby has moral claims or rights, there is in every respect a challenge to the claims put forward above on behalf of Liz. It has already been said that the principle of respect for autonomy applies to the extent that it is compatible with the autonomy of all who will probably be affected by the action being considered. There is clearly likely to be a conflict between the autonomy of Liz and the claim made on behalf of the foetus that it, too, will grow to become a person whose autonomy requires respect. Terminating this potential life also obviously militates against the other principles of beneficence, non-maleficence and justice, and dramatically limits the extent to which we can agree with Liz's claims in these respects. On the other hand, if we do not agree that the unborn child has moral claims or rights, Liz's claims remain compelling.

The moral claims of Matt

Almost from first hearing the news, Matt has been delighted by Liz's pregnancy. Does he, however, have significant moral claims in this case? There is little reason to doubt that he would suffer harm if Liz were to go ahead with the termination. The loss of his child might be devastating, and the principle of non-maleficence as applied to Matt would certainly be breached. The difficulty is that we could easily feel in an intuitive sense that Matt's claims are not as important as those of Liz or – if we agree that they exist in the first place – of the foetus. Why is this? Perhaps it is because, as has been argued, termination or otherwise will have a far-reaching effect on Liz's life. The decision will, literally, mean potential life or not for the foetus. Matt will be denied father-hood – at least for the time being – but this seems a lesser effect than the prob-able impacts of the decision on others. This moral view resembles that taken by the law which generally speaking regards the father in cases of abortion as having no legal rights.

There is at least one further interest in this case. This is of Dr Collins, Liz's GP, and of the other medical and nursing staff who might be involved if Liz decided to go ahead with termination. The 1967 Abortion Act provides a statutory legal defence through conscientious objection for health care workers who, for reasons of conscience, are not prepared to take part in termi-nations. This defence does not, however, apply if action is required to save the life of, or prevent grave permanent physical or mental damage to, the preg-nant woman. Clearly, health care workers who are – for religious or other reasons – conscientious objectors also have a moral claim in the sense of their right not to be exposed to the possibility of psychological harm through an involvement in abortion. It can of course be difficult to take the position of a conscientious objector in a busy hospital or other health care setting. The code of conduct for nursing, midwifery and health visiting does not necessarily make this easy, through its requirement on practitioners to report conscien-tious objection as early as possible. It has been argued that, for example, a midwife declaring conscientious objection to abortion at a job interview might face discrimination against being appointed (Dimond, 1994).

So what might be the view of the thoughtful health care practitioner, informed by ethics and law, on whether Liz should have an abortion? The outcome exemplifies again a key argument of this chapter – that there is a fundamental difference between what we *must* do (that which the law requires us to do) and what we *ought* to do (that which our personal and professional moral character obliges us to do). The law requires us to act in a certain way in the case of abortion, allowing a broad defence of termination up to a certain time in foetal gestation and then effectively forbidding such defence except in very grave circumstances. Given Liz's situation, she *could*, in all probability, have an abortion, and the statutory defence for the action would apply to those involved. There is, however, no such clarity over the issue of whether Liz *ought* to have an abortion (and whether the thoughtful practitioner could agree or otherwise with that decision).

Through a careful examination of the case, it has been possible to recognise that a number of different moral claims on the part of those centrally involved are present and that our reactions to these may well determine our view of whether Liz *ought* to proceed to termination. Making this considera-tion even more difficult, it seems that there are grounds to dispute the nature and extent of the claims. Furthermore, we may not be inclined to believe that a key party – the foetus – has any rights at all (or conversely, that the rights of the foetus are crucially important). There are certainly no easy answers to the question of whether Liz *ought* to have an abortion (and whether we *ought* to agree with any decision she makes), but careful thinking and analysis should make us more confident about the worth of the conclusions we even-tually draw.

SUMMARY

- The study of ethics is conceptual enquiry, largely concerned with trying to understand how people ought to behave towards one another. It involves clarifying the meaning of concepts such as 'benefit' or 'duty'

- The study of law is an analytical enquiry into the development of society's prescriptive rules or laws, and into establishing whether legal statute or precedent applies in a particular situation

- Ethics tries to describe what we *ought* to do. The law prescribes what we *must* do

- The study of ethics and law can help to identify the value placed on health over and above other values, the guides or limits to professional conduct and the scope of the obligations of health workers

- Neither ethics nor law can provide a definitive 'solution' to contemporary health dilemmas (for these do not exist), but their study can provide a framework for considering key questions. Reflecting on ethical and legal principles and dilemmas may help in forming consistent judgements and in the search for a moral life.

QUESTIONS FOR FURTHER DISCUSSION

1. Does the law's concern with prescription and attempts to establish definitive judgements help or hinder those striving to be good (moral) health workers?

2. Consider a health dilemma that you are personally aware of or have become aware of through the media. Can the application of ethical principles clarify what should be done in this situation?

FURTHER READING

Beauchamp, T. and Childress, J. (1994) *Principles of Biomedical Ethics*, 4th edn. Oxford: Oxford University Press.
Beauchamp and Childress developed the idea of the 'Famous Four principles' of health care ethics, and this is the book in which their ideas are most completely expressed. It is detailed and technical but offers many helpful points of reference, including extensive signposts to further literature.

Dworkin, R. (1995) *Life's Dominion*. London: HarperCollins.
Subtitled 'An argument about abortion and euthanasia', this is an elegantly written attempt to make sense, from a legal–philosophical perspective, of the ways in which we think about the beginning and ending of human life. The focus of ethics on health care should by no means be all about the drama of life and death, but this is such a well-constructed and closely argued book that it to some extent provides a model for thinking about how we might employ ethics and law in consideration of other areas of health and health care.

Gillon, R. (1990) *Philosophical Medical Ethics*. Chichester: John Wiley & Sons.
Writing for a mainly British audience, Gillon has 'translated' Beauchamp and Childress' ideas and arguments from the North American context in which they were originally framed.

McHale, J. and Fox, M., with Murphy, J. (1997) *Health Care Law: Text and Materials*. London: Sweet & Maxwell.

> A comprehensive collection of materials exposing many of the issues emerging from the application of law to health care. There is much reference to particular legal judgements and background provided to these. The work as a whole is detailed and perhaps best used as an ongoing source of reference.

Seedhouse, D. (1988) *Ethics: The Heart of Health Care*. Chichester: John Wiley & Sons.

> Contains an interesting view on the nature of the relationship between ethics and health care. In particular, Seedhouse develops what he calls an 'ethical grid', which he argues is a practical tool for understanding and dealing with the moral problems posed by work for health.

REFERENCES

Aristotle (1955). *Ethics*. Harmondsworth: Penguin.

Beauchamp, T. and Childress, J. (1994) *Principles of Biomedical Ethics*, 4th edn. Oxford: Oxford University Press.

Dimond, B. (1994) *The Legal Aspects of Midwifery*. Hale: Books for Midwives Press.

DoH (Department of Health) (1998) *The New NHS: Modern, Dependable*. London: Stationery Office.

Dworkin, R. (1995) *Life's Dominion: An Argument about Abortion and Euthanasia*. London: HarperCollins.

Dyer, C. (1999) Doctor cleared of murdering patient. *Guardian*, 12 May.

Gillon, R. (1994) Medical ethics: four principles plus attention to scope. *British Medical Journal*, **309**: 184–8.

Gorovitz, S. (1985) *Doctor's Dilemmas: Moral Conflict and Medical Care*. New York: Oxford University Press.

Harris, J. (1985) *The Value of Life*. London: Routledge & Kegan Paul.

Health Service Journal (1999) Doctors button up as wind of change blows through. *Health Service Journal*, 18 February: 15.

Hill, M. (1999) Uncovering the Bristol scandal. *BBC Online News*, 15 March (www.bbc.co.uk/news).

Lacey, A. (1976) *A Dictionary of Philosophy*. Routledge & Kegan Paul.

McHale, J., Fox, M., with Murphy, J. (1997) *Health Care Law: Text and Materials*. London: Sweet & Maxwell.

Mason, J. and McCall Smith, R. (1999) *Law and Medical Ethics*. London: Butterworth Heinemann.

Mill, J.S. (1962) *Utilitarianism and Other Writings*. Glasgow: Fontana.

Outhwaite, W. (1999) Indefinite articles. *Health Service Journal* Special Report, 27 May: 9–11.

Paton, H.J. (1948) *The Moral Law*. London: Hutchinson.

Pyne, R. (1995) 'The professional dimension', in Tingle, J. and Cribb, A. (eds) *Nursing Law and Ethics*. Oxford: Blackwell Science, pp. 36–58.

Rumbold, G. and Lesser, H. (1995) 'An ethical perspective: negligence and moral obligations', in Tingle, J. and Cribb, A. (eds) *Nursing Law and Ethics*. Oxford: Blackwell Science, pp. 93–9.

Russell, B. (1979) *A History of Western Philosophy*. London: Unwin.

UKCC (United Kingdom Council for Nursing, Midwifery and Health Visiting) (1992) *Code of Professional Conduct*. London: UKCC.

Health Promotion

JENNIE NAIDOO AND JANE WILLS

Learning outcomes ●●●●●●●●●●●●●●●●●●●●●●●●●●

This chapter will enable readers to:

- Understand the multidisciplinary nature of health promotion
- Define the elements of health promotion
- Be aware of the ways in which countries seek to improve the health of their populations
- Discuss critically how health promotion represents a shift in thinking about health from a disease and service focus
- Become familiar with some models of health promotion and their purpose
- Discuss critically the role of health promotion and its effectiveness.

OVERVIEW

Unlike the other disciplines discussed in this book, health promotion has a practical focus on positive health and well-being. A core feature of the discipline is its recognition that health is more than individual physical and mental well-being or fitness, relating as well to overall social factors such as the degree of equality and social support. The complexity of the concept of health means that there are many different strategies to improve health for individuals, communities and the population as a whole. The World Health Organization (WHO) has led the way in developing a framework for health promotion, and the first part of this chapter examines this framework and its five key strategies. Health promotion is a relatively young discipline, and the past two decades have seen attempts to define its niche in the area of Health Studies and health care practice. Its theoretical base is characterised by its interdisciplinary nature. Many different perspectives feed into understanding what influences health and how it might be defined. These perspectives, and their associated methodologies, contribute in a complementary way to defining core health promotion strategies. Many commentators have used models to identify contributory perspectives and their interconnectedness, this being discussed in greater detail in the second part of the chapter. The debate about what should be measured, and how, in order to assess the effectiveness of health promotion is also examined in this section. The chapter then goes on to look at the example of smoking and how health promotion, through its interdisciplinary perspective, develops strategies to reduce smoking.

INTRODUCTION

Health promotion includes a wide range of strategies designed to improve people's health. This immediately calls into question how health is defined and by whom. In 1946, the WHO defined health as 'a state of complete physical, social and mental well-being, not merely the absence of disease or infirmity', going on to set further ambitious goals by suggesting that health is an essential commodity that people need in order to achieve a socially and economically productive life (WHO, 1985).

The WHO definition challenged the dominant biomedical model of health and its emphasis on disease pathology and consequently medicine as a means of treatment. Promoting health therefore means focusing not just on preventing disease, but also on people's social and mental health. Health promotion may therefore include preventive activities, education, community-based social action, the creation of healthy environments and policy change in, for example, the areas of agricultural production or transport. Most countries have a remarkable similarity in their health promotion philosophy and policy, and recognise the social roots of health and ill health.

The core questions that health promoters seek to answer can be summarised as:

● What affects people's health status?
● What might influence the decisions that people make about their health behaviour?
● How do social conditions affect individual and population health?
● How can social conditions be changed to promote people's health?

If we can answer these questions and provide some explanatory frameworks that explain the mechanisms and processes creating or sustaining health, we will be better able to apply that knowledge to design interventions that help people to change their behaviour, make the environments in which people live and work more conducive to health and develop policies that make health choices easier.

Health promotion combines different approaches and topics, and thus draws upon many academic disciplines and knowledge bases. Health promotion incorporates perspectives from epidemiology, sociology, social policy, economics, education, marketing, communication and psychology (Bunton and Macdonald, 1992), using these different perspectives to build a more complete picture of health needs and the appropriate strategies to promote health.

THE CONTRIBUTION OF HEALTH PROMOTION TO HEALTH STUDIES

Thinking about...

Think about your own state of health. What do you think are the most important influences on your health?

The concept of health promotion is extremely broad and can seem to include any attempt to improve health. The term was first introduced in 1974 by the Canadian Minister of Health, Marc Lalonde, who suggested that different elements contributed to public health in a health field (Table 10.1).

Table 10.1   Lalonde's health field

Human biology (genetics and hereditary factors)	Lifestyle (personal behaviours that may contribute to health or illness, for example those related to exercise and diet)
Environment (including both the physical and social environment in which people live and work)	Health care organisation (the quality and availability of health services)

The most radical feature of the Lalonde Report was its assertion that an improvement in health would come not from a greater expenditure on health services for those who are sick but from a 'new perspective' that directed money to **prevention**. The arguments for this were compelling. In the developed world, it was apparent that:

- technological medicine and hospital-based services were not reducing the burden of ill health
- the major causes of mortality in developed countries are non-communicable diseases such as heart disease, cancer and respiratory illness, whose cause can be attributed to behaviours such as smoking and nutrition
- there is a growing elderly population, which is associated with an increased demand for care, although most older people remain independent and living in the community
- curative medicine involves escalating costs with no guarantee of effectiveness
- people's expectations of health services outstrip capacity.

? What do health promoters mean when they speak of improving or promoting health?

The prevention of disease and the relief of ill health in those who are sick are core aspects of health promotion, but it is also concerned with improving the quality of life. Health, as understood in health promotion, is a complex of bodily, mental, social and spiritual states rather than just the functioning of the body. Instead of the clinical gaze of medicine, which focuses on a body with a disease, there is a biographical approach viewing the individual as a whole person, embedded in his or her gender, culture and society. Health promotion is concerned with promoting health at all levels, from the individual to society to worldwide.

The WHO has been most influential in defining health promotion, its Ottawa Charter (WHO, 1986) probably being the most important document in health promotion. This represents a philosophical and practical approach to health promotion identifying five key strategies:

- reorienting health services
- developing personal skills
- building a healthy public policy
- strengthening community action
- creating supportive environments for health.

This chapter will discuss the assumptions behind each of these strategies and the ways in which they have been put into practice.

Health promotion has also been seen as an approach to health improvement that encompasses a set of values. According to the WHO, all policy and practice, whatever its focus, should give full attention to:

- equity – the equal right to health care
- community participation – the involvement of people in the planning and implementation of decisions involving their health

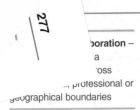

...oration –
a
...oss
..., professional or
geographical boundaries

● *intersectoral collaboration* – a recognition of the complexity of factors that affect health and the need for different agencies to work together.

REORIENTING HEALTH SERVICES: PREVENTION

The WHO argued that if countries are to achieve the ambitious goals set out in declarations such as *Health For All by the Year 2000* (WHO, 1985), they need to reorientate services towards prevention and protection and away from treatment and cure.

Prevention has become a key aspect of health policy in most developed countries. In 1992, the English government published its first national health strategy – *The Health of the Nation* (DoH, 1992) – which was followed by a revised strategy under a new government in 1999 – *Saving Lives: Our Healthier Nation* (DoH, 1999). Five areas for action were initially identified, coronary heart disease and stroke, cancer, accidents, mental illness and sexual health, as these were deemed to be major causes of mortality and morbidity and amenable to preventive action.

Caplan's (1969) well-established classification cites three levels of prevention:

● *Primary prevention* refers to strategies to reduce the risk of the onset of ill health, for example immunisation
● *Secondary prevention* seeks to shorten episodes of illness and prevent the progression of ill health through early diagnosis and treatment by, for example, screening
● *Tertiary prevention* seeks to limit the disability or complications arising from an irreversible condition, such as controlling pain or through rehabilitation after a heart attack.

Using the term 'prevention' suggests that it is possible to intervene in a causal process and implies that there are particular risks to health that we can detect and manage. The identification of risk in preventive health tends to derive from epidemiological data from large populations showing that an exposure to a particular factor is associated with an increased probability of the relevant disease occurring. Epidemiological data thus seem to set the health promotion agenda by identifying and prioritising particular health problems according to their contribution to mortality and morbidity. Risk factors get translated into health promotion programmes and become the targets for intervention.

Saving Lives: Our Healthier Nation suggests that a reduction of tobacco smoking and the adoption of a diet rich in cereals, fruit and vegetables could account for a 10 per cent reduction in the number of cancer deaths in those under 75 years of age (DoH, 1999). The National Service Framework for Coronary Heart Disease (DoH, 2000) identifies smoking, a poor-quality diet, a raised serum cholesterol level, a lack of physical activity and habitual excessive alcohol consumption as risk factors for heart disease. The focus on these risk factors for disease reflects the clinical approach that emphasises the importance of the individual patient and the biochemical basis of pathogenesis. The focus of prevention has thus been on manipulating these individual risks and ignores the social dimension of disease and debates over cause.

CONNECTIONS

Chapter 2 (Epidemiology) discusses risk and how it is assessed, and the ways in which risk factors are used in planning and target-setting

A key question in disease prevention is whether to target sections of the population deemed to be at risk or the whole of the general population. A strategy to reduce coronary heart disease, for example, might focus on people with a raised cholesterol level or those who are hypertensive. A population strategy aims to change general norms and might include a campaign to raise awareness of the need to reduce the fat intake in the diet. Rose (1992) argued that a whole population strategy will result in the prevention of more disease because a lot of people at slight risk of disease account for more of the disease than a few people at great risk. Most coronary events, for example, do not occur in men with raised blood pressure who would be deemed most at risk.

Primary care is regarded as the key site for health promotion. It is the 'first level of contact of individuals, the family and the community with the national health system bringing health care as close as possible to where people live and work and constitutes the first element of a continuing health care process' (MacDonald, 1993). The concept of health promotion as envisaged in government policy was that GPs would be able to detect the early signs of disease and could offer advice on health behaviour during a consultation. They were also encouraged, through different funding arrangements and specific targets, to monitor their practice population as the age/sex register provides information from which the GP can invite certain groups for health checks, immunisation and screening. Early studies (see, for example, Russell et al., 1979) certainly showed that brief advice given by GPs during routine consultations could help up to 5 per cent of smokers to give up.

EXAMPLE 10.1

Health checks to reduce risk factors for cardiovascular disease

Two major studies reported in 1994–95 on randomised controlled trials examining the effectiveness of health checks in primary care. Practice nurses had been trained to screen patients for coronary heart disease risk factors, assess patients' lifestyles in terms of health risk behaviours, find out the patients' views on making a change in their lifestyle, counsel patients about risk factors and negotiate priorities and targets for risk reduction.

The Imperial Cancer Research Fund OXCHECK study found that, over 3 years, health checks made little difference to smoking prevalence but that there were small but sustained changes in blood cholesterol level, blood pressure and body mass index, showing that nurses had had some effect on dietary behaviour. There were, however, concerns that nurse activity was very intensive (nurse/patient sessions lasting 1 hour) and not thought to be generally replicable. The report concludes that the use of health checks in primary care may not be cost effective. The Family Heart Study concluded that health checks that included client-centred counselling achieved a 16% reduction in coronary risk score and a 4% reduction in smoking rate. If sustained, this would amount to a 12% reduction in the number of coronary heart disease events.

The reporting of these trials in the medical press was fairly negative, many commentators questioning the value of such intensive nurse health promotion activity. Public health professionals were, however, more enthusiastic about the results, claiming a 12% reduc-

---

tion in coronary heart disease events to be a substantial and worthwhile achievement. The national service framework for coronary heart disease (DoH, 2000) now recommends that there should not be an unselected screening of the whole population but instead a system in primary care for identifying, assessing, treating and following up people with coronary heart disease or those at significant risk of developing it. This demonstrates the need to understand the different perspectives of different stakeholders involved in health promotion. Building bridges between different groups and working towards a common set of goals and understandings is one of the key challenges facing health promotion.

Sources: Doyle and Thomas, 1996; Family Heart Study Group, 1994; OXCHECK,1995

This trend to monitor health has been described as a rise in 'surveillance medicine' (Armstrong, 1995). Each stage in the life cycle is monitored, and more and more behaviours (relating to smoking, drinking, driving, eating, exercise and even sex) have been labelled as health risks. This reflects a medicalisation of people's lives: instead of only focusing on the ill, the medical gaze now extends to the healthy population. The holistic approach to health promotion also means that health workers can encroach into more and more areas of people's lives.

 What might be the criticisms of this regulatory and extended role of health promotion?

As more areas of lifestyle come under scrutiny, the public may resent this as interference in their everyday life. A common perception of health promotion is that of 'nannying' and telling people what to do. It also reinforces traditional expert/lay divisions and reinforces feelings of powerlessness, which is in itself health demoting.

DEVELOPING PERSONAL SKILLS: HEALTH EDUCATION

A central theme of government policy since the 1980s has been that individuals need to take responsibility for their own health and adopt more healthy behaviours, thus reducing the burden of care on the state. The recent health strategy for England, *Saving Lives: Our Healthier Nation* (DoH, 1999), suggests that the public, the community and government each has a role to play in health improvement. These roles have been identified as:

lifestyles – habits that promote health (for example regular exercise) or compromise health (for example smoking). Lifestyles are usually thought of as being individually chosen, but they are also influenced by social factors such as income

- government and national players assessing risks, communicating these risks clearly to the public and ensuring supportive environments for health
- communities working in partnership with other agencies to provide better information and services
- people taking responsibility for their own health and making healthier choices about their *lifestyles*.

Education is seen as the key to enabling people to change their health-related behaviours. The assumption is that if people are informed about the link between their behaviour and health, they will act in a rational manner and make efforts to change. Tones and Tilford (1994) have defined health education as:

> any activity which promotes health-related learning, that is, some relatively perma-
> nent change in an individual's capabilities or dispositions. It may produce changes
> in understanding or ways of thinking; it may bring about changes in belief or atti-
> tude and facilitate the acquisition of skills; or it may generate changes in behaviour
> or lifestyle.

The aim is to help people to feel more confident and competent in terms of accessing services, being informed about illness and chronic conditions, and understanding what might affect their health. The public have become consumers of health information, health products and services. As people become better informed, however, they are also less likely to accept advice. An example of this lies in childhood immunisation policy, in which the target uptake of 90 per cent is rarely achieved. Bennett and Smith (1992) reported that parents who did not have their children immunised appeared to have a degree of anxiety concerning the risks of immunisation and underestimated the potential benefits. The Department of Health was sufficiently concerned about the response of the public to media reports on vaccine safety and food to produce guidelines on how professionals should communicate risk to the public (DoH, 1998a).

> **?** Health care professionals frequently use the term 'non-compliance' to describe situations in which a patient or client does not follow advice on treatment. What concept of health is reflected in this term?

The use of the term 'non-compliance' suggests that the health professional gives the correct, expert advice and that the patient is irrational in ignoring it. 'Non-compliance' implies that medically trained professionals have access to the 'truth' about health and ignores the fact that lay people have their own health knowledge. The use of this term also serves to reinforce and legitimate the unequal position of professional and lay person, and suggests that this power imbalance is acceptable.

CONNECTIONS

Chapter 5 (Cultural Studies) discusses representations of health in the media and the difficulties associated with marketing health as a product

Mass communication is a central plank of health education. Health education agencies in most countries either pay for advertising or seek unpaid coverage in the media. The value of such campaigns in contributing to behavioural change is, however, much disputed. An evaluation of the extensive HIV/AIDS campaign of the 1980s found no evidence of a reduction in the number of sexual partners or an increased use of condoms among heterosexuals (DHSS, 1987). There is a hierarchy of communication effects such that simple awareness is relatively easy to achieve; to inform or reinforce attitudes is more difficult, and to have any effect on behaviour is even more so. Campaigns have an impact on behaviour only when the message is already credible to the target group, who are also able to make any changes quickly and easily. The Sunsmart campaigns

mass media – any medium that reaches a mass audience. This conventionally includes television, radio, newspapers and magazines. Posters, billboards and the World Wide Web may also be included

health education – providing health-related education, advice and the opportunity to clarify attitudes and values, and acquire skills

in Australia and the campaign to install smoke alarms in domestic premises are examples of successful campaigns because the behaviour could be easily adopted without further need for support.

Another objective of ***mass media*** campaigns may, however, be to influence the social context and create a favourable climate for health-promoting interventions at the community or social policy level. Mass media coverage can help to keep issues on the agenda and provide legitimacy for a broad range of interventions. For example, No Smoking Day in Britain results in 1 per cent of smokers quitting for 3 months or longer, but it also acts as a trigger for extensive local activities and helps to keep smoking on the health agenda.

The emphasis of most ***health education*** is on 'informed decision-making' – giving people information so that they can make decisions about their health. This approach has been criticised for relying on a deficit model whereby a deficiency (usually of knowledge or skills) is identified and then rectified. Lupton (1995) describes health education as carrying resonances of 'the passive individual requiring "facts" to defeat ignorance'. Health promotion, despite its intention to facilitate choice, is frequently a prescriptive practice that sets up a dichotomy between an expert who knows how to achieve health and a client who is in need of information. This approach has also been criticised for its tendency to 'blame the victim' – if individuals do not take the advice or information then they are seen as being at fault.

EXAMPLE 10.2

International HIV/AIDS education – the example of South Africa

More than 3.5 million South Africans are infected with HIV; 13% of them are adults aged between 20 and 64 years, half of them were infected before their 25th birthday, and over 50% will die before they turn 35. In 1990, both South Africa and Thailand had 1 per cent of their population infected. Today, the prevalence of infection in Thailand is 1.5%, whereas in South Africa it is over 22%. Women aged between 15 and 20 are at highest risk of HIV infection, and 53% of the population of South Africa is under 25 years of age. The infection level is still rising in this age group.

According to the United Nations AIDS programme, the high infection rate in Africa is generally caused by maternal transmission through breast-feeding and women passing on the virus to a higher average number of children. The combination drugs that are successfully keeping the virus in check in developed countries are not widely available in Africa. There are additional reasons why South Africa is facing an epidemic that many believe is now uncontrollable:

● established epidemics of other sexually transmitted diseases, which make the population particularly susceptible to HIV infection

● disrupted family and communal life, a migrant labour pattern and a high level of poverty

● a good transport infrastructure and high mobility, allowing for the rapid spread of infection from one community to another

- a resistance to the use of condoms, based on cultural and social norms

- the low status of women in society and within relationships. Economic dependency and the threat of physical force make it difficult for women to protect themselves from infection

- social norms that accept and encourage a high number of sexual partners, especially among men

- parallel norms that actively discourage an open discussion of sex and sexuality, particularly with children and teenagers.

Prevention campaigns have been successful in some parts of the world. The infection rate in Uganda has fallen to around 8% of the population from a peak of 14% in the early 1990s. The focus of the prevention campaigns has been sex education in schools that tries to discourage both premarital and casual sexual activity. In Lusaka in Zambia, such campaigns have led to a fall in the number of men reporting two or more casual partners and an increase in sexual abstinence among young unmarried males from a third reporting no sex in the past year to over a half doing so. Condom use is more widely promoted. In Brazil, condom sales increased from 70 million in 1993 to 320 million in 1999, and 90% of 16–25-year-old men report consistent condom use with casual partners. In Thailand and Cambodia, a '100% condom use' campaign among sex workers has increased consistent condom use with clients from 20% to 80% in 2 years.

In many countries, there have also been attempts to reduce the sex trade by developing income generation projects such as fish farming and vegetable gardening as alternatives to prostitution for girls from poor rural areas. Many countries have national sexually transmitted disease programmes and HIV/AIDS schools lifeskills programmes. Programmes in and out of school also help to train young people to teach their peers about sexually transmitted infections, HIV transmission and safer sex.

In South Africa, which is facing a major epidemic, a national AIDS Council was appointed in 1999, but it has yet to make any significant contribution. The most successful education on HIV in South Africa has been by the Soul City Institute for Health and Development Communication, which has created a multimedia vehicle to impact on priority health and development issues. Social issues are imbedded in a drama programme called 'Soul City', which is screened during prime viewing and radio time and reaches an estimated 12 million South Africans. It is a household name and, as one of the key sources of information on HIV/AIDS, it has been shown to have stimulated open discussion, which has in turn shifted knowledge and attitudes and created a supportive environment for behaviour change.

These activities have nevertheless so far been largely piecemeal, unco-ordinated and insufficient to impact on an epidemic that has already infected one in seven adults and is expected to reduce life expectancy from 60 to 40 years of age.

Sources: Abt Associates South Africa, 2000; Myer, 2000; Usdin, 2000

Health has often been linked with morality in an effort to persuade people to change their behaviour. Sexually transmitted infections in developed countries were, for example, seen as a symptom of sexual incontinence, and prevention was viewed as a matter of morality and staying faithful to one partner. Behaviours such as smoking or eating an unhealthy diet are equally seen as weakness and an inability to exercise self-control:

When risk is believed to be internally imposed because of a lack of will power, moral weakness or laziness on the part of the individual... those who are deemed 'at risk' become... sinners. (Lupton, 1995)

Nearly 20 years ago Jeannette Mitchell pointed out that:

in the health service the Victorian term 'feckless' can still be heard. Doctors have always criticised their patients who do not share their social world: 'That woman's problem isn't poverty. She should stand up to her husband. He has always got plenty of money, drinks six pints a night.' (Mitchell, 1984)

Thinking about...

Can you think of other examples of people having been criticised for their health behaviour?

A major focus of health promotion has now become to understand and address those factors which are beyond the control of individual influence.

The effectiveness of health education strategies has been called into question for assuming that if knowledge is increased, people will change their behaviour. Personal experience tells most of us that although we may know what we should do to improve our health, we do not necessarily do it. Extrapolating risk factors from epidemiological studies to derive advice and education on risks for individuals (imparted in one-to-one or small group health education sessions) is, however, flawed because health behaviour is determined not solely by rational choice on the basis of information, but also by attitudes, beliefs and contexts that encourage or hinder health-enhancing behaviours.

Health promoters and the government's physical activity task force tried to raise awareness of the physical and mental benefits of exercise through the Active for Life campaign. This recognised that physical activity integrated into people's lifestyles might be easier to achieve than participation in sport or organised activity. It did not, however, address the wider social factors that inhibit exercise, such as the gender stereotyping of physical education in schools (Murphy and Waddington, 1998) or the fact that women often do not feel safe in outdoor public facilities, or may lack the time to exercise.

CONNECTIONS

Chapter 3 (Health Psychology) discusses the relationship between attitudes, intentions and behaviour

As well as these attempts to inform or persuade, health education may involve more individually focused strategies that seek to motivate and encourage people to set their own goals. Gillies (1998) argues that individually focused interventions involving counselling, reinforcement, support, information, personal skills development and coping strategies do work 'in a modest manner'. They can encourage health-related behavioural change in up to one in four of those who participate. However, those least likely to take part in such activities are the poorest and those with little motivation.

CONNECTIONS

Chapter 3 (Health Psychology) looks at the relationship between knowledge and action, and the role of health beliefs in relation to individual behaviour.
Chapter 2 (Epidemiology) explores lay knowledge about health and illness, and how this may clash with professional perspectives

? **Why are people on a low income least likely to adopt health education messages or advice?**

Work on lay epidemiology (Davison et al., 1991; Williams and Popay, 1994) has shown how people have considerable knowledge about health and illness from observations in their own communities and consequently develop their own explanatory frameworks for illness linked to heredity, social conditions and the environment. Thus, the importance of risk factors such as smoking or diet may be overridden by personal experience or more immediate problems. Graham (1993) has drawn attention to the fact that women on a low income may trade off health for the way in which smoking is perceived to relieve their stress. Despite knowing that smoking is harmful to their own and their baby's health, many lone parents continue to smoke because it helps them to cope. Therefore not only may it be more difficult for those on a low income to act on health education messages about, for example, healthy eating (because healthy food is more expensive), but the motivation to do so may also be less (as healthy food may be a low priority when someone is preoccupied with coping on a low income).

HEALTHY PUBLIC POLICY: PUBLIC HEALTH

Another strand of health promotion sees it as forming part of the 'new public health' movement and building **healthy public policy**. This represents a reaction against the individualistic and victim-blaming approach of health education and the curative focus of biomedicine. It signals a return to the concern with environmental issues that first gave rise to public health reform in the 19th century. Then, poor sanitary conditions and housing prompted a wave of reforms to control the threat of communicable diseases. The 1848 Public Health Act, for example, required local authorities to provide clean water supplies and sewage disposal systems, the 1868 Housing Act requiring them to keep property in good repair. Yet the social reforms of the period owed as much to political concerns about the threat of revolution and the need for a healthy workforce as they did to a benevolent compassion. There was no challenge to the underlying social and economic structures that led to the mass movement of labour to the towns, where they lived in overcrowded and insanitary conditions.

In the 20th century, there was some important legislation that had a significant impact on health, such as the 1956 Clean Air Act and seat belt legislation in 1971. Yet although there has been a recognition of the ways in which health is affected by social conditions, there has been a reluctance to legislate to protect health in the UK. Bans on tobacco advertising and sponsorship have, for example, reduced the uptake of smoking by teenagers in Australia, Norway and Canada (Smee, 1992), but a complete ban has been postponed in the UK until 2006 (DoH, 1998b). Dental decay is almost entirely preventable and the fluoridation of water supplies can reduce decay by up to 50 per cent, but there has been intense lobbying to resist the extension of fluoridation on the grounds of concern about its safety.

What is different about the approach of public health is that instead of biomedicine intervening after the population has become ill and requires treatment, the approach of public health is to intervene at an earlier stage by acting on the conditions that give rise to ill health. The health education approach is often equated with lifesaving in an upstream/downstream analogy in which health promoters make frequent and frantic efforts to pull people out of the river before they drown instead of concentrating on the factors upstream that are causing them to fall in. The public health approach is to move 'upstream', trying to identify and prevent what pushes people into the river (McKinlay, 1979).

healthy public policy – policies that promote health through encouraging healthy habits or supporting healthy environment and organisations

CONNECTIONS

Chapter 9 (Ethics and Law) discusses the ethical dilemmas involved in legislating for health equity – being fair and just. This may involve targeting specific services for those most in need rather than providing the same blanket service for everyone

In the public health perspective, most social issues become subsumed under health as all have an impact on health. A recent meeting of the UK Public Health Association included presentations on food safety, homelessness, redistributive taxation and safe routes to school. Thus, health care is no longer the special concern of the doctor or nurse but of all the community and may take place in any social setting, from schools to workplaces to neighbourhoods. The Adelaide Conference (the second international conference on health promotion) defined healthy public policy as an 'explicit concern for health and *equity* in all areas of policy and an explicit accountability for health impacts' (WHO, 1988).

The social and economic determinants of health have been widely studied in all countries where there are variations in health. In the UK, there is a clear gradient of ill health and mortality closely related to position in the social order related to income, occupation, housing and educational attainment. Lower socio-economic groups are more likely not only to die prematurely, but also to suffer more ill health across a range of diseases and use services least.

The ways in which such health inequalities are created and sustained are not, however, clear. Low income can preclude the purchase of more healthy products such as healthier foods. Low-income households tend to live in poorer, less healthy environments with greater pollution, traffic and social stress, all of which impact negatively on health. Health behaviours may also be a factor in ill health. Smoking probably accounts for between 10 and 30 per cent of premature deaths, and it is lower socio-economic groups who are not only still being recruited as adolescent smokers, but are also not giving up (Stead et al., 1996).

Behaviour cannot, however, account for all the differences in health experienced by different social groups, for when behaviour is controlled for in studies, health inequalities persist. The results of the Whitehall study of civil servants show that relative social position may have an effect on mortality for all major causes of death (Marmot et al., 1996). After adjusting for smoking and physical activity, this study showed that perceived low control in the workplace is related to employment grade, and this appears to account for the four-fold difference in coronary heart disease frequency between the top and the bottom grades.

The focus of health education has been on the individual – as a member of a population group with particular health risks or concerns (the mothers of young children, gay men or middle-aged men) or as exhibiting a risk behaviour (smoking or lack of exercise). The new public health focuses instead on risk conditions such as poverty, homelessness and social isolation. Tackling these issues obviously involves many agents and agencies beyond the health services and is a demanding agenda. Reviews of interventions to reduce socio-economic differences in health have so far found that most interventions used health education methods. Most were intended to improve the utilisation of existing services by poorer groups or reduce their risk factors. Specific targets to reduce health inequalities in infant and childhood mortality are being developed, but inequalities targets can in general only be delivered by broader government policies such as Welfare to Work, the Housing Capital Receipts Initiative and Sure Start.

CONNECTIONS

Chapter 4 (Sociology) discusses the social patterning of health and ill health in more detail. It explores the relationship between health and macro social factors such as gender, ethnicity and socio-economic class

Thinking about...

Think about some situations in which a lack of control, differential status or a lack of social support might impact negatively on health

> ### EXAMPLE 10.3
>
> ### Tackling fuel poverty
>
> Cold, damp housing is a major public health problem. The English House Condition Survey of 1991 found that dampness was present in 10 per cent of occupied public sector housing and in 24 per cent of occupied private sector housing. Damp, mould and condensation are linked to a range of illnesses including respiratory disease, asthma and allergies. Cold homes can increase the incidence of chest disease, heart disease and stroke, and can lead to hypothermia. Older people are particularly vulnerable but live in the worst heated and insulated homes. They form a significant proportion of the 4.3 million households in fuel poverty (spending over 10 per cent of their income on fuel) but are often unable to afford adequate warmth because of their home's energy inefficiency. Poor people also tend to spend a higher proportion of the day at home and are more affected by damp or inadequate heating in the home.
>
> In the 1980s, government advice to old people in winter included keeping warm by going to bed and wearing a hat indoors to stop the loss of body heat. The Home Energy Efficiency Scheme of 2000 (a similar scheme in Scotland being called Warm Deal, whereas in Northern Ireland it is named the Domestic Energy Efficiency Scheme) identifies the fuel-poor and provides small grants for insulation and central heating, home safety and security, and advice on welfare benefits. Some local authorities employ young people to install the insulation under the Welfare to Work scheme. The scheme not only begins to address hidden housing needs, but also addresses the importance of using the information available from a range of practitioners to deliver 'joined up' services.

STRENGTHENING COMMUNITY ACTION

The New Public Health, the self-help movement and the women's movement were all strongly associated from the 1970s with a shift in power from experts to people themselves. By the late 1980s, the terms 'community development', *'community participation'* and 'community empowerment' were all central to the health promotion discourse. The notion that communities could identify their health needs and take action to control them signalled a definite shift in approach.

Many health promoters argue that the notion of *empowerment* is central to the process of health promotion. The WHO identify empowerment as a core health promotion principle (WHO, 1984). Empowerment is, however, difficult to define and has been used to mean different things. Rissell (1994) describes empowerment as the holy grail of health promotion, defining it as 'a process through which people become strong enough to participate, share in the control of, and influence events and institutions affecting their lives'. Tones (1995) argues that, for individuals to be empowered, they may need to acquire information or decision-making skills and has consistently argued that health education is the mainstay of population health improvement.

community participation – strategies to encourage communities to take part in identifying health problems and suggesting solutions to these problems

CONNECTIONS

Chapter 6 (Social Policy) discusses the historical development of health policy and its relationship to political ideology

empowerment – enabling others to take charge of their lives and destinies, and to feel in control of their circumstances

If people are to feel more able to make changes in their lives, they need to be supported by the people around them. Communities, be they localities or sections of the population such as students or Turkish people, can provide appropriate community-based services, be a source of networks and advice, and influence strategic change.

Community development is both a philosophy and a method of health promotion in which groups define their own health needs and decide on a strategy for change. The health promoter is a facilitator, advocate or adviser. The commitment to community development highlights many different aspects of health and how the promotion of health can be carried out (Naidoo and Wills, 2000):

- a commitment to equality and the breaking down of hierarchies and power relationships
- an emphasis on participation and enabling all communities to be heard
- an emphasis on lay knowledge and the valuing of people's own experience
- the collectivising of experience and seeing problems as shared
- the empowerment of individuals and communities through education, skills development and sharing, and joint action.

There is now considerable evidence that community-based initiatives are successful in promoting behaviour change in individuals on some issues such as condom use. However, the expectation that health promotion will have an impact on behaviour, and thus on mortality and morbidity outcomes, is inappropriate. A global review by Gillies (1998) showed that health promotion has had an effect on community participation and skills development, and it is these processes which should be taken as the indicator of health promotion's effectiveness.

Whereas there may be a commitment to a way of working, our understanding of how social and community contexts enable health is still emerging. There is some evidence that communities with a high level of social capital have a better health outcome (Baum, 1999; Lomas, 1998). There is also evidence that people who have networks of social support are more likely to survive acute and chronic illness. People are social beings, so common sense would suggest that the quality of social interaction is vital to personal and communal well-being. As Cox (1997) put it, writing in an Australian journal:

> The story goes that if we basically trust each other, our relationships work better, whether with family, friends, neighbours, work-mates... Any society which has too many distrustful members, who lack positive experience and expectations, will have serious problems with compliance, crime, self-destruction, violence, poor health and other social indicators.

Community networks may be built around activities associated with schools, workplaces, leisure or living in a particular locality. The focus of health promotion activity is moving away from health services towards the settings in which people live their lives, and it is these social systems, with their own structures and cultures, that can be made more health promoting. The school system, for example, and its objective of developing and evaluating

---

Thinking about...

Think about a community of which you are a part. In what ways does that community support or inhibit your health?

academic performance puts a strain on young people, those who rate their achievement as low being more likely to start smoking and drinking earlier and become regular users of tobacco and alcohol (King et al., 1996). One of the criteria for a healthy school is therefore the 'active promotion of the self-esteem of all pupils by demonstrating that everyone can make a contribution to the life of the school' (WHO, 1993).

SUPPORTIVE ENVIRONMENTS FOR HEALTH

Providing **supportive environments** for health involves working to achieve policy changes that impact on health. Environments include both the relatively small-scale environments of neighbourhoods or workplaces as well as the global worldwide physical and socio-economic environment. Health promoters have focused on both a 'settings' approach, which identifies settings such as schools or prisons and seeks to provide greater opportunities for promoting health within such settings, and a global approach, which stresses the importance of sustainability for health.

> **supportive environments** – environments that help to make the healthy choice the easy choice and therefore support healthy living

The WHO has, since the 1980s, advocated the use of a settings approach, launching its Healthy Cities project in 1986. The UK health strategies also all refer to settings. England's health strategy identifies schools, workplaces and neighbourhoods as contexts in which health can be promoted (DoH, 1999). For example, the Healthy Schools programme projects include: a website with health information to help young people to make informed decisions about their health; the 'cooking for kids' programme, relating to healthy food, cooking and food hygiene; and the 'safer travel to school' scheme, which encourages walking or cycling to school along safe routes. These activities all seek to integrate healthy routines into people's ordinary lives.

Communities and neighbourhoods are identified as important settings for health, a number of funded projects being targeted at neighbourhoods. England's Health Action Zones and Healthy Living Centres direct funding towards a community infrastructure that supports health through, for example, the provision of active leisure facilities. The increasingly local focus of health planning through the use of Health Improvement Programmes and the enhanced role of Primary Care Groups also highlights the importance of the local community setting.

Health is also linked to environmental factors and economic growth. The relationship between human health and the environment is part of the concern with health improvement. Not only are we now more aware of the fragility of the physical environment, but we also have a much broader understanding of the environmental determinants of health. Economic growth can have a detrimental effect on the environment by destroying non-renewable resources, breaking up traditional communities and creating pollution. These factors are not only connected, but also global in nature and not bounded by national borders or identities. There is an increasing concern about the global north/south divide and the overconsumption and depletion of natural resources by the north. The slogan 'think global, act local' has been adopted as the catchphrase for sustainability.

> **CONNECTIONS**
> Chapter 6 (Social Policy) provides further information on the policy background to the development of these initiatives

sustainable development –
development which does not
deplete natural resources
but protects or replaces
resources for future
generations

Sustainable development 'meets the needs of the present without compromising the ability of future generations to meet their own needs' (World Commission on Environment and Development, 1987). The 1992 United Nations Rio Earth Agenda 21 set out a programme of action for sustainable development into the 21st century. The Rio Declaration stated that people 'are entitled to a healthy productive life in harmony with nature' (United Nations, 1993). Agenda 21 commits governments to the following health objectives:

● meeting the basic prerequisites for health, for example access to safe food and water, sanitation and housing
● controlling communicable diseases
● protecting vulnerable groups such as children and older people
● reducing the health risks caused by pollution, excessive energy consumption and waste.

This initiative was followed by Local Agenda 21 in the UK, which brings together local government, business, voluntary and community agencies to assess and meet needs in a sustainable manner. All countries in Europe have produced National Environmental Action Plans, which provide approaches to tackling environmental health problems such as ozone depletion, air pollution, soil erosion, deforestation, water shortage and waste production and disposal.

Many national and local decisions, for example planning decisions and educational policy, can affect the health of the population. Health Impact Assessment is a form of policy appraisal in which the consequences for health of a policy are explored through community profiles and rapid appraisal methods. One example is the appraisal of the health impact of building a second runway at Manchester International Airport. Health Impact Assessment is modelled upon the well-established Environmental Impact Assessment but has a broader remit concerning the overall health of a population.

Table 10.2, displaying quality of life measures, demonstrates the growing awareness that health depends on the social and physical environment as well as on health services and individual behaviours.

THEORETICAL AND METHODOLOGICAL PERSPECTIVES

Health promotion, as seen in the first section of this chapter, draws upon a variety of disciplines, including sociology, social psychology, education and communication, economics, ethics and epidemiology, to inform its practice. This leads to a complex situation when trying to unravel the theoretical and methodological bases for health promotion practice. There is no unitary discipline or underlying theory of health promotion, which some commentators see as a strength:

Health promotion cannot really be called a 'discipline'. It draws parasitically on several existing disciplines. Nor would it want to be one if it is to effectively support

Table 10.2   Quality of life measures

The UK government is to publish a quality of life index that links health and environmental and social concerns with economic growth. The indicators are:

- Economic growth: the measurement of the total output of the economy (the gross domestic product)

- Social investment: investments in public assets such as transport, hospitals and schools

- Employment: the percentage of the working population in work

- Health: life expectancy

- Education and training: people's qualifications at age 19

- Housing quality: the number of homes unfit to live in

- Climate change: greenhouse gas emissions

- Air pollution: the average number of days on which pollution was recorded

- Transport: road traffic levels

- Water quality: the number of rivers of good or fair quality

- Wildlife: the population of wild birds

- Land use: the number of new homes built on previously developed land

- Waste: the amount of excess waste produced

Source: Department of Environment, Transport and the Regions, 1999

the empowerment of individuals and communities for a 'discipline' presupposes a top-down model in which an authoritative body defines the issues and validates solutions. (MacDonald, 1998)

Instead, there is an inter- or multidisciplinary base for health promotion. Bunton and MacDonald (1992), in their ground-breaking book, suggest that health promotion has its own integrating framework informed by the social science disciplines of psychology and sociology. These disciplines provide an account of health that embraces both the social patterning of health and disease, and individual perceptions and attitudes. This is in marked contrast to the disciplines of biology and medicine, which provide a mechanistic account of health as being the absence of disease.

The core questions that were identified in the introduction to this chapter have led health promoters to employ an interdisciplinary approach. Health promotion takes place in a context in which epidemiology and medicine have to some extent set the scene by identifying health risks and some preventive strategies. Health promoters have, however, also traditionally answered the question of what affects health by using a behavioural approach focusing on individual behaviours. The realisation that individual behaviours are not necessarily freely chosen, but may be dictated by circumstances, has led to caution in the sole use of psychological models in health promotion.

Health promotion therefore relies on a number of complementary disciplines, each with its own criteria for methodological rigour and effectiveness. The only consensus is that health promotion is a hybrid, with its roots in many different disciplines. This may lead to doubts about whether health promotion is an entity in its own right at all. The central unifying claim is perhaps that health cannot be reduced to a biomedical model but must emphasise the social, psychological and economic determinants of health. Promoting health thus depends on activities in many different spheres and is not confined to health service provision. Factors such as full employment, adequate public housing and green transport policies have more impact on health than does the provision of screening clinics.

Practitioners and commentators have tried to develop a robust health promotion identity with definitional certainty, which has resulted in a range of frameworks and **models** of practice. These have demonstrated the inclusivity of health promotion with traditional biomedical concepts of health alongside more radical public health perspectives.

A key concern for health promoters is to examine the **effectiveness** of their interventions. Yet this too is a contested area because evaluation implies underpinning theory, and the criteria for effectiveness vary according to the perspective of the evaluator. The same intervention may be deemed to be effective or otherwise, depending on the evaluator's perspective. For example, an evaluation of health checks in reducing the impact of risk factors for cardiovascular disease (Doyle and Thomas, 1996) was interpreted by primary care staff as showing this intervention to be ineffective, whereas public health practitioners suggested that it was both effective and useful.

models – abstract representations of real circumstances that assist critical thinking and analysis

effectiveness – successfully achieving the aims and goals that have been set

MODELS OF HEALTH PROMOTION

The diversity of practice in health promotion led to a desire to map or package it in ways that accommodated the very different determinants of health and the consequent range of interventions. In 1988, Rawson and Grigg identified 17 published health education models in the UK, and there have been a number of newly proposed models since then. Models provide a means of mapping health promotion and identifying the underlying theoretical perspectives. This can be done more or less explicitly, and a distinction has been made between descriptive and analytical models. Descriptive models identify the diversity of existing practice but make no judgements about which kind of practice is preferable. Analytical models are explicit about the values underpinning practice and often prioritise certain kinds of practice over others. Ewles and Simnett (1999) and Tannahill (1985) provide examples of well-known descriptive models of health promotion, while Beattie (1991) provides an example of an analytical model.

Ewles and Simnett (1999) map health promotion activity into five areas (Table 10.3). This mapping of health promotion draws upon a variety of theoretical perspectives. Social psychology and communication theory underpin the health behaviour approach, education theory the educational approach, epidemiology the medical approach, sociology and organisational theories the social change approach, and social psychology and the humanities the empowerment approach. To optimise health therefore requires a truly interdisciplinary approach, whereby the contribution of each theoretical perspective is acknowledged and respected. Ewles and Simnett (1999) state:

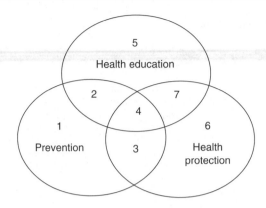

Figure 10.1   Tannahill's model of health promotion
(Tannahill, 1985, reproduced in Downie et al., 1996)

In our view, there is no one 'right' aim for health promotion, and no one 'right' approach or set of activities. We need to work out for ourselves which aim and which activities we use, in accordance with our own professional code of conduct (if there is one), our own carefully considered values and our own assessment of our clients' needs.

Tannahill's model (see Figure 10.1) describes health promotion as three inter-secting circles of health education, prevention and health protection. Within these intersecting circles lie seven possible dimensions of health promotion:

1. preventive services, for example immunisation and cervical screening

2. preventive health education, for example smoking advice

3. preventive health protection, for example the fluoridation of water

4. health education for preventive health protection, for example seat belt lobbying

5. positive health education, for example building lifeskills with groups

6. positive health protection, for example implementing a workplace smoking policy

7. health education aimed at positive health protection, for example campaigning for protective legislation.

Tannahill's model highlights the importance of complementary activity in different areas. This model, like Table 10.3, flags up the fact that practice does not conform to theoretical boundaries but overlaps and spans different theoret-ical paradigms simultaneously.

Beattie's (1991) model of health promotion (Figure 10.2) relates more directly to social theories and highlights how health promotion practice can never be value free but is underpinned by values and moral principles. Beattie's model uses two axes to generate four quadrants. The vertical axis runs from authorita-

Table 10.3   Five approaches to health promotion

	Aim	Health promotion activity	Important values	Example – smoking
Medical	Freedom from medically defined disease and disability	Promotion of medical intervention to prevent or ameliorate ill health	Patient compliance with preventive medical procedures	*Aim* – freedom from lung disease and other smoking-related disorders *Activity* – encourage people to seek early detection and treatment of smoking-related disorders
Behaviour change	Individual behaviour conducive to freedom from disease	Attitude and behaviour change to encourage adoption of a 'healthier' lifestyle	Healthy lifestyle as defined by health promoter	*Aim* – behaviour changes from smoking to not smoking *Activity* – persuasive education to prevent non-smokers from starting and persuade smokers to stop
Educational	Individuals with knowledge and understanding enabling well-informed decisions to be made and acted upon	Information about cause and effects of health-demoting factors. Exploration of values and attitudes. Development of skills required for healthy living	Individual right of free choice. Health promoter's responsibility to identify educational content	*Aim* – clients will have an understanding of the effects of smoking on health. They will make a decision of whether or not to smoke and act on the decision *Activity* – giving information to clients about the effects of smoking. Helping them to explore their own values and attitudes and come to a decision. Helping them to learn how to stop smoking if they want to
Client-centred	Working with clients on the clients' own terms	Working with health issues, choices and actions with which clients identify. Empowering clients	Clients as equals. Clients' right to set agenda. Self-empowerment of client	*Aim* – Anti-smoking issues are only considered if clients identify them as a concern. *Activity* – Clients identify what, if anything, they want to know and do about it
Societal change	Physical and social environment that enables a choice of healthier lifestyle	Political/social action to change physical/social environment	Right and need to make environment health enhancing	*Aim* – to make smoking socially unacceptable so that it is easier not to smoke *Activity* – no-smoking policy in all public places. Cigarette sales less accessible, especially to children. Promotion of non-smoking as social norm. Limiting and challenging tobacco advertising and sports sponsorship

Source: Ewles and Simnett, 1999, with permission

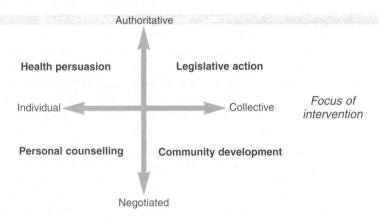

Figure 10.2   Beattie's model of health promotion
(Beattie, 1991, reproduced in Naidoo and Wills, 2000)

EXAMPLE 10.3

Models of health promotion

Strategies to address health issues may involve a number of projects. For example, one programme to reduce under-age drinking included:

● public meetings and workshops to raise the awareness of parents and teachers of the extent of under-age drinking and the problems associated with it

● curbing alcohol sales to minors through the leafleting of outlets, police enforcement and the introduction of an identity card for those over 18 years of age

● establishing alternative entertainment for young people such as youth clubs with no alcohol

● licensee training so that they may recognise and refuse to serve minors

● education sessions with young people enabling them to discuss the issues involved in under-age drinking and the pressures to drink alcohol, and to identify alternative activities and practise strategies to refuse alcohol when it is offered.

Underpinning this programme are different approaches to health improvement.

Education and awareness-raising for the community as a whole is central and needs to be appropriately targeted to different groups. The enforcement of existing legislation and policy is part of the overall strategy and is supported by training and the provision of extra resources. Recognising the social needs that are met by alcohol consumption, and the provision of safer alternatives, is also part of the health promotion response. The overall response is therefore to locate the problematic behaviour within its social and legal context, to understand the factors supporting such behaviour, to attempt to create alternative activities that meet need but avoid compromising health and safety, and to fully utilise existing policies and legislation.

tive expert-led interventions, typically based on an objective knowledge of health risks, to negotiated interventions that acknowledge and use people's lay knowledge of health. Knowledge is therefore identified as being both expert defined and defined by lay people for themselves. Activities may be tradition- ally hierarchical in nature, or more egalitarian and negotiated. The horizontal axis runs from activities directed towards individuals to activities directed towards whole populations, therefore encompassing the more psychologically or medically driven interventions directed towards individuals as well as the more public health or sociologically driven interventions directed towards groups and populations.

The four quadrants generated by the model encompass health promotion activity that reinforces the status quo (health persuasion), health promotion which is benevolent but forceful (legislation), health promotion that is communal and radical (community development) and health promotion that is aimed at empowering individuals (personal counselling). The right-hand quad- rants highlight the importance of widespread social change whereas the left- hand quadrants emphasise the importance of social continuity and consensus. The model as a whole therefore embodies very different social philosophies and values but demonstrates that each kind of activity has a role to play in promoting health.

All these models, and the many others suggested by different authors, may be used to interrogate health promotion practice, to identify underlying values and principles and to suggest ways in which practice may move forwards beyond disciplinary constraints. Some models are quite explicit about prefer- ring certain forms of practice (see, for example, French and Adams, 1986, who argue that collective action is preferable to self-empowerment or behaviour change because health is socially determined). Other models take the stance that diversity is necessary because the potential to promote health differs depending on context, role and skills. Health promotion depends on complementary activ- ities in many different spheres, and it is only by encouraging such diversity that the potential for health promotion will be fully realised.

 Is the lack of any underpinning and unifying theory of health promotion a strength or a weakness? Why?

Critics might argue that the lack of any unifying theory of health promotion demonstrates a lack of academic rigour and cite this as one reason for health promotion's relatively low profile and historic subservience to medicine. Advo- cates for health promotion might, however, argue that such eclecticism only strengthens health promotion by allowing a variety of perspectives to be used to maximum effect in the pragmatic task of promoting health.

THE EVIDENCE BASE OF HEALTH PROMOTION

All public services, including health promotion, are accountable and need to prove their worth in an economic context in which resources are finite.

England's Health Development Agency's role includes 'maintaining an up-to-date map of the **evidence base** for public health and health improvement' (DoH, 1999). This in turn raises a number of questions, including: what counts as evidence?, and who is competent to assess evidence?

Health promotion has no rules of evidence. The question of what counts as evidence relates to the theory of health promotion as different disciplines use different methodological strategies to establish the facts. The prevention of ill health and premature mortality relies on medical and epidemiological methodologies, which in turn rely on a scientific model of proof to establish cause and effect, ideally through the randomised controlled trial. While the medical dominance of health discourses means that there is a pressure to adopt this kind of research to determine effectiveness, many features of health promotion make this approach problematic.

evidence base – the sum total of research evidence that suggests which health initiatives are likely to suceed if replicated in other populations or geographical areas

> **?** **Why might it be difficult to show the effectiveness of health promotion interventions?**

1. Health promotion interventions typically have a long timescale as small changes accumulate over time to reduce the risks to health. The ultimate goal – reduced ill health and less premature death – is (if successful) apparent only years later.

2. To pinpoint cause and effect, with adequate control populations, is impossible in modern societies and for complex, community-based interventions. Indeed, one of the success criteria for health promotion interventions is the degree to which they lead to spin-off activities and spread among a population.

3. Certain health promotion outcomes are not easily measurable or quantifiable: positive health and well-being is hard to measure and has multiple determinants. Measuring positive health depends on people's subjective assessments of the quality of their lives. Factors associated with positive health, such as social capital, are in themselves difficult to measure, whereas changes in mortality and morbidity are relatively easy to assess.

Evaluating effectiveness is important in establishing the legitimacy of health promotion. What effectiveness means, however, and how it can be measured is debatable. Effectiveness has been defined as: 'the extent to which an initiative was able to achieve its objectives or to produce short-term, intermediate or long-term positive outcomes' (Dookan-Khan, 1996). This definition is useful because it includes a range of indicators of effectiveness:

- long-term outcomes, for example the reduction of risk factors
- intermediate indicators, for example an increased use of services, increased partnership working or behavioural change
- short-term changes, for example increased knowledge or skills.

Health promotion outcomes are often long term in nature, for example reduced premature mortality or a reduction in social and health inequalities.

Evaluating long-term processes in a scientifically rigorous fashion is, however, impossible. Instead, short-term indicators are often used to demonstrate that changes have occurred in the desired direction, which, it is anticipated, will lead to beneficial long-term outcomes. For example, a cancer prevention programme may include a media campaign to enable the public to assess what symptoms may indicate cancer and need rapid investigation, and encompass publicity about existing cancer screening tests. Evaluation could take place at many different levels but will entail pre-campaign as well as post-campaign testing to identify changes brought about by the campaign.

Immediate evaluation may test the public's recall of the main media messages and identify which sources were seen as being most credible and what kinds of picture and language were most persuasive. Evaluation may also assess how people feel about themselves, the degree of control or anxiety they have concerning their life and health, in the light of exposure to the media campaign. Intermediate evaluation might test people's retention of the main media messages, assess any behavioural changes and examine whether there have been changes in the number of consultations about symptoms that could indicate cancer. In addition, intermediate evaluation could monitor the take-up rate for cancer screening tests to detect any significant trends. Longer-term evaluation might examine trends in cancer screening services, including an increase in uptake and in earlier presentation.

The difficulty for health promotion is to show that such an intervention contributes to a reduction in the incidence of cancer and to rule out the many other factors that might have contributed to such an improvement. Single intervention trials that unambiguously relate one intervention to one outcome are difficult to arrange, and it is virtually impossible to prevent the spread of information or ideas to a control group. For example, a trial to see whether exercise would improve the mobility of elderly women found that those in the control group who did not receive the exercises nevertheless joined in with those who did (Tilford et al., 1997).

The evaluation of processes and short-term changes needs to be charted through individual and group perceptions and attitudes. This entails the use of qualitative methodologies. Critics argue that the use of qualitative methodologies to evaluate process outcomes such as the degree of confidence in using services or networking is too 'soft' and does not provide solid ground upon which to base interventions.

 What kind of evidence would persuade you that an intervention had 'worked'?

In practice, effectiveness is usually defined narrowly. A number of organisations (for example, the Health Development Agency and the NHS Centre for Reviews and Dissemination) carry out systematic effectiveness reviews in which they assess current evidence of the effectiveness of health promotion interventions. However, these reviews typically prioritise research that conforms to the natural science model of randomised controlled trials or quasi-experimental studies. Such research is considered to be more persuasive than qualitative research, however rigorously the latter is undertaken.

EXAMPLE 10.4

Evidence of effective interventions to prevent falls in older people

The NHS Centre for Reviews and Dissemination bulletin on the prevention of falls in older people included only randomised controlled trials evaluating the effectiveness of interventions on falls, fall-related injury or risk factors such as nutritional status, environmental hazards or medication. Intermediate outcomes such as improved balance were not given as much weight as outcomes for falls or fall-related injuries.

The bulletin identified two effective primary interventions: the promotion of exercise and home safety assessments. Based on 36 trials, the review concluded 'trials provide reasonable evidence to suggest that exercise offers potential benefits in reducing the risk of falls and some risk factors for falls. Those interventions which use balancing exercise, strength training and low impact aerobic exercise appear to be most promising' (NHSCRD, 1996). The success of assessment schemes seems to be related less to the identification of hazards than to their removal. The review stated that 'home visiting to identify and remedy environmental and personal risks for falling may reduce the risk of falling. The type of safety changes could include removal of throw rugs and objects in pathways, and installation of improved night lights and non-skid bath mats' (NHSCRD, 1996).

The limitations of randomised controlled trials become apparent when considering appropriate interventions for falls reduction. There is a focus on outcome and no information on process and how the outcomes were achieved. In the example above, the practitioner is no wiser on how best to promote exercise among older people. The perspective of older people themselves is also lacking. The focus on risks reflects the professional perspective, yet qualitative research to look at older people's feelings on risk has revealed that some older individuals reject safety precautions because they impact on their quality of life.

Sources: NHSCRD, 1996; Reed, 1998

Health promotion includes the prevention of ill health and the reduction in number of known risk factors for disease, as well as the increase in social capital and the empowerment of individuals and communities. Given such disparate aims, it is not surprising that no one methodology will suffice. What is needed is different methodologies for different objectives. As McQueen (2000) puts it, 'rather than retreating to limited rules for what constitutes evidence, there is a need to look toward analytical frameworks that recognise the complexity of the whole'.

Given the economic realities of finite resources, demonstrating the cost effectiveness of health promotion is also important. Cost-effectiveness analysis compares the costs of different interventions with the same aim. It may also examine opportunity costs – the value of using resources for health promotion rather than for alternative uses, for example health service provision:

> Cost-effectiveness analysis can be used either to identify the intervention which achieves a specific target at lowest cost or that which achieves the greatest outcome for a given cost. (Tolley, 1994)

CONNECTIONS

Chapter 8 (Health Economics) provides more details on the economic evaluation of health interventions

Although the discipline is still in its infancy, the economic evaluation of health promotion suggests that it is cost effective, although the long timescale of its benefits makes it less persuasive than interventions, such as treatment, which have immediate benefits. Reid (1995) cites brief advice from a GP and participation in No Smoking Day as the two most cost-effective smoking cessation interventions. Evidence from the USA suggests that workplace health promotion interventions result in savings to employers of at least three times the cost (Reid et al., 1992).

CASE STUDY – SMOKING PREVENTION AND CESSATION

The following case study draws together many of the themes discussed in this chapter. The identification of smoking as a health issue is linked to epidemiological evidence, and the current pattern of smoking is related to sociological factors such as gender and income. Smoking is often thought of as a personal behaviour, yet its financial links with big corporate businesses and governments reveal it to be of global concern. A range of smoking prevention and cessation strategies is discussed and the evidence for their effectiveness explored.

THE EPIDEMIOLOGY OF SMOKING

Tobacco smoking has been called the biggest single cause of preventable ill health and premature death in the UK (DoH, 1999). The decline in adult smoking rate that has occurred since the 1970s now appears to have halted, and smoking is increasingly common among children and young people. In 1988, the proportion of regular smokers in England aged 11–15 was 8%; in 1996, it was estimated to be 13% (NHSCRD, 1999). In the UK, nearly 30% of adults currently smoke, half of whom will die from smoking-related causes, one third before the age of 65.

One fifth of all deaths, or 120,000 deaths per year, are related to smoking. Smoking causes most lung cancer and is a contributory factor for many other cancers. It has been estimated that smoking leads to about a third of all cancer deaths (DoH, 1999). 'Smoking is [also] the most important modifiable risk factor for coronary heart disease in young and old' (DoH, 1999). Many other illnesses, including chronic respiratory diseases and diabetes, are also caused or aggravated by smoking.

Tobacco cultivation also harms the environment in the developing world, where farmers are persuaded to grow a single tobacco crop instead of varied food crops. In addition, advertising and promotion activities in the developing world are more blatant than in the West, with images on billboards of successful and attractive young people smoking, and promotional activities such as free cigarettes at tobacco-sponsored leisure events. Environmental tobacco smoke affects the health of others, especially children, and is linked to lung cancer, chronic respiratory illness and ischaemic heart disease. Tobacco smoking does not, however, impact solely on individuals' health; it also destroys the health of the environment.

Smoking is a legal activity that is promoted by global tobacco companies using a range of sophisticated selling methods. These include the sponsorship of sporting activities and advertising on billboards and in magazines. The UK government is committed to a strengthening of the restrictions on tobacco advertising and sponsorship, tobacco advertising being banned in the print media by 2002 and the sponsorship of all events being prevented by 2006.

Smoking remains a popular habit despite the known health risks. This is partly due to the addictive nature of nicotine. Around a quarter of young people of all social classes continue to start smoking, but people in the higher social groups are more likely to stop smoking in early to middle adulthood. This leads to a sharp social gradient in smoking, unskilled men being three times as likely to smoke as professional men. Smoking is also patterned by gender. Women traditionally smoked less than men, but this is no longer true for younger age groups. In addition, women seem to use smoking as a coping strategy in stressful situations and find it harder to stop smoking than men. Low-income women, and women carers in particular, find stopping smoking difficult (Graham, 1993). Social deprivation is generally associated with an increased likelihood of smoking, although the smoking rate for most minority ethnic groups is lower than average.

Smoking is therefore a complex issue in which many different psychological, social, physiological and economic factors interact. Epidemiological studies unequivocally demonstrate that smoking is linked causally to a variety of illnesses and a greatly increased likelihood of premature death. As mentioned above, smoking is a personal behaviour that is strongly patterned by social factors such as deprivation, income, gender, class and ethnicity. Smoking is big business, contributing approximately £10.3 billion to the government each year through taxation. Smoking contributes to environmental degradation and pollution and diverts developing countries' agricultural efforts away from food and into a single cash crop of tobacco.

SMOKING PREVENTION AND CESSATION STRATEGIES

Strategies to prevent smoking and support smoking cessation are varied, ranging from policies such as smoking bans in public places to individual support and advice on cessation. Smoking prevention activities have been evaluated by a number of research studies. The outcomes (the number of quitters and the cost of the programme) are relatively measurable, although the processes involved (increasing self-esteem and organisational policy changes, for example) remain less so. In cost terms, smoking presents a relatively clear picture. The cost to the NHS of treating smoking-related ill health can be calculated, and the funding for smoking prevention campaigns is a known factor. A cost-effectiveness formula, the cost per year of life saved, may be deduced given the number of quitters, their age and the cost of the intervention. This formula has been used to compare different kinds of intervention in order to suggest which activities should take priority.

Healthy public policies in this area include banning smoking, fiscal policies to affect the price of tobacco and policies to ban the advertising and promotion of tobacco. Such policies may be agreed and implemented at different levels, from single organisations to nations to international forums. European Union health ministers have, for example, agreed a common policy to ban tobacco advertising and sponsorship, which will be fully implemented over a number of years.

Tobacco pricing policy remains within the remit of nation states and is a contentious issue. For every 1 per cent increase in real price, consumption falls by about 0.5 per cent (Reid, 1999). However, increasing the price of tobacco impacts negatively on the most deprived groups, who are least able to stop smoking and who then spend even more of their limited income on cigarettes. While increasing the price of tobacco is associated with a reduction in consumption, it does not necessarily reduce the prevalence of smoking among young people. The huge growth in tobacco smuggling also limits the effectiveness of this strategy. It is therefore debatable whether a further increase in the price of tobacco is an effective or ethical strategy.

Banning smoking in public places is becoming more common and is important in establishing non-smoking as the norm and in protecting the health of non-smokers from environmental tobacco smoke. Smoking control policies are an important factor in establishing non-smoking environments that promote health. This includes schools and colleges, NHS premises and workplaces, most of which now have a written smoking policy banning smoking except in specified places. More than 90 per cent of large UK companies, for example, now have workplace smoking policies to restrict smoking at work. A further restriction on smoking in public places is desirable, but the process needs to be one in which everyone participates and hence has a stake in seeing it succeed.

Other policy interventions include the enforcement of the current legislation banning sales of tobacco to the under-16s and the use of stronger health warnings on cigarette packets, which are likely to cover 40 per cent of the pack face by 2001. Both of these activities are likely to have only a small effect yet politically they are important in establishing the unacceptability and high risk of smoking.

There are various community campaigns that focus on smoking issues. These are usually set up and supported by health staff but focus on issues such as children's exposure to smoking and can be useful in countering tobacco industry messages. There is, for example, a network of Smokebusters clubs for non-smoking teenagers in the UK, which provides useful media publicity but has no proven effect on smoking prevalence among teenagers.

Education on the harmful effects of smoking appears to be ineffective by itself in smoking prevention. The health risks of smoking have been known and publicised since the 1960s, yet smoking continues on a mass scale. New recruits are attracted by the image of smoking and then become addicted. Knowledge-based interventions in schools do not prevent uptake, but social reinforcement that raises the awareness of social pressure and develops resistance skills is more effective in possibly delaying a recruitment to smoking for a few years (Stead et al., 1996).

Persuading individual smokers to give up is a well-established strategy, various different methods having been tried and evaluated. Many smokers (70 per cent at any one time) say that they would like to quit. The challenge is to channel the desire to stop into an effective strategy for stopping and staying stopped, and to continue reminding 'contented' smokers of why they should quit. These activities can also be thought of as empowering and enabling people to break free of an addiction that controls them. Reinforcing young non-smokers' intentions never to smoke, for example through school health education programmes, is also important.

Persuasion can be through the use of mass media or through individual contacts. Both have been used and evaluated as smoking prevention strategies. Mass media events, such as England's No Smoking Day, are relatively effective. Although the quit rate is only 0.3 per cent, a mass exposure to the media campaign means that this translates into a respectable number of quitters. A fall in consumption of up to 5 per cent is also reported for No Smoking Day. Quitline is a national charity to help smokers to stop; it claims to give advice and support to 0.5 million callers a year. Proactive telephone counselling, in which a counsellor initiates contact with the smoker, has also been shown to be effective (Lichtenstein et al., 1996).

Psychological theories of behaviour change have informed a number of interventions designed to persuade smokers to quit. For example, Prochaska and DiClemente's (1986) cycle of change is a popular model used by many health workers to structure their interactions with smokers. There is, however, little evidence of its effectiveness, and it has been criticised for failing to address socially deprived or low-income individuals, who find it hardest to quit yet who have most to gain from quitting. Conversely, there is evidence to show that brief advice from health professionals, especially GPs, leads to a quit rate of up to 5 per cent.

Nicotine replacement therapy is of proven effectiveness and doubles the effectiveness of other interventions. The government has recently announced that nicotine replacement therapy will be available free for one week in Health Action Zone areas. This is a welcome initiative, although it probably merits extension into other areas and for a longer period of time.

The government has recently announced increased funding for smoking cessation activities, with a new public education campaign costing £50 million and smoking cessation services costing £60 million, both over 3 years. Other costs are borne by existing budgets, such as NHS staffing and treatment costs. This level of funding is still low in comparison with that seen in other countries (for example in Australia and in California in the USA) and remains only a fraction of the revenue produced by tobacco taxation.

Reid (1999) argues that, to tackle the smoking epidemic effectively, social inequalities need to be addressed on a broad front through the use of diverse social policies directed towards reducing poverty, unemployment, social exclusion and environmental degradation:

> Those who rely on nicotine to anaesthetise them against the stresses of lone parenthood or long-term unemployment are unlikely to turn to free [nicotine replacement therapy] as an effective substitute. While the cost of effective anti-deprivation measures would amount to several £ billion annually, the health benefits would be far wider than the prevention of smoking related disease. (Reid, 1999)

This case study has shown how smoking prevalence is related to many different individual, social and environmental factors. Evidence for the effectiveness of different prevention strategies has been assessed.

SUMMARY

- Health promotion is a way of looking at health that draws together all the factors that shape and influence the health of individuals and communities

- Health promotion sees health within its social and political context rather than as an isolated medical event

- The context of a dominant medical paradigm leads to a focus on risk factors for disease. In practice, many interventions focus on individual behaviour rather than the structural determinants of health

- The contribution of health promotion to overall health improvement is difficult to measure

- Health promotion has no integrating theory or model, much of the theoretical debate centring on questions of definition and purpose.

QUESTIONS FOR FURTHER DISCUSSION

1. How do you account for the current focus on health promotion in government health strategy?

2. 'Health promotion is part of a nannying society that dictates how people should live their lives.' Discuss.

3. As we enter the 21st century, what have we learned about what makes people healthier?

FURTHER READING

Bunton, R. and MacDonald, G. (1992) *Health Promotion: Disciplines and Diversity*. London: Routledge.
An edited collection highlighting the contribution of different disciplines to health promotion. It explores whether health promotion is a discrete discipline.

Naidoo, J. and Wills, J. (2000) *Health Promotion: Foundations for Practice* 2nd edn. London: Baillière Tindall.
An accessible, introductory text on the principles and practice of health promotion.

Tones, K. and Tilford, S. (1994) Health Education: Effectiveness, Efficiency and Equity. London: Chapman & Hall.
Explores the issues involved in evaluating the effectiveness of health promotion and provides some evidence of successful interventions. Explores the concept of empowerment in health promotion.

REFERENCES

Abt Associates South Africa (2000) *The Impending Catastrophe: A Resource Book on the Emerging HIV/AIDS Epidemic in South Africa*. Johannesburg: LoveLife. Website: www.lovelife.org.za.

Armstrong, D. (1995) The rise of surveillance medicine. *Sociology of Health and Illness*, **17**(3): 333–40.

Baum, F. (1999) Social capital: is it good for your health? Issues of a public health agenda. *Journal of Epidemiology and Community Health*, **53**: 195–6.

Beattie, A. (1991) 'Knowledge and control in health promotion: a test case for social policy and social theory', in Gabe, J., Calnan, M. and Bury, M. (eds) *The Sociology of the Health Service*. London: Routledge, pp. 162–202.

Bennett, P. and Smith, C. (1992) Parents: attitudinal and social influence on childhood vaccination. *Health Education Research*, **73**(3): 341–8.

Bunton, R. and MacDonald, G. (1992) *Health Promotion: Disciplines and Diversity*. London: Routledge.

Caplan, G. (1969) *An Approach to Community Mental Health*. London: Tavistock.

Cox, E. (1997) Building social capital. *Health Promotion Matters*, **4**: 1–4.

Davison, C., Davey Smith, G. and Frankel, S. (1991) Lay epidemiology and the prevention paradox: the implications of coronary candidacy for health education. *Sociology of Health and Illness*, **13**(1): 1–19.

Department of Environment, Transport and the Regions (1999) *A Better Quality of Life: A Strategy for Sustainable Development for the United Kingdom*. London: Stationery Office.

DHSS (Department of Health and Social Security) (1987) *Anti-heroin Campaign: Stage Five Research Evaluation*. London: HMSO.

DoH (Department of Health) (1992) *The Health of the Nation*. London: Stationery Office.

DoH (Department of Health) (1998a) *Communicating about Risks to Public Health: Pointers to Good Practice*. London: Stationery Office.

DoH (Department of Health) (1998b) *Smoking Kills*. White Paper. London: Stationery Office.

DoH (Department of Health) (1999) *Saving Lives: Our Healthier Nation*. London: Stationery Office.

DoH (Department of Health) (2000) *Coronary Heart Disease: National Service Frameworks*. London: Stationery Office.

Dookan-Khan, B. (1996) *The Proceedings of a Symposium on the Effectiveness of Health Promotion*. Toronto: Toronto Centre for Health Promotion, University of Toronto.

Downie, R.S., Tannahill, C. and Tannahill, A. (1996) *Health Promotion: Models and Values*, 2nd edn. Oxford: Oxford Medical Publications.

Doyle, Y. and Thomas, P. (1996) Promoting health through primary care: challenges in taking a strategic approach. *Health Education Journal*, **55**: 3–10.

Ewles, L. and Simnett, I. (1999) *Promoting Health: A Practical Guide*, 4th edn. London: Baillière Tindall.

Family Heart Study Group (1994) Randomised control trial evaluating cardiovascular screening and intervention in general practice. *British Medical Journal*, **308**: 313–20.

French, J. and Adams, L. (1986) From analysis to synthesis: theories of health education. *Health Education Journal*, **45**(2): 71–4.

Gillies, P. (1998) The effectiveness of alliances for partnerships for health promotion. *Health Promotion International*, **13**(2): 1–22.

Graham, H. (1993) *When Life's a Drag: Women, Smoking and Disadvantage*. London: HMSO.

King, A., Wold, B., Tudor-Smith, C. and Harel, Y. (1996) *The Health of Youth: A Cross National Survey*. Copenhagen: WHO.

Lichtenstein, E., Glasgow, R.E., Lamb, H.A., Ossip-Klein, B. and Boles, H.R. (1996) Telephone counselling for smoking cessation: rationales and meta analytic review of evidence. *Health Education Research*, **11**(2): 243–57.

Lomas, R. (1998) Social capital and health: implications for public health and epidemiology. *Social Science and Medicine*, **47**(9): 1181–8.

Lupton, D. (1995) *The Imperative of Health*. London: Sage.

MacDonald, J. (1993) *Primary Health Care – Medicine in its Place*. London: Earthscan.

McDonald, T.H. (1998) *Rethinking Health Promotion: A Global Approach*. London: Routledge.

McKinlay, J.B. (1979) 'A case for refocusing upstream: the political economy of health', in Jaco, E.G. (ed.) *Patients, Physicians and Illness*, 3rd edn. Basingstoke: Macmillan – now Palgrave, pp. 263–72.

McQueen, D. (2000) Perspectives on health promotion: theory, evidence, practice and the emergence of complexity. *Health Promotion International*, **15**(2): 95–7.

Marmot, M., Shipley, M.J. and McQueen, D. (1996) Do socio-economic differences in mortality persist after retirement? 25 year follow up of civil servants from the first Whitehall study. *British Medical Journal*, **313**: 1177–80.

Mitchell, J. (1984) *What Is To Be Done about Illness and Health?* London: Penguin.

Murphy, P. and Waddington, I. (1998) Sport for all: some public health policy issues and problems. *Critical Public Health*, **8**(3): 193–207.

Myer, L. (2000) New directions for improving condom use in South Africa. *AIDS Bulletin*, **9**(2): 15–17.

Naidoo, J. and Orme, J. (1998) Qualitative and quantitative research: an opportunity to restore the balance? *Critical Public Health*, **8**(1): 93–5.

Naidoo, J. and Wills, J. (1998) *Practising Health Promotion: Dilemmas and Challenges*. London: Baillière Tindall.

Naidoo, J. and Wills, J. (2000) *Health Promotion: Foundations for Practice*, 2nd edn. London: Baillière Tindall.

NHSCRD (NHS Centre for Reviews and Dissemination) (1996) *Effective Health Care Bulletin: Preventing Falls and Subsequent Injury in Older People*. York: University of York.

NHSCRD (NHS Centre for Reviews and Dissemination) (1999) *Effective Health Care Bulletin: Preventing the Uptake of Smoking in Young People*. York: University of York.

OXCHECK Study Group (1995) The effectiveness of health checks conducted by nurses in primary care: final results from the OXCHECK study. *British Medical Journal*, **310**: 1099–104.

Prochaska, J.O. and DiClemente, C.C. (1986) 'Towards a comprehensive model of change', in Miller, W.R. and Heather, N. (eds) *Treating Addictive Behaviours: Processes of Change*. New York: Plenum, pp. 3–24.

Rawson, D. and Grigg, C. (1988) *Purpose and Practice in Health Education*. London: South Bank Polytechnic/HEA.

Reed, J. (1998) 'Care and protection for older people', in Heyman, B. (ed.) *Risk, Health and Health Care – a Qualitative Approach*. London: Arnold, pp. 241–56.

Reid, D. (1995) *Is Health Education Effective? Health Promotion Today*. London: Health Education Council.

Reid, D. (1999) ' Tobacco control: a losing battle?' in Griffiths, S. and Hunter, D.J. (eds) *Perspectives in Public Health*. Oxford: Radcliffe Medical Press, pp. 95–106.

Reid, D., Killoran, A., McNeill, A. and Chambers, J. (1992) Choosing the most effective health promotion options for reducing a nation's smoking prevalence. *Tobacco Control*, **1**: 185–97.

Rissell, C. (1994) Empowerment: the holy grail of health promotion. *Health Promotion International*, **9**(1): 39–47.

Rose, G. (1992) *The Strategy of Preventive Medicine*. Oxford: Oxford Medical Press.

Russell, M., Wilson, C., Taylor, C. and Baker, C. (1979) Effectiveness of general practitioners' advice against smoking. *British Medical Journal*, **2**: 231–5.

Smee, C. (1992) *The Effect of Tobacco Advertising on Tobacco Consumption: A Discussion Document Reviewing the Evidence*. London: DoH.

Stead, M., Hastings, G. and Tudor Smith, C. (1996) Preventing adolescent smoking: a review of options. *Health Education Journal*, **55**: 31–54.

Tannahill, A. (1985) What is health promotion? *Health Education Journal*, **44**: 167–8.

Tilford, S., Delaney, F. and Vogels, M. (1997) *Effectiveness of Mental Health Promotion Interventions: A Review*. London: Health Education Authority.

Tolley, K. (1994) *Health Promotion: How to Measure Cost-effectiveness*. London: Health Education Authority.

Tones, K. (1995) Health education as empowerment. *Health Promotion Today*. London: Health Education Authority.

Tones, K. and Tilford, S. (1994) *Health Education: Effectiveness, Efficiency and Equity*, 2nd edn. London: Chapman & Hall.

United Nations (1993) *United Nations Conference on Environment and Development 1992: Rio de Janeiro, 3–14 June 1992*. New York: United Nations.

Usdin, S. (2000) Soul City – innovations in media and AIDS in HIV/AIDS 2000 – local level response. Medical Research Council of South Africa. *Urban Health and Development Bulletin*, **3**(2): 15–24.

WHO (World Health Organization) (1946) *World Health Organization Constitution*. Geneva: WHO.

WHO (World Health Organization) (1984) *Health Promotion: A Discussion Document on the Concept and Principles*. Copenhagen: WHO Regional Office for Europe.

WHO (World Health Organization) (1985) *Health For All by the Year 2000*. Geneva: WHO.

WHO (World Health Organization) (1986) *Ottawa Charter for Health Promotion*. Geneva: WHO.

WHO (World Health Organization) (1988) *Adelaide Recommendations on Healthy Public Policy*. Adelaide: WHO.

WHO (World Health Organization) (1993) *The European Network of Health Promoting Schools*. Copenhagen: WHO.

Williams, G. and Popay, J. (1994) 'Lay knowledge and the privilege of experience', in Gabe, J., Kelleher, G. and Williams, G. (eds) *Challenging Medicine*. London: Routledge, pp. 118–39.

World Commission on Environment and Development (1987) *Energy 2000: A Global Strategy for Sustainable Development: A Report for the World Commission on Environment and Development*. London: Zed Books.

11

Integrating Perspectives on Health

JENNIE NAIDOO AND JANE WILLS

This book has sought to introduce the reader to the interdisciplinary field of Health Studies. This includes the 'core' disciplines of sociology, psychology, ethics and physiology as well as the more applied disciplines of social policy, organisation and management, cultural studies, epidemiology, health promotion and economics. These disciplines are not exhaustive, but they do provide a solid, comprehensive grounding in the kinds of academic tradition that contribute most to Health Studies. There are inevitably tensions between the different cognate disciplines, the applied disciplines and the interdisciplinary hybrid of Health Studies. Students of particular academic disciplines are introduced to specific ways of thinking about health issues and the specific methodologies used by their discipline. Ontology – concerning what counts as truth or the facts – and epistemology – relating to what is seen as a valid means of establishing the facts – are themselves contested concepts that different disciplines answer within their own terms of reference. The concept of health provides a good example of this, and the different chapters in this book have sought to clarify how and why health is regarded as a key issue by very different disciplines. For each, health, or some particular aspect of health, has come under investigation, albeit in a very different way.

Reading through this book, you may find that some perspectives appeal to you more than others. Depending on your background, experiences and values, you may find some approaches immediately resonate more powerfully. The content of some perspectives will probably be more compelling and interesting than that of others, and you may also be more sympathetic to certain kinds of investigation or methodology. You may, for example, be drawn more towards the 'hard' scientific disciplines of physiology and epidemiology, or the analytical rigour of ethics and law, or the qualitative methodology used by social sciences such as sociology.

Each chapter is a springboard for further study in that area. A further study of sociology and cultural studies may, for example, lead you to examine postmodernism in more depth, debating the nature of social identity and the way in which we experience our physical bodies as social constructs. To what extent are seemingly natural phenomena, such as body shape and size or procreation, moulded and shaped by social forces? Studying organisations and management in greater depth may help you to identify the different types of workplace culture and enable you to suggest how changes may be most effectively introduced and managed. For example, how can a large organisation introduce communication channels that help employees to feel more valued and hence committed to organisational goals?

A further study of ethics and law may help you to analyse the ethical bases underpinning the different positions taken with regard to many health issues, for example euthanasia. As a society, we are now in a position to make technical interventions affecting the boundaries of life and death, but unless this is done within an ethical framework, such interventions may be seen as harmful and open to abuse.

A deeper study of economics may help you to assess the economic advantages and disadvantages of different kinds of intervention. The allocation of funding for different kinds of services is, for example, affected by traditional patterns of spending and the relative power of different specialities. An economic analysis may suggest more rational ways of reallocating funding to maximise health output, away from the high-technology, high-visibility services such as surgery and towards lower-technology interventions such as primary and social care.

The usefulness of Health Studies is that it provides a way of thinking about health that draws together different perspectives in a complementary manner. Traditionally, each perspective would approach health in its own way, addressing certain issues and not others. This would lead to piecemeal insights and conclusions, valid within their own term of reference but not accessible to people from outside the unifying disciplinary frame. While academically respectable and supported by the traditional divisions of knowledge and research, such an approach is inevitably limited in its ability to impact on health issues in the real world.

The approach of Health Studies is to highlight the real health issues of the day and then draw together insights from different disciplines in an attempt to create viable strategies and solutions to problems. As such, Health Studies seeks to be an applied discipline that engages with and addresses topical health issues. Major health issues, such as how and at what level health care services should be funded and provided, demand such an interdisciplinary approach and will benefit from it.

For example, the recent decoding of the human genetic code, the Human Genome Project, raises fundamental questions about the practicalities and realistic expectations of genetically tailored cures for diseases, the ethics of ownership of, and access to, such knowledge, and the funding and management of this global project. While the content of the project is embedded within the disciplines of biology and physiology, its impact and usefulness will depend on many factors that are addressed by different disciplines, including management, social policy and ethics. The Human Genome Project has already raised ethical and technical dilemmas that would have been inconceivable just a few decades ago and will undoubtedly give rise to many more in the near future.

The following figure uses the example of teenage pregnancy to illustrate how the different disciplines might address this issue, the connections between them and how using different perspectives provides a more rounded picture of the issue. It also highlights how the taken-for-granted reality of each perspective is challenged by insights drawn from other perspectives.

Organisation and management
By understanding the ways in which the public sector is organised, we can identify how to deliver more effective and accessible services:
● What factors make services more accessible to users?
● Are small, local services more acceptable?
● How can different organisations work together to co-ordinate strategies and services targeted at young women?

Social policy
By understanding the links between trends in welfare provision and associated ideologies, we can identify different views on the role that the state should take in tackling health and social problems:
● Is teenage pregnancy a legitimate concern of government?
● What accounts for the current focus on parenting support programmes?
● Do early education programmes break the 'cycle of poverty'?

Physiology
By understanding the physiological process of pregnancy, we can identify what might be the health-related consequences:
● What contributes to the complications, including anaemia, toxaemia and hypertension, that are associated with teenage pregnancy?
● What is the lower age at which pregnancy presents a significant physiological burden and risk to women?
● What are the physiological links between teenage pregnancy and the increased rates of low birthweight babies and premature birth?

Cultural studies
By understanding concepts of health held by particular groups, we can design better interventions targeted at these groups:
● Is teenage motherhood the norm among certain groups?
● How do young women's views on motherhood relate to their views on adulthood?
● What is the perspective of the men who father children born to teenage women?

Ethics and law
By understanding what we (individuals and society) value, and whether there are universal moral rules, we can identify principles that can be applied to decision-making related to why, how and when to intervene in individuals' fertility:
● What are society's views on the appropriate and acceptable age of pregnancy and motherhood?
● What are society's views on the relationship between marriage and motherhood?
● At what age and in what circumstances should medical confidentiality be respected?

TEENAGE

Figure 11.1   Disciplinary perspectives on teenage pregnancy

PREGNANCY

Economics

By understanding economic principles, we can identify rational criteria on which to base decision-making related to resource allocation:

- What are the economic effects of teenage pregnancy on mothers, families, health and welfare services and society in general?
- Are young people's contraceptive services cost effective?
- What criteria should be used to assess the effectiveness of contraceptive services?

Health promotion

By understanding the factors contributing to health status and behaviour, we can better plan strategies and services focused on educational and behaviour change in young people:

- How effective is school-based education in reducing early sexual activity and pregnancy?
- Which is most effective – abstinence programmes, lifeskills or factual information?
- Are pharmacies an appropriate venue for providing emergency contraception?

Sociology

By understanding social patterns and societal structures, we can identify the causes of health inequality:

- Is teenage pregnancy linked to socio-economic position?
- Why might economic hardship or low educational attainment be more common in young women who become pregnant?
- What generational and cultural factors influence teenage pregnancy?

Psychology

By understanding people's health beliefs, we can identify what might influence their health-related decisions:

- Why do young women first become sexually active?
- What are young women's attitudes towards contraception, and what inhibits or prompts its use?
- How are decisions about pregnancy termination made?

Epidemiology

By understanding what factors are associated with teenage pregnancy, we can identify which groups of young women are more likely to become pregnant:

- What are the trends in age of first intercourse?
- What proportion of sexually active young women become pregnant?
- What is the incidence of related health problems such as sexually transmitted disease?

Teenage pregnancy is often cited as a major health problem. The teenage pregnancy rate in the UK is the highest in Western Europe, with nearly 30 live births per 1,000 women aged 15–19. It is not, however, a simple issue to address. The nature of the problem is defined in different ways by a variety of perspectives and includes:

● societal concerns about teenage pregnancy
● the size and scale of, and trends in, teenage fertility
● the health outcomes of teenage pregnancies on mothers and children
● the effects of teenage pregnancy on maternal circumstances and life chances.

The different academic disciplines use very different paradigms, which are not capable of being synthesised into one discipline. Whereas this may be confusing for the reader in that no final truth is offered, it reflects the real world in which competing paradigms sit alongside each other. These paradigms in turn inform different kinds of human intervention designed to promote health, ranging from the risk factor analysis of individual lifestyles to an economic cost–benefit analysis of different health policies, and to social policy and organisational change analyses suggesting how organisations and societies may become health promoting. What is most important is for readers to understand why and how such different interpretations and explanations are offered, and to seek to combine interventions so that they build upon and reinforce each other.

There has in recent years been a general encouragement for health and welfare professionals to learn and work together. This is partly a response to a need to rationalise resources and lessen duplication, but there is also a recognition that the factors affecting health are the same as the factors affecting social welfare in general. In addition, the complexity of health services and the need to understand the roles of others, especially in relation to the care of people in the community, has made partnership working a necessity. Until recently, traditional professional boundaries and specialist training have made such partnership working difficult, but there is now an increased move to shared learning in education in which professional groups (for example social workers, health visitors and radiographers) may learn together on common core programmes, specialist elements being presented separately for each professional group. The intention of such programmes is to increase mutual professional knowledge, promote teamwork and encourage multiskilled professionals who can look beyond their particular specialism.

A common grounding in Health Studies provides a central strategy for achieving interprofessional and interdisciplinary education and training. This often happens during the first years of further and higher education and is particularly useful as it establishes collaborative understanding and working at the outset, before professional and disciplinary boundaries become reinforced and hardened. It is our intention that this textbook will be used, by both students and tutors, to further these aims.

Many students of Health Studies will go on to pursue a career in health and welfare services, some as front-line practitioners, some as managers. We hope that this textbook will provide students with the necessary knowledge and skills to enable them to work effectively across disciplinary boundaries with other practitioners. By understanding and appreciating the insights of different disciplines, more effective teamwork and collaboration can occur.

Some students will already have a clear career path in view and will go on to build on the introduction to their chosen discipline provided in this book. Others may find during the course of their study that some specialism particularly appeals to them, and that through studying Health Studies their future specialism and role is clarified. We hope that all students will find Health Studies an enriching area of study, as we ourselves have.

Index

Page numbers printed in **bold** type refer to figures; those in *italic* to tables. Asterisks (*) against page numbers indicate the presence of glossary points in the margin in addition to material in the main text.

A

abbreviations xvi
aberrant coding 154
abnormality 47–8, 49, 50
  see also normality
abortion, as depicted in *The Silent Scream* 154–5
Abortion Act 1967 268, 271
acetylcholine 23, 24
Acheson Report 45, 65, 109, 174
actin 25
action, theory of reasoned action *89
action potentials (nerve impulses) 20, *21, 21–2, 22, 33
Active for Life campaign 284
Acts of Parliament 257
  see also individual Acts of Parliament
Adelaide Conference, World Health Organization 286

adenosine diphosphate (ADP) 12
adenosine triphosphate (ATP) *12*, 13
adherence, *see* compliance
administration *207
  v. management and leadership 212–14
ADP, *see* adenosine diphosphate
adrenaline (epinephrine) 23, 24
adrenocorticotrophic hormone 24
advertising, commercial products 144–5
  see also tobacco advertising and sponsorship
advocacy services, in the NHS 178
aetiology *40
  see also cause
African-Caribbean *v.* white patients, views of health and illness 146–7
age
  chronological *v.* biological/social 187–8
  as criterion for health care rationing 176, 187
ageing 186–9
  demographic time bomb 187–8
  health issues 187
  and memory 80

see also older people
Agenda 21 290
AIDS
  representations of people with 137
  see also HIV/AIDS education
Airedale NHS Trust (Respondents) v. *Bland* 257–8
airways 17
albumin 26
alcohol
  and cancer 73, 95
  health promotion programme 295
  and heart disease 278
  socio-economic status and 108
  under-age drinking 295
alimentary canal (gastrointestinal tract) 14–15
allocative efficiency *236, *239
Althusser, Louis 150
amino acids 18, 25
amphetamine 24
anabolism *18
anaemia 17
  testing 47
anaesthetics, local 23–4, 35
analgesics (painkillers) 24, 35
  endogenous 36–7
  placebo effect 37
  tolerance to 36

'anomalous categories' 136
anorexia 140
antibiotics 28
anti-depressant medication, as a cultural phenomenon? 145
anxiety, affecting pain perception 84–5
appraisal, in self-regulatory model 94
Aristotelianism 253–4
artefact explanations
  country of birth as ethnicity measure 114
  for health inequalities 108
arteries **14**
arthritis, rheumatoid arthritis 28
asbestos 125–6
aspirin 35
assisted conception 158
association
  disease and *56
  pain and 84
asthma 17, 24
atoms 12
ATP, *see* adenosine triphosphate
atropine 24
attitude, towards behaviour or object *89
attribution, dimensions of 73–4
attribution theory *73–4

314